SCIENCE AND THE BRITISH EMPIRE

This book studies the linkages between science, technology and institution building in Colonial and Modern India. It discusses the advent and growth of modern science in India in terms of a nested three-stage model comprising the colonial-tool stage, the peripheral-native stage and the Indian response stage, each leading to and coexisting with the next. The book gives an account of developments in various fields of science and education in the latter half of the 19th century and the beginning of contributions made by Indian individuals, continuing into the 20th century. It traces the process of colonization and how it led to studies in astronomy, meteorology, natural history, geography and medicine in India.

Rich in archival resources, this book will be indispensable for scholars and researchers of history of education, history of science, colonial education, science and technology studies, South Asian history, Indian history and history in general.

Rajesh Kochhar was a former Professor of Astrophysics and former Director, National Institute of Science, Technology and Development Studies, New Delhi, India. An astrophysicist turned historian, he published original research with a special focus on the history of science and education in British India. He was a former President of International Astronomical Union Commission on History of Astronomy, a Fulbright Visiting Lecturer, Jawaharlal Nehru Fellow and British Council Visiting Scholar at the University of Cambridge, UK. He is the recipient of the Indian National Science Academy's 2014 Indira Gandhi Prize for Popularization of Science. He published original research in a number of fields and lectured extensively in India and abroad including Harvard, Cornell,

University of Texas at Austin, Belfast, Brighton, Royal Dublin Society, Tubingen, Copenhagen University and National Museum Copenhagen. He is the author of *The Vedic People: Their History and Geography* (2000), *English Education in India, 1715-1835: Half-caste, Missionary, and Secular Stages* (2020) and *Sanskrit and the British Empire* (2022).

SCIENCE AND THE BRITISH EMPIRE

Rajesh Kochhar

Routledge
Taylor & Francis Group

LONDON AND NEW YORK

First published 2024
by Routledge
4 Park Square, Milton Park, Abingdon, Oxon OX14 4RN

and by Routledge
605 Third Avenue, New York, NY 10158

Routledge is an imprint of the Taylor & Francis Group, an informa business

British Library Cataloguing-in-Publication Data
A catalogue record for this book is available from the British Library

ISBN: 978-1-032-43518-3 (hbk)
ISBN: 978-1-032-73871-0 (pbk)
ISBN: 978-1-003-46640-6 (ebk)

DOI: 10.4324/9781003466406

Typeset in Sabon
by SPi Technologies India Pvt Ltd (Straive)

CONTENTS

TABLES

ACKNOWLEDGEMENTS

This book is published posthumously. The author Dr Rajesh Kochhar passed away in March 2022 a few months after completing this manuscript.

While writing this book, the author would have contacted several colleagues and organizations. Unfortunately, I do not have that information available to me to acknowledge each one by name and contribution. I thank everyone who directly and indirectly contributed to this work by way of discussion, guidance and sharing their insights. Those who worked with the author know of his passion for Indian science and history and I thank you for enabling this work to come into being.

I would like to thank the editorial team at Routledge, Taylor and Francis Group – Dr Shashank Sinha, Antara Ray Chaudhury and Anvitaa Bajaj – for their patience as we navigated the process to get this manuscript ready for publication.

Thank you to Dr Partha Majumder for his kindness after the author's death, for guiding the initial stage of the publishing process and helping us find reviewers.

Thank you to Dr Jagdev Singh, Dr Tushar Prabhu, Dr Ramesh Kapoor and Dr Krishna Kumar. They were the author's dearest friends through decades – his sounding board not just on academic topics as in this book but in all his day-to-day discussions whether mundane, serious or humorous. They deserve an extra special mention just for enduring all his jokes. Their presence and support after his death has been key in getting this work published.

Without exaggeration, this book would have never moved from manuscript to publication without Dr Ramesh Kapoor. Dr Kapoor worked with the reviewer comments and the editorial team to incorporate feedback and get the manuscript publication ready. He spent over a year working through new content, making sure his expertise was augmented with the right additional knowledge to do justice to this book. And, he did all of this with his characteristic steady patience and good humour. Thank you, Kapoor Uncle.

Garima Kochhar
(Author's daughter)

1

INTRODUCTION

Our school textbooks and other writings at times give the impression that British soldiers, armed with science and technology, marched to India and conquered it. This is not true. When the English East India Company was established in 1600, the telescope had not yet come into existence. It is no more than a coincidence that the first English ship reached the Indian waters off Surat the same year (1608) the telescope made its appearance in the Netherlands. This numerology brings home the point that modern science grew hand in hand with oceanic voyages, maritime trade and colonialism. The Age of Reconnaissance was a necessary prerequisite for the Age of Renaissance, of which Europe became exceedingly proud.[1]

The Portuguese Prince Henry, the so-called Navigator, his sailors, Columbus and Vasco da Gama were all products of the Middle Ages. In 1434, Portuguese sailors ventured beyond Cape Bojador (not the Bojador of today but the present-day Cape Juby) notwithstanding the widely held belief that monsters resided there. Even though the ancient Greeks had warned that the seas would be boiling at the equator,[2] the Portuguese crossed the equator in about 1473 and emerged unscalded.

King Manuel I, during whose reign, extending from 1495 to 1521, Portugal reached India and Brazil, recognized the contribution of the navigational astronomy of his day by adopting the armillary sphere as his personal emblem.[3] He developed an elaborate architectural and decorative style, since designated Manuelino, which employed traditional Christian symbols as before but added such motifs as the armillary and others like twisted ropes connected with ships, oceans and distant lands. The armillary sphere also came to adorn the Portuguese national flag. Afonso de Albuquerque (1453–1515), who conquered

DOI: 10.4324/9781003466406-1

Goa in 1510, emulated his king and depicted the armillary sphere on the gold and silver coins minted by him.

The excitement and profitability of sea voyages triggered boldness of thought and action, broke old taboos and brought about new discoveries and inventions. The expansion of economy and encounters with diverse geographies, ecologies and peoples transformed the European mindset. For the first time in the history of humankind, production of wealth depended not upon the mercy of God or the goodwill of the King, but on human endeavour. The hold of feudal lords, kings, God and armchair academic authorities weakened and, in the course of time, sailors, merchants, carpenters and artisans became respectable and influential members of society.

Vasco da Gama did not make any geographical discovery, but the commercial discovery that he made on arrival in India in 1498 changed the course of world history. The pepper which sold at 160 ducats per quintal in Venice was available in Calicut for as little as six ducats. European merchants, on arrival in the Indian Ocean, discovered the value of intra-Asian or country trade. The first 12 English voyages to the East Indies during 1601–1612 yielded an average profit of 138%. Huge profits were waiting to be made if ships could reach their destination and return to the home port safely. There were two sources of death on high seas: shipwreck and death due to scurvy, now known to be caused by Vitamin C deficiency. A seasoned sailor could steer his ship safely, but there was no avoiding scurvy.

Scientific Aids to Navigation

A ship on the high seas did not have the advantage of any familiar landmarks. That is how the expression "at sea" arose to denote "not knowing what to do." The sailor must turn to the sky to know his position on the Earth. Ascertaining the latitude was relatively a simple matter because it involved measurement of angles. Determination of longitude however posed a non-trivial problem because it hinged on the determination of local time aboard the ship.

Scientific, commercial and nationalist causes all converged and the best European scientific brains of the time applied their minds to help the sailor. In 1597, Gresham College, named after the founder of the Royal Exchange, was established not at Oxford or Cambridge but at the new commercial centre, London. Henry Briggs (1561–1636), a mathematics professor at Gresham College and later at Oxford, invented, during 1615–1616, the logarithm to the base 10, which greatly simplified calculations. His reputation as a mathematician made him a leading member of the London Company and his advocacy of a northwest passage helped colonize Virginia. Ship captains took lessons from him before embarking on their voyages. In gratitude, two competing explorers independently named geographical features after him in North America: an island in the Hudson Bay; and an entire Bay.[4] Complementing Briggs' theoretical work, his astronomy colleague at Gresham, Edmund Gunter (1581–1626), invented the Gunter scale, for computing with logarithms, a forerunner of the slide rule.

It was at Gresham College in November 1660 that the Royal Society was formally constituted, though the name came later. It was a voluntary association for "the promoting of Experimental Philosophy,"[5] which stood apart from what Robert Boyle had in 1647 dubbed "the prattling of our book-philosophers."[6] The same year, that is 1660, John Graunt (1620–1674), a London draper, who laid the foundation of modern epidemiology by his analysis of bills of mortality, was made a fellow of the Society on the recommendation of King Charles II himself. When objections were raised within the Society because of Graunt's humble origins, Charles issued a Royal admonition: "if they found any more such tradesmen, they should be sure to admit them without much ado."[7] Graunt was imposed on the Society from above, but by and large it remained a club of the privileged for a long time.

English as well as French companies started compiling sea charts and keeping records of voyages. Observatories were opened at Paris in 1667 and Greenwich in 1675 for advancing navigational astronomy. The first Astronomer Royal supplemented his meagre salary by offering tuition to young men who wished to be appointed cadets in the East India Company. It paid to learn astronomy and it paid to join the Company. What was now needed were new instruments.

Sextant

In 1730, a young American glazier, Thomas Godfrey (1704–1749), in Philadelphia invented the (precursor of) sextant. It was successfully tested first during a voyage to Jamaica in November 1730 and then on a voyage to Newfoundland in 1731. Since ideas travel faster than things, the possibility exists that the news of Godfrey's instrument reached England. It has however consistently been asserted that sextant was "independently" invented in England by John Hadley in 1732. Godfrey's well-wishers in America requested the Royal Society for recognition for him, but without success.[8] North America was a lesser territory and not worthy of accommodation. Priority of invention apart, America of the day did not need a sea-faring instrument. Godfrey's creativity was a personal invention. Hadley's instrument however filled a felt need and immediately became a systemic innovation, and was widely accepted. The octant was improved into a sextant in 1767 by John Campbell. While ruthlessness and cruelties prevailed on high seas and distant lands, co-sharing of knowledge was considered purely scientific.

Longitude

British naval establishment paid a heavy price for contemptuously and cruelly disregarding the tacit knowledge residing in unlettered sailors. In 1707, four warships of the Royal Navy were wrecked off the Isles of Scilly in Great Britain itself which killed 2000 sailors. It was said that a common sailor on the flagship who was a native of Scilly and knew the waters tried to warn the Admiral that the fleet was off course. Instead of listening to him, the Admiral had him hanged. Even if the story is a myth, the fact remains that English establishment was loath till much later to take note of common people's tacit knowledge.

Determination of longitude was taken up as a British national mission in response to Scilly. In 1714, the British government formed the Board of Longitude which would award attractive prizes for one who solved the longitude problem. The solution was finally found by a carpenter-turned-clock maker John Harrison (1693–1776) who perfected his marine chronometer over a period of 40 years and was amply rewarded by the British Parliament, in instalments, the last one coming in 1773. Isaac Newton, the greatest scientist of the time, doubted the success of a sea clock, but Harrison persisted and proved Newton wrong. Those were the days when in their own domain self-taught artisans could confidently stand their ground against established names.

Scurvy

The human body can store only about six weeks' worth of Vitamin C. In longer voyages, if no preventive steps are taken, the sailor will start suffering from scurvy. In 1617, the Company surgeon general, John Woodall (1570–1643), recommended the use of "the Lemmons, Limes, Tamarinds, Oranges" against scurvy, adding that "[T]he use of the juice of Lemmons is a precious medicine." More than a century later, in 1747, pioneering clinical trials were conducted by the Scottish naval surgeon Robert Lind who concluded that oranges and lemons were the best cure for scurvy. The Navy, however, treated lemon juice to be too commonplace to be considered a medicine.

Finally, it was only in 1795 that the British Navy made lime a compulsory part of the diet on the sea. It is not that the Navy carefully evaluated available evidence and arrived at an informed decision. The decision was taken as a result of successful lobbying by a Scottish ship surgeon Gilbert Blane (1749–1834) who "did dearly love the society of lords and of senior officers," was popular with Admiral Rodney and the rulers of the King's Navy, and used "cajolery and flattery" to achieve his purpose.[9] In the period 1795–1814, the Admiralty issued a total of 1.6 million gallons of lemon juice.[10] This earned the epithet limey for British sailors and the British in general.

Control of scurvy along with scientific navigation drastically brought down the death rate on high seas. Sea voyages became safe so that the colonial service started attracting young men from better families.

European Interest in India

Europe's basic scientific interest in India was latitude-driven in the sense that it was dictated by the novelty of the landmass (in contrast, the current software-facilitated globalization-era Western interest in India is longitude-driven). The British were not interested in the scientific or industrial development of India. Their focus remained on field sciences. Whenever colonial requirements or European scientific interests pointed towards a particular discipline, such as geography, botany, astronomy, meteorology, geology, geodesy, animal husbandry, etc., attention was paid to it. Science was colonial in the sense that the agenda was colonial, but the science that emerged was not tainted on that count. Exceptions were ethnology and anthropology. Another tainted discipline was history. Since harnessing of science enriches it, in the process of Empire building, India was added as a field station to the world edifice of modern science. In the course of time, technological tools like steam, telegraph, railway and radio were introduced. Thus, ironically when we celebrate anniversaries of scientific institutions like the Survey of India, Geological Survey, telegraph, or railways, we are also unwittingly celebrating the step-wise entrenchment of the British colonial power in India.

The novelty of India made world-class scientists out of ordinary colonialists. Contribution to science removed the stigma of birth and poverty and made European colonial scientists important and respected members of their society.

India was a nice country to own but its people could not be wished away. It was a vast, thickly populated and culturally advanced country. It was necessary for the British to involve Indians in the administration of their own country. The French in Algeria excluded French-speaking Arabs from the Bar and practically confined them to a single profession – that of medicine.[11] Such a strategy would have been counter-productive in India. Here, the British made conscious efforts to connect with, and enlist support from, the leading sections of the Hindu society. In 1977, the noted film-maker Satyajit Ray (1921–1992) made a Hindi/Urdu film *Shatranj ke Khiladi* (chess players), set in 1856 Oudh (Avadh, corresponding to the present-day Eastern Uttar Pradesh). The story dealt with two Muslim noblemen who were so obsessed with chess that they had no time or concern for either their families or their official duties. Ray's story ends on an anti-climax.[12] The noblemen take note of the capture of their King by the British forces by declaring: "The rules of game have changed. The piece so far known as Vizier shall now be the Queen."

The denouement is subtle but unhistorical. In the original story, written in 1924 by Hindi writer Munshi Premchand (1880–1936), the two noblemen pick up a quarrel over a trifling and kill each other. This is consistent with the fact that the Muslim nobility chose to perish rather than support the new rulers. It was the Hindus, especially in Bengal, who enthusiastically took to British rule. Taking artistic license, Bengal-born Ray transports the Bengal phenomenon into Oudh.

Nested Three-stage Model

The advent and growth of modern science in India can be conveniently discussed in terms of a nested three-stage model comprising (i) the colonial tool stage, (ii) the peripheral native stage and (iii) the Indian response stage, each leading to and coexisting with the next.[13] The colonial tool stage consisted of the introduction and use of science, especially by the British, as an imperialist tool. It can be taken to begin with the appointment of James Rennell as Bengal Surveyor, in 1767, two years after the grant of Deewani. The colonial science effort involved persons from other European nations also. Science had an ideological dimension also. As authors of a powerful knowledge system, Europeans considered themselves to be superior to others and therefore entitled to rule.

In the "peripheral native stage," for reasons of economy, Indians were assigned the role of providing assistance to the colonial science machinery. The role increased and improved with time. In the first sub-stage, non-English-knowing natives were utilized. Next, help was drawn from the English-educated new middle class. This stage began in 1831 with the appointment of a number of Hindu college-educated boys (including Radhanath Sikdar) as sub-assistants for mathematical work in the Trigonometrical Survey.

The third stage, "the Indian-response stage," arose as a reaction to the preceding two stages and is characterized by scientific activity by Indians themselves. It can be taken to begin with the 1876 establishment of a pan-Indian, but essentially Bengali, Indian Association for the Cultivation of Science. We use the term native to refer to Indians in a subservient role, using Indian itself only when there is exercise of, or desire to exercise, free will or the desire thereof. It should however be noted that modern scientific research was initiated by Indians who were trained in Britain.

The phenomenon of colonial science in all its manifestations needs to be studied in detail not only because of its intrinsic historical value but also because Independent India's attitude towards science has been fashioned by the colonial experience.

Notes

1 Parry, 1982.
2 Goodman, 1991, 123.
3 Lach, 1970, 59.
4 Neither of the name survived.
5 Birch, 1756, 1, 3; McKie, 1960, 1.
6 McKie, 1960, 4.
7 Sprat, 1722, 67.
8 Real Admiral A. T. Long, 1931, The Godfrey Sextant, https://journals.lib.unb.ca/
   index.php/ihr/article/download/28527/1882521282.
9 Carpenter, 1986, 97.
10 Carpenter, 1986, 95.
11 Kennedy, 1910, 312.
12 Pritchett, 1986.
13 Kochhar, 1992, 1993a.

2
ENGLISH SURGEONS AND COMPANY TRADE CONCESSIONS

Medical men were the first Europeans to command any respect from Indian rulers. In later years, they would enrich the world of science in various ways, but in the purely trading days of the East India Company, they served as frontmen in obtaining trading concessions that gave English merchants a decided advantage over their European competitors and even Indians. In many cases, the concessions were not authentic but forged. The various official orders granting trade concessions gave the British a cause to defend, with military strength if needed. Indeed, the transformation of the Company from a trading outfit to a ruling organization was brought about by its desire to enforce its own version of the official charters issued in its favour and to continue with their misuse. It must be said, however, that on their part, the Mughal functionaries, from the head of the province downwards, tended to treat the European traders as milch cows.

There were three kinds of European medical men in India. Some were educated in a university and carried regular degrees. At the other end of the spectrum were those who had no medical expertise when they arrived in the East; they read a few Western medical books and successfully passed themselves off as doctors. Whether their success was due to their intuition, the quality of the books or plain exoticism is difficult to say. In most cases, however, candidates served as apprentices in England hospitals and sought employment as surgeons in ships and colonies. They differed widely in their professional attainments.

George Strachan in Iran and North West India

The earliest self-styled physician in the East was a Catholic Scotsman George Strachan (c. **1572–1635**). He came to Aleppo in about 1615, furnished

DOI: 10.4324/9781003466406-2

himself with some prescriptions from a Flemish doctor, bought a book or two and started to practice which became very successful. When the Company set up its first factory in Iran at Isfahan, under the control of Surat, Strachan was appointed surgeon. He served interruptedly till 1622, did not return to Europe and is believed to have died in 1635 in North West India where he was buried. Thanks to his successful practice and contacts with important people, he was able to collect books and manuscripts in Arabic, Persian and Turkish. He even translated some Persian works into Latin. His collection and works came to adorn European libraries. History remembers him as an Orientalist rather than a medical man.[1]

The presence of a European surgeon, Robert Surtees, at Surat was a great help to the local population. In 1636, the president of the Surat factory recorded:

> A young Bramene about the age of 14 years, washing himself in the river not far from the customhouse, a fish or crocodile (I conceave rather a sharke) sheared off his right arm in the midst betwixt the elbows and shoulder; who being the only child of his mother, a poor widow, I commanded the surgion to undertake the care for God's sake; who sawed off the boone, being shattered, and clipping of some torn flesh and then, applying such powders and other means as the case required, he bound it up very hard to stop the bleeding, all which the boy indured with manlike patience.

Another case occurred ten days later. It involved a "Banian called Cullian Vesse [Kalyan Vaishya] … an undertaker betwixt the rustickes and the Governor concerning the payment of their rents, who had received a great wound upon his head and another upon his leg." The surgeon, called at about ten at night, "used his best meanes," but "before midnight the Banian dyed."[2]

Nicholas Manucci

The first European doctor in Mughal India was a self-styled one. Nicholas Manucci (1638–c. 1720) left Venice in 1651 at the young age of 13 and arrived in Surat via Persia sometime between 1653 and 1655. After about 1656, Manucci came to Delhi and worked as the Mughal Emperor Shah Jahan's son Dara Shikoh's artilleryman at a monthly salary of 80 rupees. At the end of five or six years, he asked for and obtained from his relatives various books on medicine whose titles he specified (How did he learn about the books?). With the help of these books, he was able to declare himself to be a physician. During 1671–1678, Manucci practised medicine in Lahore and then, during 1678–1682, served as physician to Shah Alam, the eldest son of Aurangzeb.

He arrived in Madras in 1686 and remained here for the next 30 years till his death. Manucci wrote *Storia do Mogor* or *Mughal India*, which however is discursive and not very reliable.

Francois Bernier

Francois Bernier (1620–1688) with an MD from Montpellier arrived in India in 1658 or 1659 and served for a while as a surgeon to Dara Shikoh and then to his brother Aurangzeb. Bernier returned to Europe in 1667 through Persia. He published *Travels in the Mughal Empire* originally in 1670–1671 in French from Paris. It is considered to be an authoritative document for the period it covers.

John Fryer

John Fryer (c. 1650–1733) obtained an MB from Cambridge and arrived on the Indian west coast in the Company's service in 1673. He was sent to Iran 1677–1679. He returned to England in 1682, and the next year he obtained an MD from Cambridge. He was elected a Fellow of the Royal Society in 1697, becoming its first India-connected fellow. In 1698, he published a valuable book on his travels, called *A New Account of East India and Persia in Eight Letters, begun 1672 and finished 1681*. Fryer notes in passing that one Dr NG (from India) sent an account of the manufacture of ghee (clarified butter) to the Royal Society.[3] This must be one of the earliest examples of Europe trying to formally acquaint itself with Indian practices.

Where Iranian medicine stood at the time was placed on record by Fryer. Some of these details must be relevant for North West India also. Anyone who wished to join the profession took instruction from a master and then set up his practice where there were the fewest physicians already. His fame spread by degrees which in turn brought in many students. The patient would consult a physician for two or three weeks. If that did not work, the patient would move to consult some other. If the physician failed to set up a successful practice, he would "fall upon other Trades to get a Livelyhood." "In the matter of their Physick, Extracts or Essences of Plants, Roots, or Minerals, are beyond their Pharmacy; only they use cooling Seeds, and medicines of that nature." "Rhabarb, Turbith and Scammony are dreadful to them; but Senna, Cassia, Manna and Turpentine are swallowed without any apprehension of evil." They think that "if their own Nation cannot give them a Remedy... none other can." They however concede that "as to Chyrurgery" the Europeans were "better at Manual Operation than themselves."[4]

Manucci mentioned several European surgeons in India. An Armenian, called Sikandar Beg, was a surgeon to Suleiman Shikoh, Dara's eldest son, in

1658. A Dutch surgeon, Jacob Minues, was in Agra in 1663 and had fled Goa after killing a man there. Another Dutch surgeon, Geimer Vorburg, was in Assam the same year. Other names are Luis Beicao with Mirza Raja Jai Singh in the Deccan (1664); a Venetian, Angello Legrenzi, in the court of Shah Alam at Aurungabad (1679); d'Estremon, with the Sultan of Golconda (1684); and a Frenchman, Cattem, in Bengal (1700). From Tavernier, we learn about a French physician, Francois de la Palisse, alias St Jacques, as being at the Mughal court, and Claudius Malle, of Bourges, as surgeon to the governor of Allahabad, both about 1666. The Company tried to draw on their help. In 1684, the Company asked d'Estremon in Golconda for help in obtaining a *farman* that would permit the Company to coin rupees. Similarly in 1693, Johannes Petuliet ("from his name probably an Armenian") who was physician to the Nawab of Carnatic "tried to help the English get a *Farman* from the Emperor at Delhi for free trade on the Coromandel coast."

A *farman* was an executive order issued by the Emperor which was applicable to the entire Empire, while the order issued by a Governor for his own province was known as Nishan [Nishaun]. The Mughal administration as well as the peripheral kingdoms were fully aware of the benefits European trade bestowed on the economy in general and on high functionaries personally. Permission to open factories was given as a matter of course, and the Mughals routinely gave *rahdari* [transit duty] exemptions.[5] In reality, these exemptions did not mean much, because irrespective of the higher orders, bribes had to be paid at the lower levels. Moreover, any concession that was available across the board to all competitors still kept the playing field level. In addition to *rahdari* were the custom duties [*mahsul*]. What the British were looking for were concessions that would give them an edge over others. They soon got their chance, thanks to a combination of their medical expertise, mis-representations, fraud and low cunning.

The Boughton Legend

The most notable name in the Company's medical annals is not the surgeon who attended on the local populace, but the one doctor who served the Mughal nobility. "One of the most widely known stories of the early history of the English in India is the legend of Gabriel Boughton, Surgeon of the *Hopewell*."[6] It first appeared in print in 1778, but was subjected to historical scrutiny only in 1911, by Sir William Foster, the historiographer to the India Office. By this time, it had served the colonial cause well.

In the intervening period, it appeared in so many otherwise scholarly publications that it came to be accepted as one of the romances of history. A detailed and picturesque account appeared in 1813 in Major Charles Stewart's *History of Bengal*. It mixes up dates and names, but its essence is as follows.

Emperor Shah Jahan's daughter was "dreadfully burnt" in an accident. As he desired "the assistance of an European Surgeon," Gabriel Boughton was brought from Surat who "had the good fortune to cure the young Princess of the effects of her accident." When he was asked

> to name his reward, he, with that liberality which characterizes Britons, sought not for any private emolument; but solicited that his nation might have liberty to trade, free of all duties, to Bengal, and to establish factories in that country. His request was complied with, and he was furnished with the means of travelling across the country to Bengal. Upon his arrival in that province, he proceeded to Pipley, and in the year A.H. 1048 [AD 1638] an English ship happening to arrive in that port, he, in virtue of the Emperor's firman and the privileges granted to him, negociated the whole of the concerns of that vessel without the payment of any duties.[7]

It is now considered certain that Shah Jahan's *farman* never existed; it was a myth created to derive commercial benefit. The sequence of events can now be reconstructed with reasonable confidence.

(i) On 2 October 1637, Shah Jahan issued a routine *farman* exempting English traders from paying transit duties.

(ii) In 1643 (or 1644), at Agra, the Emperor's daughter Jahan Ara met with a fire accident, "Anitulla, the most famous physician of the age, was brought express from Lahore," and the Princess was cured. No European surgeon was involved in this and there was thus no question of Shahjahan's rewarding the Company by issuance of a duty-exemption *farman*.

(iii) Boughton arrived in Surat in 1644, near about the time of Jahan Ara's accident and found an attractive appointment waiting for him. Asalat Khan, *Mir Bakshi* (or paymaster general) of the Mughal empire and a special favourite of Emperor Shah Jahan, had been keen to obtain the services of a European surgeon and had asked the Company at Surat to send him one. Boughton accepted the appointment and came to Agra early 1645. The next year he even accompanied his patron to Balkh. At about the same time, in Basra, the Company surgeon was providing medical assistance to "the Governour's kinsman and ally Agha."[8] On Asalat Khan's death in 1647, Boughton accepted the patronage of Shah Shuja, emperor's son and the *subahdar* (governor) of Bengal and moved to his capital Rajmahal. "One of the princes (sic) concubines, which woman the Prince greatly loved, had a great pain in her side, and could find no cure." The lady was cured by Mr Boughton "in a very short time." In return Shuja issued a *nishan* ordering that imperial officers should not interfere with Boughton for the payment of customs. The duty exemption however was for the surgeon's personal trade and not the Company's. Two years later (that would be 1649) a ship arrived from London (under Captain Brookhaven) and bought several goods free of duties "upon the account of Mr Boughton's nishauns."

English traders' fraud operated at two levels. Shuja's custom concession to Boughton as an individual was made into a concession for the Company, and a provincial *nishan* passed off as an all-encompassing Emperor's *farman*. In subsequent years, the Company traders were able to persuade post-Shuja governors to issue *parwanas* [permits] in their favour based on Shah Jahan's non-existent *farman*.[9]

The British traders were not the only ones trying to pull strings in the Mughal capital. In 1711, a Dutch embassy arrived from Surat to the court of Aurangzeb's successor, Bahadur Shah. Their helper in the court was a Portuguese lady, Donna Juliana Dias da Costa, whose late father had been a doctor in the service of Aurangzeb and Bahadur Shah. She held the well-paid job of the "governess of the harem and commanded influence both over the Emperor and his Court." Her efforts however were nulled by the fast-changing political scene. She helped the Dutch get a favourable *farman* from Bahadur Shah, who unfortunately died soon thereafter of old age. She did manage to get a new *farman* from his successor, Jahandar Shah, but he lost his throne and life within a year, making way for Farrukh Siyar, the benefactor of the British.[10]

In 1715, a Company embassy led by John Surman came to Farrukh Siyar's court from Calcutta. It included a surgeon, William Hamilton. In August, he was required to treat the King for swellings in the groin and did so with success. Two months later, in October, the King was again attacked by violent pain, and it was feared that he would develop fistula. Hamilton's treatment was again successful, and on 7 December the King's marriage to the daughter of Raja Ajit Singh of Jodhpur, which had long been delayed by his illness, was celebrated. "Hamilton was richly rewarded, receiving an elephant, a horse, five thousand rupees in money, two diamond rings, a jewelled aigrette, a set of gold buttons, and models of all his instruments in gold."

More important than the personal enrichment of Hamilton was the fact that his professional success placed the Company's embassy in high regard in the Emperor's court. In April 1717, the Emperor's *farmans* were issued, meeting all the demands that the Company had made in its petitions. The favours included permission to purchase 38 villages surrounding the three already held by the Company (Sutanuti, Gobindapur and Kalikata). After issuing the *farman*, and not before it, Farrukh Siyar expressed a wish to retain Hamilton in Delhi as his personal surgeon. "As Hamilton was unwilling to stay, much further trouble and delay were caused; but finally Farakh Siyar consented to let him go, on his promising to return to Delhi, after a visit to Europe." This was not to be, because Hamilton died the same year, in December 1717, at Calcutta. A British medical historian commenting on the above in 1914 wrote patronisingly "the King's consent to his (Hamilton's) departure shows a more reasonable and more kindly disposition than might have been expected in an Oriental potentate."[11] Farrukh Siyar was murdered barely two years after the *farmans*, but the favours he bestowed on English traders remained and influenced the course of history.

Given the chaotic condition of the Mughal Empire, Farrukh Siyar's *farman* giving concessions to the Company was unenforceable, at least in Bengal. However, trade exemptions, no matter how obtained, gave the British traders a decided commercial advantage over other European companies and even over native traders. More importantly, the various official orders granting trade concessions gave the British a cause to defend, with military strength whenever needed.

Notes

1 Yule, 1888, 314–315; Winstone, 1984; Glazier, 2020, https://euppublishingblog. com/2020/08/12/george-strachan-of-the-mearns-a-historians-biography/.
2 Crawford, 1914, 1, 64–65.
3 Elgood, 1951, 397; Crawford, 1914, 1, 66–67.
4 Elgood, 1951, 401–405.
5 Prakash, 1998, 125.
6 Crawford, 1914, 1, 37.
7 Crawford, 1914, 1, 37.
8 Crawford, 1914, 1, 66.
9 Hasan, 1991, 353.
10 Sharma, n.d., 370.
11 Crawford, 1914, 1, 120.

3

GEOGRAPHY

In the early days when Europeans were full-time merchants, they had no reason to venture into the interior. However, once they developed territorial ambitions, it became necessary for them to gather geographical information and prepare maps. Without intelligence on terrain, rivers, hills, roads, bridges, etc., the European military might be useless. The French, thanks to the Jesuit connection, took the lead in modern Indian map-making, but soon the initiative passed on to the British, who had their tasks clearly laid out: to survey the territories they already held, increase revenue earnings, and learn about Indian geography, for the sake of administration and future conquests. Military geography thus went hand in hand with the administrative. Whatever geographical information had been obtained by the Europeans in relatively recent times was located and made use of. At the same time, still older sources like *Ain-e-Akbari* were consulted.

As soon as a territory came under British control, a systematic field survey was ordered. There was already a precedent from Scotland, where immediately after the 1746 suppression of the Jacobite rising, a survey was ordered in 1747 of confiscated estates, which comprised the greater portions of the Scottish Highlands. One of the Scottish officers involved in the survey, Major General William Roy (1726–1790), would later initiate England's Ordnance Survey and inspire its Indian counterpart.

Early Geography 1759–1818

In 1761, one Hugh Cameron (d. 1764) was appointed "Surveyor of the New Lands," acquired during 1757–1760. This was the first regular appointment of a surveyor anywhere in India.[1] On his death, the appointment went to

DOI: 10.4324/9781003466406-3

Major James Rennell (1742–1830). In 1767, two years after the grant of Deewani, Rennell was made the Surveyor General of Bengal. While discussing the early days of the Company administration, it is not quite meaningful to talk of British India as a single entity, because the three Presidencies functioned more or less independently. Bombay appointed Charles Reynolds as its Surveyor General in 1796 and Madras Colin Mackenzie in 1807. The latter became India's first Surveyor General in 1815. Rennell remained in office till 1777, after which he worked at the East India House in London. There he prepared maps which were sent out to Bengal in Company ships.[2] His *Bengal Atlas* in 1779–1781 was followed by his magnum opus, the *Map of Hindustan* accompanied by a Memoir, with the value of the memoir long outliving that of the map. The two first appeared together in 1782 but separately underwent revisions till 1793 to incorporate new and improved data. As Rennell wrote to India in 1808, "at that day we were compelled to receive information from others respecting the interior of the country, but in your time you explored for yourself."[3] A substantial body of early geographical information came from the Jesuits.

Jesuits as Geographers

The European mercantile interests were fortunate to have valuable secondary tools of the Empire in the form of Jesuit priests, who had the time, scientific training and opportunity to criss-cross the country. They collected valuable and reliable geographical data partly out of curiosity and partly on instructions from France.

The Jesuits in India or elsewhere were not interested in reaching out to the European public at large. They dutifully sent their accounts to their headquarters. From the beginning of the 18th century, these accounts were incorporated in *Lettres edifiantes et curieuses* (Edifying and Curious Letters) of which a total of 36 volumes were published from Paris between 1702 and 1776, the oldest letter being dated 1699. The early geographical information they sent back home had limited immediate appeal if any. Europe was not yet ready for India. It was only when knowing India became a paying proposition that Jesuit data came to be valued. An abridged two-volume translation of the first 25 volumes of the Jesuit *Lettres* (up to 1741) was edited in London in 1743 by John Lockman and titled *Travels of the Jesuits into Various Parts of the World: Particularly China and the East-Indies*. Lockman hoped that the Jesuits' "literary productions" would be found as "acceptable" as "the Tenets and Practices ascribed to them must be distasteful."[4] Predictably, he deleted accounts of conversions and miracles, as being "quite insipid or ridiculous to most English readers, and indeed to all persons of understanding and taste." English readers were undoubtedly interested only in those parts of the Jesuit work which would further their own overseas interests. Lockman's edition was obviously important enough to warrant a corrected second edition in 1762. Over the years, the Jesuit *Lettres* were translated into Spanish, German and Italian. France on its part brought out a fresh edition of the original Jesuit work. It was published in Paris between 1780 and 1783 in 26 volumes by Querboeuft, who conveniently arranged the letters in geographical order. Volumes 10–15 give information about India. Thanks to the Jesuits, the French were more successful in India on the scientific front than they were on the colonial.

Bouchet

The first dependable map of the interior of the southern peninsula was due to the efforts of Fr Jean-Venant Bouchet (1653–1732) who had the inconvenient distinction of landing in India from the east rather than the west. Born at Fontney-le-Comte in France, he joined the Society of Jesus in 1670 and was a member of the expedition sent to Siam (Thailand) in 1687 by King Louis XIV. There were 14 Jesuits in all, formally designated "The Mathematicians of the King." They arrived in Siam in 1688 but were expelled the same year as a result of a revolution that overthrew the king. The missionaries left for India, but only three survived the ordeal and reached Pondicherry on 17 February 1689, two of them being Fr Bouchet and Fr Jean Richaud. It is not clear who the third Jesuit was. On arrival in India, Bouchet joined the Madura Mission but left it in 1703 to set up the Carnatic Mission.

Bouchet covered the Coromandel coast on foot, made astronomical obser-vations at Pondicherry, and prepared maps and sketches. In 1719, he sent to France his map of Madurai and the neighbouring kingdoms, extending it slightly to the north of 14°. The map was drawn on a small scale of not quite an inch to one degree of latitude, with the result that it was not capable of giving any considerable detail of the territories covered. Obviously, there was some sort of coordination between the Jesuit data collectors on the one hand and the French commercial and political interests on the other. The Jesuits next sent over several manuscript charts and other materials from which a new map was prepared by the famous French cartographer Jean-Baptiste Bourguignon D'Anville (1697–1782). It was drawn on a scale nearly twice as large as the former and was a great deal more particular as well as accurate and extended further north. D'Anville published his map of the southern peninsula in 1737 and followed it by his famous *Carte de l'Inde* in 1752. An important feature of this map was that instead of speculating, he very consci-entiously left blank those parts of India about which he did not have authen-tic knowledge. D'Anville consulted tables in Ain-e-Akbari, Ulugh Beg and others to get or compare data. There was a tacit understanding in Europe that commercial and military rivalries notwithstanding, scientific knowledge would be unreservedly shared. D'Anville's Memoir was translated, annotated and published with a reprint of his map in London in 1754 and 1759.

Richaud

In passing, we may note the scientific activities of Bouchet's co-surviving colleague, Richaud. He discovered in 1689 that the bright southern star Alpha Centauri was in fact a double star. This was the second binary ever discovered. Earlier in 1685 another Jesuit, Fr Fontenay, had discovered from the Cape of Good Hope, the first binary Alpha Crucis. Richaud's was the first recorded astronomical discovery from India. The 1680s thus marked a significant step in the European observation of the southern skies.

Boudier

The next stage was the geographical exploration of Hindustan (North India) undertaken by Fr Claude Stanislaus Boudier (1686–1757). Born at Sens in France, Boudier left France for Chandernagore in Bengal in 1708. His chance to traverse north India came about as a result of the astronomical pursuits of Sawai Raja Jai Singh of Jaipur who wanted the Jesuit to visit him for scientific consultations. Accordingly, Boudier and another Jesuit Pons set out from Chandernagore on 6 January 1734. "[O]n their arrival they seem unfortunately to have wasted much time in disputing with the local Brahmins as to the extent to which Indian astronomy was indebted to the ancient Greeks." The two Jesuits worked in Jaipur during August and September 1734 and returned to Chandernagore about a year later.

The Jesuit mission was a failure from Jai Singh's point of view, but seen from the colonial angle, it was a huge success. During his journey both ways, Boudier fixed the longitude and latitude of many important places and kept a survey of his route between Agra and Allahabad. He described various places on the road from Agra to Bengal and computed their distance from the course of Yamuna and Ganga. Boudier's work was extensively used by D'Anville as well as Rennell. The latter depended on Boudier for his 1774 general map of Bengal and used his values as late as 1793.

Tiefenthaler

A rather pathetic figure was Fr Joseph Tiefenthaler (1710–1785) who survived the dissolution of the Society of Jesus in 1773 by working under British auspices. Born at Bolzano in the Austrian Tyrol, he joined the Order in 1729 and left Germany for Spain in 1740. In 1742, he sailed from Lisbon for Goa and arrived in Goa the next year. He was apparently intended originally for the Jaipur Observatory, but Jai Singh's death in 1743 cut short these plans. He was accordingly sent to Agra to work at the Jesuit College there. Shortly, afterwards, he began his wanderings to Mathura, Delhi, Narwar (now in Shivpuri district of Madhya Pradesh), Goa, Surat and numerous other places.

In 1747, he commenced service as a priest at the Bourbon colony at Narwar where he remained for about 18 years.

In 1759, the King of Portugal banished all Jesuits from his dominions. Consequently, the Jesuit presence in Goa ceased and with this, the Mughal Mission as a Jesuit enterprise came to an end. Tiefenthaler found himself in such financial straits that in 1756 he boldly decided to appeal for financial help to the "famous English nation so well known for their humanity, liberality and charity to the poor." He travelled to Calcutta keeping surveys on the way. Apparently, he found the help he needed and settled in Oudh for the rest of his life. Till 1771, he was continuously on the move making astronomical observations and surveys, employing also one or more local assistants "versed in geography," whom he sent to explore the sources of the Ganga and Gogra. Tiefenthaler was a tireless explorer. The publication history of Tiefenthaler's works draws attention to the complexity of the times. In 1772 or 1773, he sent a voluminous collection of his works in Latin to Christian Gottlieb Kratzenstein (1723–1795), a professor in Copenhagen, through the agency of a Danish doctor, Dr Flor, whom he had met in India.[5] In 1759, while in Surat Anquetil Duperron had been in correspondence with Tiefenthaler in Narwar. Almost two decades later, in 1776, he received a packet from Tiefenthaler (then at Faizabad). It included many maps, including a 15-foot-long map of Ganga. Anquetil Duperron very promptly prepared a treatise on these maps and published it in the *Journal des Savants*, making it a point to mention Tiefenthaler's works that lay unattended in Copenhagen. Anquetil Duperron's publication spurred the Berlin-based German astronomer and mathematician John Bernoulli. He obtained Tiefenthaler's geographical work *Descriptio Indiae* from Copenhagen and collaborated with Anquetil Duperron in its translation and publication along with that of an expanded version of Anquetil Duperron's edition of Tiefenthaler's treatise. The work was published in three volumes in German (1785–1787) and French (1786–1789). Bernoulli's publication reached Rennell in England in time for Tiefenthaler's work to be incorporated into his 1788 map. Thomas Call (c. 1749–1788), Rennell's successor as Surveyor General of Bengal, had already received copies from Tiefenthaler himself. Call's *Atlas of India* embodies routes taken between Goa and Agra by Tiefenthaler and a survey of the country northwest of Delhi by him and Fr Francis Xavier Wendel (d. 1803).

Wendel

The sad state of the last days of the Mughal Mission is best epitomized by the rather shadowy Wendel who like Tiefenthaler survived the Mission. It is not possible to construct a connected account of his life.[6] Wendel was a German who came to India in 1751. By 1763, he was in Lucknow. In 1764, he sent Duperron a map showing the strategic position of the Mughal and

British armies at the time of the Battle of Buxar. He spent almost four years, 1764–1768, with the Jat Raja Jawahar Singh at Bharatpur, Deeg and Agra. The French commandant at Chandernagore complained to Paris that Wendel was a British agent. It is certain that

> he was in the pay of the English and that his real object was to keep the Bengal Government informed of any hostile designs of the powerful and ambitious Jat Raja who held the balance in Northern India between the Abdali and the Maratha.[7]

In 1768, he wrote his memoirs on the origin, growth and present state of Jat power in Hindustan (1768). Wendel was closely associated with Tiefenthaler in geographical pursuits. From a scientific point of view, his most notable contribution is his *A Memoir on the Land of the Rajputs and other Provinces to the South and South West of Agra*, along with a map which he drew in 1779. These were afterwards presented by Colonel Popham to Rennell, who acknowledged Wendel's help in the preparation of his great map of Hindustan. In 1780, Wendel met a Russian named Czernichef who had travelled from Bukhara through Kashmir to Lucknow and sent the latter's diary to Colonel Francis Wilford at Benares. Wendel died on 20 March 1803 and like Tiefenthaler was buried at Agra. With his death, the last links with the Mughal Mission snapped.

Monserrate

The earliest Jesuit geographical work carried out in India was the last one to be taken into account. Fr Anthony Monserrate (1536–1600) was born in Vic de Ozona, 30 miles from Montserrat in Catalonia (Spain). He joined the Order in 1568 and left for India in 1574. In 1579, he was chosen to be a member of the first Jesuit mission to Akbar's court and was asked by his superiors to keep a diary. This he did most faithfully, adding greatly to its value by his geographical and astronomical observations. On his journey from Surat to Fatehpur Sikri in 1580, he made a survey and took observations for latitude. When in 1583 Akbar marched to Kabul against his half-brother Mirza Muhammad Hakim, he took Monserrate along to continue the education of his second son Murad (1570–1599). Akbar encouraged Monserrate to take observations en route which he did as far as Jalalabad. Akbar however does not seem to have shown any interest in the data collected by Monserrate who kept it with himself when he returned from the journey.

On the basis of his observations, Monserrate, in about 1590, prepared a small map, $5^{1/2}$ in. $\times 4^{1/8}$ in. in size. This little map was a tremendous improvement over all previous efforts. It was based on actual observations rather than on travellers' tales. It gave a better idea of the Himalayas and the upper course of Punjab rivers than Rennell would do two centuries later. Expectedly, Monserrate did not have any knowledge about regions east of Yamuna. Keeping in mind the times when it was first prepared, its value cannot be overestimated. It however had no contemporary significance. Monserrate's work, carried out when the Mission was just established, came to light only when the Mission was closed in 1803.

In the opening years of the 19th century, Monserrate's manuscript was dusted out of the archival shelves and incorporated into the corpus of geographical knowledge. The timing was not fortuitous. The British struggle for territorial control over north India was almost over, and the British were finally in Delhi. The territory west of Delhi was now of strategic importance. Monserrate was able to do his fieldwork when Akbar marched to the north west to secure his fledgling empire. The British needed Monserrate for the same reason. Monserrate's geographical work thus neatly brackets the Mughal Empire's history. It is reasonably certain that a copy of Monserrate's manuscript was kept at the Jesuit College at Agra from where it was taken by Tiefenthaler who may have passed it on to Wilford in 1784 a year before his own death. The manuscript went into the valuable *Map of the Countries West of Delhi as far as Cabul and Multan*, which Francis Wilford brought out in 1804. This was a tremendous improvement on anything that had been produced before. It stretched as far as Sukkur and Dera Ghazi Khan on the southwest, Kabul on the west, and to Chitral, and Gilgit in the north. For additional information, Wilford employed a "properly instructed native," Mirza Mogul Beg, who carried out extended fieldwork between 1786 and 1796.

Military Geography: The Moonshee Phase

Indians were first hired as servants and then as assistants. This early employment of Indians to serve the European geographical cause constitutes the little-known Moonshee–Pundit phase, identified here for the first time. Old spellings are advisedly used to convey the flavour of the time and to distinguish from other uses of the terms. The term Pundit was invariably used for Hindus, irrespective of whether they were Brahmin or not, learned or not. Muslims so employed were designated Moonshees, although Hindus could also carry the designation. In this phase, suitably instructed Indians were hired to facilitate the Europeans' work. This phase, transitional by its very nature, preceded the better-known Baboo phase in which the Europeans educated the upper-caste Hindu youth in their own fashion with a view to preparing them for lower-level appointments in the new administration. The Baboo phase was necessitated by reasons of economy, while the work which the Moonshees did could have been done only by them.

Surveys were continually required for military purposes. The geographical location of important places in the country was determined by "borrowing a sextant here, a watch there, and a quadrant in another quarter, from different officers at Calcutta who happened to possess them." Surveyors were sent out with every army to prepare route maps. Intelligence on south and western India was very greatly valued because of the stiff resistance offered to the British by Mysore and the Mahrattas. In 1774, a Sepoy Officer Golam Mohammad was sent to explore the roads and countries of the Deccan and "to gain intelligence about the Mahratta powers."[8] In the 1780s, Thomas Call while working on his *Atlas of India* employed "Munshys to survey some roads between places well ascertained in the Map" and "procure some very useful information." His expenditure of Rs 12,000 on this count was reimbursed by the Company.[9] In 1791, the Bengal surveyor Reuben Burrow while budgeting for his journey asked for "a Moonshy at Rs 25 a month," adding "This last article is more necessary than at first sight may appear, as it is often requisite to send a Moonshy to make enquiries and to take bearings, and to get copies of routes, etc." The value of military geography can be seen from the fact that in 1793, the Company paid a fabulous sum of Rs 6,000 to a surveyor, Lieutenant Robert Hyde Colebrooke (1762/3–1808), for a map of Mysore accompanied by a memoir. Colebrooke later served as Surveyor General of Bengal, during 1794–1808.

Charles Reynolds

The most spectacular use of the local surveyors was made by Colonel (later Lieutenant General) Charles Reynolds, Surveyor General of Bombay, who employed them for 12 years from 1795 to 1807 to collect data for a large-scale map of western India, especially of territories outside the Company's control. He even offered to pension them off on his own. As a part of his work, Reynolds discovered that the river Ghaggar does not cross the desert to reach the sea as had been supposed by earlier geographers, but instead loses its way in the sands near Sirsa. Reynolds received the princely sum of two lakh rupees for his valuable map.[10]

The Company surveyors hired "Native assistants" or harkaras (messengers) to do the leg work. The Company refused to reimburse these expenses. It was one thing for the Company to pay for inside information on the Mahrattas, but the Company had no intention of spending its hard-earned money on such useless piece of information as that the rivers Sone and Narmada do not spring from the same source as Rennell had supposed but arose 40 miles apart.[11] The Company, not yet sure of itself, was never very comfortable with the use of the natives, which though convenient and economical, was risky. While adding to the knowledge of the British, they might become knowledgeable themselves, or worse, sell the information to the French, Dutch, or others. Finally, in 1813, the use of harkaras for survey work was banned, "as Government were anxious to prevent the Natives from obtaining, or being taught, any knowledge of the kind."[12] Only the Company's own covenanted or military officers could carry out surveying and map-making within India. The use of Indians for revenue work was a different matter. Here there was no security risk; the only apprehension was of untrust-worthiness and corruption, which could be averted by better supervision.

Company Surveyors

An early British geography-oriented astronomical observer in India was Calcutta-based Colonel Thomas Dean Pearse (1741/2–1789), the first profes-sionally educated artillery officer in the Company's service in India. Pearse was born in a respectable but impoverished family. He joined the Royal Artillery for prestige and in 1768 was transferred to the Company service for money.[13] He set up a private observatory at his residence in Calcutta and regularly made observations of longitudes and latitudes. He had the ingenu-ity to modify his wooden and brass instruments to serve his purpose better. He also recorded meteorological data. On his way from Calcutta to Madras for the 1781–1784 Mysore War, he made astronomical observations. On his way back from Madras to Calcutta, he carried out a systematic survey mea-suring distances with perambulator and fixing positions astronomically. For the latter, he was handed over a 15-inch radius land quadrant which the Company had sent out for the 1761 transit of Venus observation by Reverend William Hirst (page 52). Additionally, and more importantly, he trained his young assistant, Robert Colebrooke.[14] India-based Englishmen sought pa-tronage from the British establishment which was not always forthcoming. Pearse contacted the Astronomer Royal Nevil Maskelyne (1732–1811) as well as the president of the Royal Society Joseph Banks for recognition in England. At the time, Banks and Maskelyne were in opposing camps in the Royal Society, with Maskelyne charging Banks with bias against mathemati-cal sciences. But poor Pearse stood disowned by both. Recognition in the home country was keenly sought and was a great incentive for the British in India to indulge in scientific pursuits.

Reuben Burrow

Starved of European talent, colonial India happily offered opportunities to Englishmen who in the country of their birth were considered low-bred. Born in a poor family and irregularly educated, Reuben Burrow (1747–1792) was a brilliant mathematician. Had he come from a better social background, he would have been a great intellectual asset, but England was not ready to ig-nore his personality traits or condone his anti-social behaviour.

An erstwhile assistant to the Royal Astronomer, Dr Nevil Maskelyne, he was fortunate to receive patronage from Henry Watson (1737–1786) of Bengal Engineers who was in England during 1772–1776. On his advice, Burrow arrived in Calcutta in 1783 without any appointment. He began giving private tuition to European officers in Calcutta who were interested in learning mathematics.[15] In 1783 itself he was hired to start a school of mathematics and astronomy for young engineer officers stationed at Fort Williams. The teaching arrangement lasted only three years. In 1787, the Company purchased a number of astronomical instruments for his official survey work. Using them, he fixed the geographical points from Haridwar to Assam.[16] He made a proposal for the establishment of a permanent observatory, but it was brusquely turned down by the Company.[17]

Sir William Jones arrived in Calcutta a few months after Burrow, as a Supreme Court judge. Burrow became a founding member of the Asiatic Society (1784) and seems to have contributed several notes on astronomy in Francis Gladwin's Ayeen Akbery [Ain-e-Akbari].[18] While out surveying he acquired old manuscripts and interacted with learned pundits. History remembers Burrow as one of the earliest investigators of ancient Indian mathematics. In 1790, he published "A Proof that the Hindu had the Binomial Theorem."[19]

Half-hearted Geodesy

So far the British Indian interest in geography had been purely for utilitarian reasons. Now, scientific Europe took note of the vast Indian land mass accessible to the British. In 1783, Cassini III, the director of Paris Observatory, suggested that the difference in the longitude and latitude of Greenwich and Paris observatories be precisely ascertained through triangulation. The task was entrusted to William Roy, who measured the baseline in 1784, while actual triangulation was begun in 1787. This diplomatic initiative led to the establishment of the British Ordnance Survey in 1791 and gave great fillip to the making of mathematical instruments. In 1787, before starting the triangulation, Roy suggested that measurements be made in peninsular India for determining the length of a degree at lower latitudes. In April 1790, following explicit orders, Burrow began work on measuring the degree of longitude near the Tropic of Cancer. The work was however interrupted by Burrow's death and not resumed. Burrow's results were finally published by his friend in 1796.[20] British India's first half-hearted foray into geodesy was a non-success.

Dr James Dinwiddie (1746–1815)

A first-hand account of where science generally stood in Calcutta at the end of the 18th century comes from Dr James Dinwiddie (1746–1815), a well-regarded science educator from Scotland, who was part of the embassy under Lord Macartney which was sent out to China by East India Company in 1792. Dinwiddie was designated mathematician and made superintendent of a large number of astronomical and other scientific instruments meant to be presented to the Chinese Emperor. The embassy however was a total failure. The instruments were given away to Dinwiddie as part of payment for his services. On his request, Dinwiddie was dropped at Calcutta, while the rest of the embassy returned home. Dinwiddie lived in Calcutta from 1794 to 1805.

In 1791, when Cornwallis laid siege to Bangalore, no one man among his engineers could measure the distance of the enemy's targets. It was determined to be 1200 yards, but when the battery began to play, the fire could not reach the target. In this dilemma, Colonel Patrick Ross (1740–1804) was sent from Madras who determined the distance to be 2000 yards.[21] Mathematics was generally at "a low ebb" among officers. Dinwiddie filled that gap. Receiving "ample encouragement" from the Governor General, Dinwiddie advertised a course of 25–30 lectures, beginning April 1795, on natural philosophy and chemistry at a substantial fee of ten gold mohurs.[22] The introductory lecture was attended by as many as 180 of "the first ladies and gentlemen in the settlement." Dinwiddie was able to raise a subscription of £2250, "the greatest sum that, probably, ever was received for one course in any part of the world."[23]

The public enthusiasm for the lectures waned in later years, but his early success did fetch him a regular though short-lived employment. In 1795, he was asked "to extend his advice to any subjects that should be referred to him" by any department. He was also "to communicate any observations on manufacture, chemistry or science, that might be useful in promoting the prosperity of the Company's provinces." The appointment which carried a monthly salary of Rs 500 was terminated in January 1797, because "it did not appear to us...that the prospect and advantage to the Company was sufficient to justify a continuance of his salary."[24] While the appointment lasted,

> we find him testing and reporting on the qualities of indigo, cochineal, saltpetre, flax and hemp, and the native timbers of the country, in regard to the purposes of architecture and ship-building. He also attended to the erection of lightening-rods, the management of fire-engines, pumps; to regulating chronometers, and a variety of other matters.[25]

This gives an idea of the administration's scientific activities at the time.

Dinwiddie noted that Calcutta "was considered the most expensive city in the world." He drew attention to the "abominable trash" that was "poured into this country, by every ship from Europe, under the name of hats, boots, shoes, telescopes, with a long list of et cetra." He observed that "The cockney phrase-My dear sir, this hat is not for sale-it is for the Ingee market-is well known here." Of immediate concern to Dinwiddie in Calcutta were the quality and price of sulphuric and nitric acids. Being hazardous, these chemicals could only be brought in as deck cargo, which entailed heavy freight, making the landed cost prohibitively high. On top of it, he found the nitric acid sent out by the British manufacturer to be adulterated; "the bottle had been filled, at least three-fourths of the whole contents, with water." Manufacturing of sulphuric acid was taken up by the government on his suggestion and placed under his management. At the same time, he privately undertook the manufacture of nitric acid "for supplying by contract to the dispensary."[26] The manufacturers however did not survive Dinwiddie's departure.

In April 1801, Dinwiddie was appointed teacher of mathematics at the newly opened College of Fort William, Calcutta. He held the post till 1805 when the College was downsized and his post abolished. He lectured on natural philosophy, chemistry, mathematics, and the ancient and modern art of war.[27] His Analysis of a Course of Lectures in Experimental Philosophy was published in 1801. But much to his disappointment, the College emphasis remained on oriental languages.[28]

Dinwiddie's lectures were particularly helpful to officers entrusted with a government survey, who found Dinwiddie's lecture room useful in getting their mathematics brightened up for the field.[29] Dinwiddie had high hopes for the large-scale use of modern science in British India. He invested a considerable amount of his money in importing scientific instruments in the hope that the College, government and the public at large would buy them. His hopes however were belied. British India was not interested in initiating or promoting manufacture.

Tafazzul Hussain Khan Kashmiri

The first Indian to acquaint himself with Western scientific learning was an 18th-century aristocratic Shia Muslim. Tafazzul Hussain Khan (1727–1800) was a mathematically oriented learned scholar who became the Company's ally in its political machinations in Avadh (Oudh, Oude) and interacted with the British officials at various levels.[30] From 1788 till 1797, Tafazzul served as Nawab Asaf-ud-Dowla's vakil (agent) at Calcutta. He returned to Lucknow as the Prime Minister but quit the position on the Nawab's death that took place a few months later. Sa'adat Ali, on his installation as Nawab in January 1798, appointed Tafazzul as vakil in Calcutta. He could enjoy the position for a very short period because he died in early 1800.

He was useful to the British not only on the political front but also on the intellectual. Europe at the time was very greatly interested in recovering the Greek originals from under the layers of Arabic scholarship. Warren Hastings asked Tafazzul to obtain for him copies of Greek books that Tafazzul might come across. Another European interest at the time was the ancient Indian astronomy. In 1792, Anderson writing from Edinburgh on behalf of his "literary friends" asked Tafazzul to get some information on the topic from Sanskrit pundits. On his part, Tafazzul was keen to learn about European astronomy and mathematics. Dr Dinwiddie recognized his mathematical abilities, adding in a superior tone that "his knowledge was purely speculative, being unable to apply it to any practical purposes."[31] More consistently, Tafazzul depended on Reuben Burrow for instruction. The list of books Tafazzul was given to read is impressive indeed: William Emerson's *Mechanics* (1769), Thomas Simpson's *Treatise of Algebra* (1745) and Guillaume de l'hopital's *Treatise on Conic Sections* (1706). Burrow was very keen to involve Tafazzul in translation work. Apollonius' *De Sectione Rationis* had been translated from Greek into Arabic, but the Greek original was lost. It was later translated from Arabic into Latin, but the Arabic version got lost. Finally, Burrow, while still in England, had translated it from Latin into English, and now seeing himself in the historical role of completing the circuit asked Tafazzul to translate it into Arabic. Another spectacular project of Burrow's was the translation of Newton's Principia into Arabic, which caught the establishment's attention.

Tafazzul also interacted with leading Europeans of Calcutta including Sir William Jones and Sir John Shore (Lord Teignmouth) who counted Tafazzul among his personal friends.[32] Shore served as Governor General during 1793–1797 and played a role in Tafazzul's career. Shore wrote in his memoirs that Tafazzul's "fame as a scholar and a mathematician was established by a Translation of Newton's 'Principia' into Persian, and an original treatise on Fluxions." Note that no mention is made of Apollonius, and Newton's translation is said to be in Persian rather than Arabic. Tafazzul even accompanied Shore to England where Shore "persuaded him to enter upon the irksome and disgusting, but patriotic task of superintending and reforming the Vizier's Government."

Tafazzul left behind three "Mathematical MSS. Compositions," which became the property of his son Tajammul Hussain Khan (Tujummool Hoosyn Khan) in Lucknow. "One of them exhibits a view of the Copernican System of Astronomy, the other two are Algebraic treatises."[33] These were copied by the Calcutta School Book Society. Maulvi Hyder Ali [Mowluwee Hydur Ulee] prepared an account of these for publication in the Society's 1818 report. The account was accompanied by a copper-plate engraving of the Solar System. The account was published separately as a 23-page booklet from Calcutta in 1819. This publication, which seems to be Tafazzul's only one, does not seem to have been mentioned before. It would be interesting to examine its contents.

It is probable that Tafazzul became Burrow's pupil in 1783. Tafazzul's translations of Newton or Apollonius have not survived. They were probably never made. No details or remnants are available of Burrow's ambitious project to render Newton into Arabic or Persian, but we do know from another context what Burrow meant by translation. Burrow's claimed translation of Bijaganita and Lilavati from Persian simply consisted of writing the English of each word above the Persian. Tafazzul's intellectual achievements under British patronage appear to be exaggerated. Neither were his intellectual interests typical of the time nor was he representative of his community.

Trigonometrical Survey (1800)

The 1799 defeat of Tipu Sultan of Mysore at Seringapatam was an event of great administrative and scientific significance. So far the Company had been confined to the peripheral areas in South India, but now it became a successor to a well-run state. Its territories now extended from the east coast to the west. From a scientific point of view, this was an exciting development because the new lands presented different flora and geology. Post-Tipu, the first task for the Company was the compilation of maps from whatever "meagre and unsatisfactory material" was already extant. Next, the Governor General ordered a thorough and systematic Mysore survey, the details of which were soon worked out. It was to comprise two components. The mathematical survey would fix the external boundaries and also lay down the "Country in detail" through primary triangulation. Numerous peaks and hills, "many of them remarkable for buildings on them" rendered the territory particularly favourable for the exercise. The physical survey would deal with botany, mineralogy, medicine; diseases, weather, rains, soil, agricultural produce, animals, revenue, population, etc. Colin Mackenzie was made overall in charge of the survey. Within the survey, Francis Buchanan was appointed to investigate "the state of agriculture, arts, and commerce." The departments of botany, mineralogy and natural history were entrusted to Benjamin Heyne. The geodetic survey was a new initiative which we shall now discuss. The other parts will be taken up later.

Lambton

Just as Plassey had produced its Rennell, Seringapatam produced its Lambton, only more quickly. Unlike Rennell's survey which was run in traditional route survey style, Major William Lambton (1756–1823) modelled his on the lines of the recently started survey in England. He was born "of humble parents." Fortunately, locally influential persons became his patrons, "interested themselves in his education," and gave him access to their libraries.[34] In 1782, he joined the 33rd Regiment on Foot and left for New York. On the 1783 signing of peace with the American states, Lambton was entrusted with the task of settling the royalists in Canada. That is where he applied himself to the study of mathematics. In early New Brunswick maps, the Big Bald Mountain was shown as Lambton's mountain. Lambton came to Calcutta in 1797. Arthur Wellesley (1760–1852), the future Duke of Wellington, had joined the 33rd in 1793 in England, and Lambton met him in India. This connection would stand Lambton in good stead.

Lambton carried a letter of introduction addressed to Sir Alured Clarke, then Commander-in-Chief in India. It was written by merchant politician Sir Brook Watson who presumably knew Lambton from America. The letter did make a difference. Lambton had been stagnating as a subaltern and had no money to purchase promotion. But now he was promoted as Brigade Major to the King's troops in Madras. At the same time, the 33rd Regiment was ordered to participate in the final war against Tipu.

Inspired by the geodetic survey in Britain, Lambton proposed a similar survey in peninsular India where the hills and tall temples would greatly facilitate the work. He was enthusiastically supported by his commanding officer Wellesley. This support was doubly important because Arthur's brother, Richard Wellesley (1760–1842), Earl of Mornington, was the Governor General. While other officials down the line were also very supportive, the sailing was not entirely smooth. The Court of Directors consulted the old-fashioned London-based Rennell who opposed it. Those were the days when social networking could influence final decisions. The Astronomer Royal Reverend Dr Nevil Maskelyne was the maternal uncle of the Madras Governor Lord Edward Clive (1754–1839). This connection was invoked to win over Rennell.[35] The British geodetic survey was a military engineering operation in which the Astronomer Royal was not involved. The survey in India would also remain a strictly military affair.

The requisite instruments reached India from England via China. Many instruments similar to the one made for the English survey were purchased by the Company for presentation to the Chinese Emperor. They however ended as the personal property of Dr Dinwiddie in Calcutta from whom they were officially purchased for Lambton's use. The first task before Lambton was to put the Dinwiddie instruments in working order, which because of disuse and neglect had fallen into a "wretched state." In October 1800, Lambton measured a baseline near Bangalore. This was more in the nature of a dry run because the real work on the Trigonometrical Survey of India began on 10 April 1802 with the measurement of a new baseline in Madras in a plain near St Thomas Mount. In 1809, when the 33rd Regiment returned to England, Lambton was permitted to stay back and continue his work.

In 1808 a baseline was measured at Tanjore. In this flat country, *gopurams* or lofty towers of the temples were utilized as points for triangulation. While the theodolite was being hoisted to the summit of the Tanjore temple, it dashed against the temple wall with great force and was severely damaged. Lambton brought the theodolite to Bangalore, and, with the help of ordnance artificers, brought it back nearly to its original form. The repair took six weeks but the instrument was used for all the subsequent observations up to 1830. The incident is dramatic but not untypical. India in general did not receive a continuous supply of scientific equipment from England; it was received in spurts. It was the existence of a workshop facility and trained mechanics that kept them in working order.[36]

A fellow officer of Lambton's in the 33rd Regiment was a French nobleman with the anglicized name, John Warren (1769–1830). As part of the post-Tipu Mysore survey, he became in 1801 the first European to notice the presence of gold in workable quantities at Kolar near Bangalore. Warren worked as an assistant to Lambton from 1802 till 1805. In 1816, on the death of his elder brother, Warren became the 24th Comte de Warren. Colonial service was a great European social equalizer. In spite of the sharp contrast in their social backgrounds, humbly-born Lambton and aristocratic Warren became very good friends and remained so up to the former's death.[37] Warren served as the acting director of Madras Observatory from 1805 till 1811 (p. 54) and determined its longitude. His value continued to be used in official maps till as late as 1905.

Lambton's initial goal was rather modest. He wished to connect the two coasts of Coromandel and Malabar and determine the latitudes and longitudes of the principal places both on the coasts and in the interior. He however realized that the survey would need to extend to latitudes further north and suggested as early as 1807 that it be taken over by the Supreme Government.[38] The survey was subsequently enlarged in scope. With effect from 1 January 1818, when the final defeat of the Mahrattas was in sight, the survey was transferred from the Madras to the Supreme Government, renamed the Great Trigonometrical Survey of India (GTS) and extended to the whole country. Lambton was designated superintendent and George Everest (1790–1866) his assistant. Everest came to India in 1806 as a 16-year-old cadet in the Bengal Artillery. He was selected by Sir Stamford Raffles to take part in the reconnaissance of Java, 1814–1816. On Lambton's death in 1823, Everest was appointed the GTS superintendent. In 1830, he was in addition made the Surveyor General. He held both these appointments till retirement in 1843 when he returned to England.[39] Everest conceived the gridiron system of triangles and quadrilaterals which covered the whole country. The details were then filled in by the Topographical and Revenue Surveys. In 1878, the three surveys were merged under the name Survey of India (both the names GTS and Survey of India are applied retrospectively).

From his great arc of the meridian, stretching from Cape Camorin in the south to Banog near Mussoorie in the north, Everest calculated the shape of Earth, known as Everest geoid, on which all subsequent observations were computed. On 1 March 1856, Everest's successor Andrew Scott Waugh (1810–1878) communicated to the Royal Geographical Society the result of the long-drawn calculation of the height of the highest Himalayan Peak XV and the reasons for naming it after Everest. Though the name came into vogue almost immediately, it was formally approved by the Society in 1865. This is the only peak given a personal name. The peak is too distant and insignificant as seen from India to carry a traditional name. The British may or may not have known of the names for it in use in Tibet or Nepal. But since both these countries were closed to the British, they could claim ignorance and give a name of their own. Peaks in India already had names; they were not disturbed. New peaks were identified in the Karakoram range, but they were not given any name. The naming of the highest point on Earth after a Surveyor General was not only a tribute to the person but also a recognition of the organization.

There are two instances of Everest utilizing the services of two Indians, Syed Mir Mohsin Hussain and Radhanath Sickdhar, in instrumentation and calculation, respectively, and standing up for them when needed.

Syed Mir Mohsin Hussain (d. 1824)

An example of how Indian talent was spotted and utilized by colonial scientists is well illustrated by the case of Syed Mir Mohsin Hussain. He was born near Madras and was described as of partial "Arab descent," and "[O]f good family, connected with the Nawab of Arcot." He came to Madras and took employment with a well-known European jeweller's shop run by George Gordon. Here he was spotted by Colonel Valentine Blacker, the Quarter Master General, who was struck by "his uncommon intelligence and acuteness." Blacker got some instruments repaired by him, and when in 1823 Blacker moved to Calcutta as Surveyor General, he brought Mohsin over in place of the local *siclegur* (polisher; sword or knife grinder). In 1824, Mohsin was appointed instrument maker at the Surveyor General's office at a salary of Rs 25 a month. Blacker's successor John Hodgson, during 1826–1829, taught Mohsin to take astronomical observations and found him "a most respectable man and steady observer."

Mohsin's rise began when Everest took over as Surveyor General. In 1830, Henry Barrow (1790/1–1870, later FRS) was specially brought from England and appointed as the Mathematical Instrument Maker to the East India Company at a monthly salary of Rs. 500 plus house rent; a workshop was set up for him at Calcutta (the workshop is now known as the National Instrument Factory). Gifted but headstrong, Barrow fell out with Everest and was discharged from service in 1839. On return to England, Barrow set up his own manufactory and supplied instruments to the GTS.

For repairs during the field trips, Everest took Mohsin along. In 1832, Mohsin was drawing a salary of Rs 90. In 1836, while recommending him for appointment as sub-assistant, Everest reported him as "particularly remarkable for his inventive talent, the facility with which he comprehends all mechanical arrangements, and the readiness with which he enters into all new ideas of others." Everest went on to declare that "Without the valuable aid... rendered to me, it would...have been utterly out of my power to carry into effect my various projects for the remodelment of the instruments...." On Everest's recommendation, the Court of Directors appointed Mohsin successor to Barrow, but with a lowered designation of "Head artificer to the department of scientific instruments." Overcoming prejudice in high quarters, Everest finally in 1843 got Mohsin the same official designation as enjoyed by his English predecessor, if not the salary. Mohsin was given a monthly salary of Rs 250. In 1854, he was given a personal monthly allowance of Rs 150. It was said of him that "though he could not read English, he would have taken a leading place even among European instrument makers."[40]

Radhanath Sickdhar and the Himalayan Peaks

Everest was away from India on furlough from 1825 till 1830. "The greatest years of his work" began on return when he was given the twin charge as Superintendent of Trigonometrical Survey Surveyor General. In 1829, in his minute on the organization of the Survey, the Governor General, William Bentinck, wrote: "It is by a more enlarged employment of the native agency that the business of a Government will be at once more cheaply and efficiently transacted."[41] Everest proposed the establishment of a computing office comprising a chief computer and his deputy, both European, and a number of "young native computers" who possessed a competent knowledge of arithmetic, practical use of logarithms and English. The office would be distinct from the survey staff and complement its work.[42] It would clear the vast backlog of calculations and prevent future accumulation. The government hoped that "all the requisite computers may be drawn from existing establishments in the Presidency." The supply came from Hindu College, Calcutta, which in 1828 had obtained the services of a brilliant mathematics professor, Robert Tytler. Subsequently, in 1835, Survey of India even seconded an officer, Vincent Louis Rees, to teach mathematics at Hindu College.

Offers of employment were sent to a number of Bengali students. Radhanath Sickdhar (1813–1870) (his spelling), a Hindu College student since 1824, joined on 19 December 1831. Within a few months, eight more young men were appointed. These eight remained in service only for a few years. The computing office however stabilized in course of time. Coming across dhoti-clad Bengalis was a new experience for Everest. Rather imperiously, he desired that those attending office should "wear trousers or paijammahs." Yielding to the protests, he suggested, as a concession, that those who found themselves "unable to meet his wishes" should at least be out of his sight and be placed in a special workroom.[43]

Everest was immediately struck by the mathematical abilities of Radhanath and took him under his wing. A few months later, he was appointed sub-assistant. In 1833, he was attached to the Surveyor General's office at Dehradun. He would remain here for the next 15 years. His starting salary was Rs 107 per month comprising a pay of Rs 50, a tent allowance of Rs 40 and a horse allowance of Rs 17. Under normal rules of promotion every three years, Radhanath was placed at Rs 140 in 1835 and Rs 173 on 7 May 1838. In 1838, many computers left GTS, in most cases without taking Everest into confidence, to accept newly established posts of Deputy Collector. Radhanath also expressed a wish to leave GTS to become a "teacher to a public institution." He was placated through a special increase of Rs 100 from 1 June 1838, which meant a 60% addition to his emoluments. While building the case for him, Everest told the government that Radhanath had been "trained from boyhood under my own eye;" and that his mathematical attainments "would rank very high" "even in Europe." Radhanath was, Everest argued, "the cheapest instrument that government ever could employ in a task of this kind."[44]

Everest noted in 1836 that Radhanath has imbibed "our regard for truth, integrity, and manly virtue." On his part, Sickdhar noted with pride that Everest admitted him "in his own table."[45] Sickdhar's "hobby was beef, as he maintained that beef-eaters were never bullied, and that the right way to improve the Bengalees was to think first of the physique or perhaps physique and moral simultaneously."[46] He certainly had moral courage. Whether it was due to beef or not is difficult to say. In 1843, he stubbornly confronted an English magistrate on the latter's maltreatment of "paharee coolies." Although the colonial administration fined him Rs 200 for his "criminal" action, he was hailed as a hero by his countrymen.[47] This was a significant incident, because a "native" employee was taking on an arrogant European officer and coming out unscathed.

In 1840, Radhanath went down to Meerut to meet his father who was on pilgrimage to Badrinath. Everest sent with Radhanath a letter inviting his father to come to Dehradun. This would have given an opportunity "to show you personally how much I honour you for having such a son as Radhanath." Father would have been infinitely gratified at witnessing the high esteem in which he is held by his superiors and equals."[48]

In 1845, Radhanath was appointed the Head of the Computation Department with the designation Chief Computer. In 1851, two artillery officers Captains R. Smyth and H. L. Thuillier published *A Manual of Surveying for India* in the Preface of which they handsomely acknowledged Sickdhar. He wrote Chapters 15, 17–21 and 26 of Part III and the whole of Part V, and in addition, gave advice "on all subjects connected with his own department."

Radhanath had become dispensable by 1875 when a third revised and enlarged edition was published. By this time, Smyth was already dead, and revisions were carried out by Thuillier, who retained the material written by

Sickdhar but deleted acknowledgement to him. A junior Survey officer, Lieutenant Colonel Macdonald, who publicly objected, paid a price for his outspokenness. On Thuillier's insistence, who later became the Surveyor General (1866-1895), Macdonald was suspended for three months, demoted and debarred, at least for the time being, from holding any position at the headquarters.[49]

Radhanath was elected a Fellow of the Royal Astronomical Society in 1853, the first Indian to be so honoured. After retirement in 1862, he worked as a teacher of mathematics at the General Assembly's Institution (now Scottish Church College).

Himalayan Peaks

The Trigonometrical Survey commenced its "North-Eastern Himalayan Series," directed at Nepal Himalayas, in 1845 and completed it in 1850. It spanned 2,720 km from Dehradun to Sonakhoda, in Purnia, Bihar. The mightiest of the Himalayan peaks are visible from the principal stations of this series. Everest's successor, Andrew Waugh, Surveyor General from 1843 to 1863, ordered that every visible peak, great and small, should be observed from every observing station, but that the identification of peaks must be left to the computers.

Under normal circumstances, Sickdhar's mathematics department would have carried out the computations. But in 1849, in a cunning move, he along with his computing office was shunted to Calcutta. He and the staff under him left Dehradun at the end of January 1849 and reached Calcutta on 2 May 1849. As soon as he retired, in 1862, the office was brought back to Dehradun. Immediately after Sickdhar vacated Dehradun, a "small office" was established there under the superintendence of J. B. N. Hennessey, first assistant in the GTS. It was "composed of native Surveyors, and newly joined Sub-Assistants, who thus had an opportunity of being rigorously trained in the theoretical portion of their new duties." True to form the native sub-assistants associated with computations were never named.

Peak XV was observed from six distinct stations between 27 November 1849 and 17 January 1850. Its height was then calculated for each of the stations. The results were made public in 1856. It was a great source of comfort that the numbers in all cases were mutually consistent, ranging from 28990 ft to 29026 ft, yielding a mean value of 29,002 ft. The next three highest in the Series were Kanchenjunga or Peak IX (28,156 feet) in Sikkim, and Dhaulagiri or Peak XLI (26,795 feet) in Nepal.[50]

In March 1856, Waugh wrote a near-official letter to his deputy, Major Thuillier, and authorized him to read it before the Asiatic Society of Bengal. The letter, read at the August 1856 meeting, announced the "discovery of a mountain [Peak] in the Himalayan range, the measurement of which...

assigned it a place above that of any previously ascertained height in the range."[51] He "determined to name this noble peak of the Himalaya as Mont [later Mount] Everest." Note the caution in Waugh's choice of words. At this stage, he is talking only of the highest peak in the North-Eastern Series, not the entire Himalayas, because the survey of North-Western mountains was still in the future.

The Karakoram range lay outside the area covered by GTS. On 10 September 1856, Captain Thomas George Montgomerie sketched the two most prominent peaks of the Karakoram range, calling them K1 and K2. K1 is the Mashabrum Peak, the most conspicuous mountain in the Mustakh and Karakorum range. Behind it lies K2, which is surrounded on all sides by very lofty peaks, and is consequently never seen to great advantage.[52] In July–August 1857, Elliot Brownlow estimated K2's height to be more than 28,000 feet. Finally, in 1858, Montgomerie gave a precise value for the height: 28,287 feet, placing it next to Peak XV.[53] In 1865, the Royal Geographical Society approved the name Mount Everest. This is the only peak that was named. The proposal to designate K2 as Mount Godwin-Austen was rejected.

To sum up, so far, the heights of peaks in the Nepal Himalayas were first estimated in 1852 and finalized in 1856 when the name Mount Everest was publicly suggested for the highest peak in this range. No generalization could be made at this point because the survey of Karakoram was still into the future. As it turned out, K2 failed to out-top Mount Everest. Thus, when the name Mount Everest was first suggested it was merely the highest peak in the North-Eastern series, but by the time the name was universally accepted, it had already been recognized as the highest peak in the world. Table 3.1 summarizes the observations of Peak XV and K2.

TABLE 3.1 Observations of Peak XV and K2

No.	Year	Description
1	1849 Nov. 27–1850 Jan. 17	Peak XV was observed from six distinct stations.
2	1852	Preliminary heights of Peak XV and others were ascertained.
3	1856 Mar. 1	Peak XV was assigned a height of 29,002 feet. Designated Mount Everest in Survey records.
4	1857	K2 was estimated to be above 28,000 feet.
5	1858	K2 height was precisely calculated to be 28,287 feet, lower than Mount Everest's.
6	1865	The name Mount Everest was officially accepted by the Royal Geographical Society.

While the GTS' calculations of peak heights were universally accepted, there was a prolonged controversy whether Peak XV was really nameless as Waugh had claimed or a name for it existed in Tibet or Nepal. Curzon, the Viceroy of India, succeeded in obtaining permission from the Nepalese Government to send an English survey officer to proceed to Kathmandu in order to identify the peaks visible from the heights in the neighbourhood of that city, and, further, to ascertain what names, if any, were given to them respectively by the natives of Central Nepal. In 1904, Captain H. Wood published his *Report on the Identification and Nomenclature of the Himalayan Peaks as seen from Katmandu, Nepal*. It is in this setting that in 1904, Sidney Gerald Burrard (1860–1943) wrote an article in *Nature*. He served as the Superintendent of the Trigonometrical Survey from 1899 till 1908, and as Surveyor General from 1908 till 1914. Choosing his words carefully, he wrote: "About 1852 the chief computer of the office at Calcutta informed Sir Andrew that a peak designated XV had been found to be higher than any other hitherto measured in the world."[54] He does not mention any physical encounter between Waugh and Sickdhar, and refers only to the Nepal Himalaya.

The transition from the solid grounds of history to the slippery slopes of screenplay writing was made in 1921 by Sir Francis Younghusband, Imperial explorer and at the time President of the Royal Geographical Society. In his Introduction to *Mount Everest: The Reconnaissance, 1921*, he dramatically declared that in 1852, "one day the Bengal Chief Computer rushed into the room of the Surveyor General, Sir Andrew Waugh, breathlessly exclaiming, "Sir! I have discovered the highest mountain in the world."[55] Younghusband in turn became the uncritical second-hand source for Major Kenneth Mason, who was awarded the Royal Geographical Society's Founder's Gold Medal in 1927 and served as Oxford University's first statutory geography professor from 1932 till 1853. In 1928, at the Himalayan Club, Simla, which he had helped establish, he gave a lecture on Himalayan Romance, which was reported in "The Englishman" dated 12 November 1928, accompanied by the note: "The following is the summary of a lecture delivered in Simla by … Mason …and reproduced in the Journal of the Society of Arts, with the sub-heading. "Babu's great discovery." Mason wrote:

> It was during the computations of the north - eastern observations that a babu rushed on one morning in 1852 into the room of Sir Andrew Waugh, the successor of Sir George Everest and exclaimed: Sir. I have discovered the highest mountain on the earth.[56]

In 1933, Jogesh Chandra Bagal published a magazine article in 1933 in which he quoted both Burrard and Mason and declared Radhanath to be the discoverer of Mount Everest.[57] Bagal assumed that their remarks were mutually supportive which is not the case. Mason's Radhanath barges into Waugh's room, whereas according to Burrard, he merely informs Waugh. One may argue that Radhanath travelled from Calcutta to Dehradun for a face-to-face meeting. This is unlikely because in that case there would have been an official record of the visit. More importantly, the context in 1852 was the Nepal Himalaya rather than the whole of it. Radhanath wrote an autobiography. He never married. His heirs were the family and descendants of his younger brother, Srinath, who joined the Survey as a Computer but resigned before 1861. The autobiography was with the family as recently as 1935. Apparently, Radhanath himself chose not to say anything about Peak measurements, because otherwise Bagal would have either quoted from it or any member of the family.

The Great Trigonometrical Survey (GTS) was an extremely well-documented enterprise, both scientifically and administratively. In the absence of any other material of a personal or non-official nature, one must necessarily depend on official records. In 1933, Burrard in the second edition of his well-regarded *A Sketch of the Geography and Geology of the Himalaya Mountains and Tibet* addressed the question of the "discovery" of Mount Everest. Noting that "an incorrect story was obtaining circulation," he decided to "state the simple facts." He discounted Younghusband's version.

The computations of the height of Mount Everest were not the work of a single computer; all the calculations were made in duplicate, the horizontal angles were computed first and the vertical angles at a later date, and not necessarily by the same computer. The work of different computers was compared at intervals and the Chief Computer were consulted when any unusual result was obtained.

While horizontal angles were a straightforward affair, vertical angles had a major "source of perplexity." A ray of light emanating from the cold peak and received at a relatively high-temperature station in the plains, passed through layers of differing density, necessitating refraction corrections to be applied. Radhanath had been studying refraction for a long time and was "unofficially in touch with the Surveyor General." In 1852, Radhanath "sent his official intimation to the latter that a new peak had been computed from the angle books to be higher than any peak hitherto observed." To sum up, so far, peak XV was calculated at Dehradun under Hennessey, while Calcutta-based Radhanath Sickdhar was unofficially consulted by Waugh whenever needed. There is merit in the assertion that the "discovery of Mount Everest was due to the organized cooperation of observations and computers."[58]

An imaginary dialogue created by an Imperial explorer (Younghusband) 70 years after the event became the point on which Bagal and following him others have erected an inverted pyramid, unhistoricizing Sickdhar. Exaggerated and imaginary claims on his behalf divert attention from the core issue that has not so far been addressed. How is it that when the efforts of GTS were reaching their peak, the Chief Computer was nowhere in the picture? Under ordinary circumstances, Radhanath's office would have remained in Dehradun and taken up the task of calculating the heights of Himalayan peaks. In that case, in the Royal Geographical Society and other Imperial forums, Waugh would have been acknowledging the assistance of a native and not a fellow Englishman Hennessey. I suspect that Radhanath's removal from the scene just before computations began at the Survey headquarters was deliberate and with a view to deny him, a high-profile native, a place in history.

Theory of Isostasy

In Waugh's time, there was an able mathematician in Calcutta. The Venerable John Henry Pratt (1809–1871) arrived in India in 1838 and became the Archdeacon of Calcutta in 1850. He had been third wrangler of his year at Cambridge and a fellow of Caius College. Waugh placed the vast GTS data in Pratt's hand pointing out "the problem of computing the attraction of the Himalayas and the Tibetan plateau on the plumb line. This was in 1852."[59] Two years later, that is in 1854, he published a 75-page research paper in *Philosophical Transactions*. It was postulated that the mountains stood on matter of low density so that the actual attraction exerted by them was less than suggested by their size.

Pratt's pioneering work eventually led to the important concept of isostasy.[60] Pratt's was the only major theoretical work carried out in India.

Trans-Himalayan Explorers

While the Indians were largely kept out of the actual survey work within the country, there was one type of survey which they alone could do. And that was the late 19th-century clandestine exploration of Trans-Himalayan regions, where Europeans would have been immediately spotted and killed. In 1816, the British took over Kumaon from the Gorkha with the result that they now share a border with Tibet. The exploration of Tibet was driven by a desire to continue the Trigonometrical Survey beyond the Indian frontier coupled with an unhealthy neighbourly curiosity. The Central Asian work was of great strategic importance and necessary to fill the gap between the Indian and Russian surveys. Spy geographers in Tibet were Hindus who disguised themselves as pilgrims or Buddhists, while the explorers in Central Asia were, with rare exceptions, Muslims. The pattern already established in other fields was seen here as well. Early explorations were carried out by individual European officers on their own initiative who employed native assistants. Institutionalized training and employment of the latter came later, in

1861, when the British mooted a proposal for a systematic clandestine survey of areas beyond the Himalayas.

With characteristic British thoroughness and disdain, the Indian surveyors were only taught how to take observations. They were not instructed in the reduction of data lest they cheated. It is said that as a matter of policy, the government "suppressed" their names as long as "they were still strong and vigorous, and liable to be again employed."[61] This may at best be only part of the reason. The names were publicly announced by the Schlagintweit brothers. Denial of identity is a very effective put-down. Coded names of explorers were revealed after their superannuation or dug out from official records. All explorers sent to Afghanistan and Central Asia were Muslims; those sent to Tibet were Hindus or Buddhists. Many of them were known by titles: Pandit (Nain Singh), Mullah (Ata Mahomed), Mirza (Mirza Shujah), Havildar (Haider Shah), Syud, Hakim, etc. In other cases, codes were constructed out of their names. To create a code name for say Kalian Sing[h], the name was first spelt backwards, and the first letters of the reversed name, supplemented with dashes, were used: G_K. According to this formula, Kishen Sing[h] would also get the same code as Kalian; he was called Krishna and designated A__k. Similarly, Abdul Subhan became N-A; another coded name was S_M_.

The Rawat Family moved into the British orbit in stages over half a century. In the 1810s, they pulled Moorcroft out of trouble when he was in Tibetan territory; in the 1840s, they assisted the Strachey brothers in their surveys, and in 1851, the Schlagintweit brothers; and finally, they became paid servants of the Survey of India.

Moorcroft

An early adventure was due to William Moorcroft (1767–1825), otherwise Superintendent of the Company's Stud at Pusa (p. 130). In 1812, when Kumaon was still a Gorkha territory and four years away from British control, Moorcroft accompanied by a young half-caste, Hyder Jung Hearsey,[62] surveyed it from south to north (p. 131). They then decided to enter Western Tibet. They disguised themselves as Hindu pilgrims under the assumed names of Mayapuri and Hargiri (thus preserving the first letter of their last name) and visited Manasarovar [Lake Manas][63] and Rakas Tal, and made an important geographical discovery which however did not have any colonial or commercial value. Contrary to popular belief, Satluj did not arise in Manas but in Rakas. The two were detained by the Tibetan authorities at Daba Dzong, some 80 miles north-west of Manasarovar. Two Kumaon-based Bhotia Rawat brothers, Bir Singh and Deb Singh (Debu) interceded on their behalf, stood security for them and got them released. This incident brought the family to the notice of the British and went on to provide the Europeans with distinguished clandestine explorers.

The Bhotia Rawat Family

Nain Singh Rawat (1830–1882) kept a diary in Hindi which has recently been published as part of a well-researched work.[64] It helps correct various mis-statements about his family background that have been extant in English language colonial-time sources. Whenever an Indian proved to be useful to the British Indian establishment, he was projected as coming from a respectable and influential family. Nain Singh's real life was not as smooth as has been made to be by his colonial biographers.

According to Nain Singh, his remote Rawat Rajput ancestors migrated from Rajasthan to Garhwal. Eighteen generations before Nain Singh, Dham Singh was instrumental in expelling robbers from the Kingdom of Darikursum (which included Western Tibet of today). The grateful King Bot-chogyal showered a number of concessions on Dham Singh, the most important of which ensured a permanent source of income. He was given a title to 10% custom duty on all barter trade. With the King's permission, Dham Singh chose to settle in Kumaon rather than in Western Tibet and made Milam in Johar (or Juhar) valley his home (now in Pithoragarh district of Uttarakhand). He then used his good offices to get duty exemption for all Johari traders winning their gratitude for times to come. Some generations later his clan started marrying locally into the Bhotiya people of Tibetan origin, and in the course of time, rose to great wealth and influence. The Rawats, their surname notwithstanding, are Bhotias who are classified as Scheduled Tribes. The family also came to enjoy the title *Boorha* literally meaning old, but here a designation for village elder or head. The starting point for the present narrative is Dham Singh II or Dhama who had ten sons from three wives each of whom maintained a separate household. It is the household of the third wife with five brothers which furnished the Survey of India with many famous clandestine explorers. Here below, we give a partial genealogy to illustrate the relationship among the names that figure in the Survey chronicles.

Moorcroft's benefactors, Bir Singh and Debu, were among the ten sons of Dhamu. The eldest was Jaspal Singh whose descendant Uttam Singh Rawat became a Christian in 1878. Debu was the father of two real brothers: the elder Man Singh was nicknamed Mani Compassi, possibly because of his use of a compass as a surveying assistant, and the younger Kishen Singh. Dhama's ninth son Amar Singh nicknamed Laata (1795–1848) begot Nain Singh and Kalyan Singh from different mothers. Another of Dhama's sons was Fateh Singh whose son Mani Boorha (distinct from his cousin Mani Compassi) is important because of the support he extended to Nain Singh in the latter's difficult times.

Laata turned out to be the black sheep of the family and his sins visited his progeny. Notwithstanding the family's wealth and prestige, Nain Singh was brought up in an environment of financial insecurity and social isolation.

Although Laata was already married, he forcibly brought home the wife of another resident of the village who was his casteman. As a consequence, he was turned out of home and village by his brothers who additionally confiscated his share of the inheritance. Laata migrated to a non-Bhotiya village Bhatkura in the same area. His exile would last 25 long years. His 1824 appeal for restoration of his inheritance was turned down by the British Commissioner of Kumaon, George William Traille. As a result, a few days later, his dejected two wives jointly committed suicide by drowning. Next year, that is in 1825, Laata married a non-Bhotiya Rajput girl from whom he got four children, Nain Singh being the second. On his third wife's death in 1838 Laata married again, this time a girl of his community for the sake of the younger children and again became father of two sons including Kalyan Singh.

Laata returned to Milam in 1847 but died the next year. The uncles and cousins were generally against restoring the Laata family's share in the ancestral property; the sole exception was Mani Boorha who gave some money of his own, looked after the family and involved the family in some profitable trade deals. But generally, the family simply borrowed money and lived off it. In 1851 when Nain's stepmother remonstrated with him, he chose to leave home and go on a journey to Badrinath. During this journey not only did he gain valuable experience, but also a wife. His wife was the cousin of Mani Boorha's wife and hence the already cordial blood ties were strengthened further.

Nain Singh lived with his well-off in-laws for three years. But for a man to reside with the in-laws was a practice then as now considered undignified. Finally in 1854, he along with his wife returned to Milam without even informing his hosts. Fortunately, Nain Singh was cordially received by his uncles and cousins but shortage of funds remained a problem. He went out on two trade expeditions in the Himalayas and through Tibet. Though they turned out to be commercial failures, the travel experience would stand him in good stead.

In 1846, Henry Strachey (1816–1912) reached Manasarovar and Rakas Tal. He concluded that Satluj emanated from Manasarovar, and not Rakas Tal as stated earlier by Moorcroft. Subsequently, the contradiction was resolved by the Swedish geographer Sven Hedin (1865–1952). A short-term visitor's perception was fashioned by the season of his visit. In the dry season, the neighbouring Manasarovar and Rakas Tal were distinct entities, with a dry channel running between the two. If because of rains, the Manasarovar level rises by six feet, there will be water outflow to Rakas making the two lakes one. Strictly speaking, Satluj did emanate from Rakas. In 1848, his brother Richard Strachey (1817–1912) and botanist J. E. Winterbottom explored Western Tibet. The Stracheys together entered Tibet in 1849. "Mani Compassi had once been engaged by the Stracheys, during their travels in

Tibet."[65] He might have earned the name Compassi during his stint with the Stracheys. In 1851, Mani Compassi was appointed by the Government as a patwari of Juhar and stationed in Tejam. When the Schlagintweit brothers embarked on their scientific mission to High Asia, Dhama's family contributed three of its members to their staff. Mani Compassi was an obvious choice. He proved to be "of the most essential service" during the brothers' Tibet journey and was "the only one of our establishment considered trustworthy enough to be taken to Turkistan." Mani's cousin Dolpa was hired as a subordinate attendant and was described as a rough kind of man but full of courage, energy and devotedness. High praise was reserved for Nain Singh who went with Herman and Robert Schlagintweit to Ladakh in 1856. He was described as "well disposed and intelligent." The brothers wrote:

> He took a great interest in our operations and though at first unacquainted with instruments was soon taught their use as he showed a very great desire to be able to read off the scales and write the readings in English numbers. He could also read and write Tibetan.

The brothers in fact took tuition in Tibetan from Nain Singh.

> We had proposed, and with apparent acquiescence on his part, to take him to Europe [for three years on good salary] but like all hill men he was too much attached to his native mountains to bring himself to leave them and he unexpectedly went away from us at Raulpindi leaving behind a long letter of apologies.[66]

The reason recorded here for Nain Singh's not going to Europe is a classical Orientalist construct. We learn the real reason from Nain Singh's diaries. Mani Compassi did not wish to take Nain Singh on the Schlagintweit establishment. He was forced to do so because of family pressure, especially from Mani Boorha, and took his revenge by treating Nain Singh as a menial. On his part, left to himself Nain Singh would have gone to Europe but was forced to say no by his domineering and jealous cousin.

The stint with the German brothers brought Nain Singh to the notice of the British Indian establishment. In 1859, he was appointed teacher in the newly opened municipal school in Milam. His relatives were still not ready to forgive him for his father's sexual transgression. They wanted him to be removed from the school, but the administration refused. Nain Singh acquitted himself well and continued here till 1862 when he joined the new school in Dharchula. His salary was only 15 rupees and he still carried old debts. The murder of Adolphe de Schlagintweit at Kashgar in 1857 focused attention on the risk inherent on Europeans' venturing outside India as surveyors. A new policy was therefore adopted.

Nain Singh

Captain Thomas George Montgomerie (1830–1878) proposed in 1861 that Trans-Himalayan exploration should be entrusted to carefully selected and trained Indians who should suitably disguise themselves for the task. The proposal was accepted and Major Edward Smyth, Inspector of Schools, Kumaon, was asked to suggest names. On his suggestion, Mani Compassi and Nain Singh were selected. They joined the Survey in February 1863 at a monthly salary of Rs 50 and Rs 40, respectively. Nain Singh at long last had found his true calling. Financial difficulties and the hurt of being disowned by kith and kin impelled Nain Singh to succeed, while the comfortable family conditions robbed Mani Compassi of ambition. He and Nain Singh were trained at the Survey head office in Dehradun first by J. T. Walker, the Survey Superintendent, and then by Montgomerie. A first attempt to penetrate Tibet from Kumaon was unsuccessful, and the following year, a second effort was made via Nepal. Here, too, difficulties were encountered. The two explorers then separated and tried to get through independently. Nain Singh alone was successful. During 1865 and 1866, disguised as a Tibetan lama, and on behalf of the Great Trigonometrical Survey, he made a 1200-mile route survey. During this survey, he traced the route of Brahmaputra from its source near Manasarovar to Lhasa. In addition, he fixed the altitude of 31 distinct locations including Lhasa. He also made observations of the temperature of air and boiling water, by which heights of 33 points were fixed. He also provided "Notes as to what was seen, and as to the information gathered during the expedition." For his work, Nain Singh was provided with a fake rosary and a fake prayer wheel both of which were adapted to serve his needs. Noting with great relief that the prayer wheel was "free of all examination by custom-house or other officials," the Survey took full advantage of "this immunity" for the future and custom-made several copper prayer wheels in the workshop which could hide compasses, etc, for later use.

In 1868, Montgomerie gave a detailed report to the Royal Geographical Society on Nain Singh's work,[67] except that he was mentioned as "Pundit----" as though the mention of a native name would have been a breach of etiquette of an elitist English club. The Society awarded a "Gold Watch, value thirty guineas" to the "Pundit employed by Captain Montgomerie for "his route-survey from Manasarovar to Lhasa in Great Thibet." The award ceremony was held at the Society's anniversary meeting, on 25 May 1868. Nain Singh was not only absent but also personally irrelevant. There was much idle talk on who would have been the best person to physically receive the award: Lord This, or Sir That. The award was "presented to Lord Strangford on behalf of the Pundit." The Lord was quite ignorant about the awardee. He described the Pundit as "a native of the plains," who has "emulated the

Alpine Club, by climbing to a height of 15,000 feet, and showing wonderful endurance."[68] Had the Pundit been from the plains he could not have accomplished what he did.

The Pundit was described as "wily" and "skilful" no doubt because he was able to maintain his disguise and bring reliable data. It is clear from the remarks at the award ceremony and in the discussion that followed Montgomerie's presentation that the real hero of the Geographical Society was the latter.[69] The Pundit "had proved himself in every way worthy of Captain Montgomerie's selection."[70] Even though others before the Captain had employed the native agency "for the purpose of acquiring political and statistical information," it was he who made really a most valuable discovery, namely that natives "could use a sextant or a theodolite as well as Europeans." It was now hoped that further explorations would be carried out by "native enterprise directed by English intelligence."[71]

Nain Singh was further honoured in 1877 when the Society conferred on him its coveted Victoria or Patron's medal. The same year when Queen Victoria was proclaimed to be Empress of India, he was made Companion of the Indian Empire. More substantially, he was given a jagir in Rohilkhand which yielded a revenue of 1000 rupees. Probably, Lord Strangford confused the location of the jagir with the place of birth.

Google's Doodle

For his fieldwork, Nain Singh disguised himself as a Tibetan lama and went to extreme lengths to hide his true identity. He kept aloof from others so that he could focus on counting his paces and made his astronomical observations only at night when no one was around. Google's Doodle is misleading and unhistorical. It shows a tall dark man in a European dress, a frockcoat and tight trousers. He has a tripod in front of him and is observing the Sun in full glory. If Nain Singh had dressed like that and observed like that in Tibet, he would have been jailed or expelled or killed. There then would not have been anything to google or doodle about him.[72]

After completing actual field service, Nain Singh was entrusted with the task of training new recruits for route surveys. Three of the pupils are particularly noteworthy: his cousin Kishen Singh; "a native gentleman of the Muhammedan faith," M—S; and Sarat Chandra Das. M—S "contributed enormously to the existing geographical knowledge of Badakshan" during 1877–1878.[73]

Kishen Singh

Kishen Singh followed in his elder cousin Nain Singh's footsteps and came to be recognized as a great explorer (the Survey records carelessly describe the two as brothers). His journeys covered the period 1872–1882. His most famous journey which took him to Mongolia is the last one.

Kishen Singh left Darjeeling in April 1878, entered Tibet and moved northwards till he reached Saichu in Mongolia. He took a different but longer route for return, returning to Darjeeling in November 1882. During his journey of four and a half years, he traversed 3000 miles. He took observations for latitude at 22 stations and heights by boiling point at 69 places. The "hardships and anxieties undergone" during the long journey "incapacitated" him "from undertaking any similar work in future."[74]

At the International Geographical Congress[75] held at Venice in 1881, the Italian Geographical Society placed two gold medals, gold and silver, in the hands of J T Walker for award to the two native explorers "whom he considered the most meritorious." M—S was given the silver medal and Kishen Singh the gold. He was also awarded a gold medal by the French Geographical Society. Unlike Nain Singh, he did not get any medal from the Royal Geographical Society which however gave him an inscribed golden watch and a grant of Rs 500. The Indian Government made him a Companion of the Indian Empire and awarded him a jagir in the Satapur district of the United Provinces yielding a revenue of Rs 1850.

Sarat Chandra Das

Sarat Chandra Das (1849–1917) was a student in the Engineering Department of Presidency College, Calcutta, when through the good offices of his mentor, Sir Alfred Croft, he was appointed headmaster of the newly opened Bhutia Boarding School at Darjeeling. The post of Tibetan teacher at the school was held by Lama Ugyen Gyatso, who was a monk of the Pemayangtse monastery of Sikkim and related to the royal family of Sikkim. Das learnt Tibetan and paid several visits in subsequent years to the monasteries and other places of interest in Independent Sikkim, where he made the acquaintance of the Raja, his ministers, and other persons of importance. In 1878, it was decided to send Lama Ugyen Gyatso to Tashi Lhunpo and Lhasa with a tribute from the Pemayangtse monastery. Das accompanied the Lama and their fruitful visit lasted about six months.

For his second journey, Das accompanied by Ugyen Gyatso left Darjeeling on 7 November 1881 and proceeded to Tibet. He visited several monasteries and important places and closely observed the cultural and social life, as well as the religious and political scenarios of Tibet. During his visit to the ancient monastery of Sakya, he found many rare books in Sanskrit hundreds of years old that had been believed to be lost forever. On his return to India in late 1882, he brought back over 200 volumes of manuscripts and block prints, a number of them in Sanskrit, obtained from the great libraries of Tibet. On return, from 1881 till 1900, Das worked as the official translator of the

Tibetan language for the Government of Bengal. In October 1885, Das accompanied the civil servant Colman Macaulay on his official visit to Peking regarding diplomatic negotiations on trade with Tibet. In Beijing, Das met the American diplomat and Tibetologist, William Woodville Rockhill who edited and published Das' "Journey to Lhasa and Central Tibet" in 1902.

On return from Peking, Das was titled Rai Bahadur. He was also made CIE. At a professional level, the Royal Geographical Society awarded him the Back Premium. Rockhill wrote trenchantly in 1891:

> If any British explorer had done one-third of what Nain Singh, lama Urjyen jyats'o, Sarat Chandra Das, or Kishen Singh (alias A_ K_), accomplished, medals and decorations, lucrative offices and professional promotion, freedom of cities, and every form of lionizing would have been his; as for those native explorers a small pecuniary reward and obscurity are all to which they can look forward.[76]

Very audaciously, the colonial surveyors approached the Nakshabandi Fakir Kwajah Ahmed Shah for collaboration. He lived in Kashmir and was constantly in the habit of travelling in Eastern and Western Turkistan. His son, Gafur Khan, accompanied him in 1852–1853 from Kashmir via Ladakh to Yararkand, Kashgar, Kokan and back via Kabul.

> [b]oth father and son have, in their clerical character, considerable facilities in moving about Turkistan, where the mass of the population is Mahomedan, and where the Shah (the son) tells me they have a good many followers (mureed) of their own, and would consequently not be likely to be interrupted in their travels.
>
> I should propose that either the father or son should be asked to undertake the guidance of two trained native explorers, and I understand from the son that they would be willing to undertake such a charge. He said that he thought that there would be no danger to natives, who accompanied him into Turkistan.[77]

In 1876, the Mullah ascended the Indus River from the point where it entered the plains of the Punjab at Attock to the point where it is joined by the Gilgit River. In 1877, M_S_, "a native gentleman of the Muhammadan faith, and of much repute among his co-religionists," explored the area beyond the Hindukush. An Indian official of GTS, sub-surveyor Imam Baksh Bozdar (b. 1834) took part in eight different expeditions during his service. He explored the Gilgit area, Zhon, Gomal, Shirani Hills, Kandahar, Kabul, etc. On his retirement in 1884, he was given a grant of 250 acres in the Dera Ghazi Khan district and the title of Khan Bahadur. Similarly, in 1896,

Muhammad Yusuf Sharif Khan Bahadur was given Murchison Grant for his work in Persian Balochistan.

Outstanding explorers were given professional awards, which however celebrated European patrons rather than the native winners. The government gave Indians honours and benefits which would enhance their prestige in their own society, but never thought of accommodating them in its establishment.

In 1834, on orders from the government, astronomical instruments from the Survey were issued to enable the former Bombay Astronomer to observe the phenomenon of the opposition of Mars. This happened when Everest was out on a field tour. On his return, Everest made a strong protest against the loan, saying: "The discoveries which the late Astronomer of Bombay is likely to make in science would hardly repay the inconvenience occasioned by retarding the operations of the Great Trigonometrical Survey..."[78] The astronomer John Curnin did not enjoy much of a reputation having been dismissed as the first Director of the Colaba Observatory in 1828.

Everest's imperious put-down of pure astronomy was in conformity with the government's disdain. As can be seen by the price placed on various services. At the beginning of the Trigonometrical Survey, in 1801, the Superintendent was getting a monthly salary of Rs 980 marginally higher than the Madras Astronomer's Rs 672. Seven decades later, in 1877, while the Astronomer's salary had crawled up to Rs 800, the Survey Chief's had jumped to a substantial Rs 2565. Fifteen surveyors were getting more than the Astronomer, three of them being Fellows of the Royal Society. While most scientific activities were suspended in wartime, the work on the Trigonometrical Survey continued uninterruptedly.

On the eve of the transfer of Lambton's survey from Madras to the Imperial Government, Lieutenant Colonel J. Young, Secretary to the Governor General, Military Department wrote an official letter on 25 October 1817 declaring that

> this single public act has raised the name of the English East India Company in the eyes of the scientific world to a level with those of the great sovereigns of Europe, who have been their only rivals in similar undertakings.[79]

It would be simplistic to say that this was "an early corporate public relations idea."[80]

The Company was not content with being a corporate body. It wanted to be seen as the sovereign ruler of India and divert gaze away from its unsavoury activities. Support for Western scholarship was a means of achieving this. The government's distribution of Sanskrit manuscripts and botanical specimens in the Western world was carried out as part of diplomacy. While revenue and topological surveys filled the felt needs of the Company, utilitarian aspects were not important in the case of the Trigonometrical Survey. European men of science were aware of the vast land mass the Company had under its control or had access to. The Trigonometrical Survey and the associated extra-Indian explorations constituted an ambitious project requiring sustained support and organization of a high order. In it, geography, geodesy, and geopolitics coalesced, and scholarship and prestige fed each other.

&&&&

What was the attitude of European scientific officers towards their Indian staff? No fixed pattern is discernible. There were variations in the outlook of the officers. The Indians they dealt with would also have varied among themselves as far as personal attributes were concerned. The superiority which the Europeans felt over Indians transformed into paternalism in some cases and bad behaviour in others. Europeans who viewed their own work in India as historical tended to take the Indians along, but there were others who showed open contempt.

In his 1879 official report, Medlicott, the head of the Geological Survey, responded thus to the appointment of two Indians as sub-assistants:

> It is still, however, very doubtful if they can ever prove competent for independent field-work. Geologist's work may not demand high mental powers, but it inevitably requires some originality of thought in dealing with observation and induction, that peculiarly modern turn of mind to which we owe the present development of natural science, the very quality which more than any other makes the western man different from the eastern.[81]

What Medlicott was saying was that by definition Indians could not do what Europeans could.

In sharp contrast to Medlicott there stood Henry Francis Blanford (1834–1893), the first head of the India Meteorological Department. Ruchi Ram Sahni, the first Indian officer in the Department who joined in 1885, described him as "an angelic officer." On the other hand, his successor John Elliot was universally described as a "native hater."

Notes

1 Phillimore, 1945, 1, 324–325.
2 Phillimore, 1945, 1, 375.
3 Phillimore, 1945, 1, 215.
4 Lockman, 1762, i.
5 Noti, 1906, 5.
6 This paragraph is based on Maclagen, 1932, 141–143.
7 Natwar-Singh, 1981, 115.
8 Phillimore, 1945, 1, 30.

9 Phillimore, 1945, 1, 286.
10 Phillimore, 1945, 1, 278.
11 Phillimore, 1950, 2, 354.
12 Phillimore, 1950, 2, 355.
13 British Indian Military Repository, 1822, 1 (Jan.), 1.
14 Phillimore, 1945, 1, 155.
15 Phillimore, 1945, 1,318.
16 Phillimore, 1945, 1, 318.
17 Phillimore, 1946, 1, 171.
18 Phillimore, 1945, 1, 318.
19 Burrow, 1790.
20 Phillimore, 1945, 1, 165.
21 Proudfoot, 1868, 104.
22 Carey, 1882, 1, 180.
23 Proudfoot, 1868, 98.
24 Phillimore, 1950, 2, 395.
25 Proudfoot, 1868, 99.
26 Proudfoot, 1868, 99.
27 Proudfoot, 1868, 113.
28 Proudfoot, 1868, 119.
29 Proudfoot, 1868, 104.
30 Asiatic Annual Register, 1804, ("Characters"), p. 1.
31 Proudfoot, 1868, 104.
32 Basu, 1943.
33 CSBS, 1819, 18.
34 Ingledew, 1858, 299.
35 Warren, 1830, 77.
36 Markham, 1871, 52.
37 Lambton's biographical sketch published in 1830 is based on Warren's material, which was recast because the Frenchman Warren was not quite familiar with the idiom of the English language; Warren, 1830, 73.
38 Phillimore, 1954, 3, 225.
39 Everest married in 1846 at the age of 56 and begat children. He however does not have any lineal descendants.
40 This section is based on Phillimore, 1954, 3, 485; Phillimore, 1958, 4, 458; Kochhar, 1991, 89.
41 Phillimore, 1954, 3, 388.
42 Pres. Coll. 100, 1956, 3.
43 Phillimore, 1958, 4, 339.
44 Phillimore, 1958, 4, 341–342.
45 Phillimore, 1958, 4, 461–462.
46 Mittra, 1878, 31.
47 Bengal Spectator, 1843 Sep. 16, reproduced in Chattopadhyay, 1978, 265.
48 Bagal, 1933b, 292; Phillimore, 1963–1964, 33.
49 Sanyal, 1894, 25–26; Bagal, 1933a, 459.
50 Waugh, 1857, 1, 347.
51 *Journal of Asiatic Society of Bengal*, 1856, 25, 437–438.
52 Montgomerie, 1866, 163.
53 Phillimore, 1959.
54 Burrard, 1904, 43.
55 Younghusband, 1922, 10.
56 Das, 1991, 43. I thank Wg Cdr Sudhir Kutty, Honorary Secretary, Himalayan Club, Mumbai for help on this reference.
57 Bagal, 1933a, b.

58 Burrard & Hayden, 1933, 194.
59 Lenox-Conyngham, 1944, 511.
60 The term was first used by the American geologist, Clarence Edward Dutton (1841–1912), in 1882.
61 Walker, 1885, 65.
62 Most accounts give only his last name, hiding his mixed origin. He Anglicized his Urdu middle name, meaning war, to Young. Full name is given by Mason, 1956, 170.
63 Lake Manasarovar would be tautological, because Sarovar means lake.
64 Bhatt & Pathak, 2008.
65 Schlagintweit et al., 1861, 39.
66 Schlagintweit et al., 1861, 39.
67 Montgomerie, 1868.
68 Royal Awards, 1868, 217.
69 Royal Awards, 1868; Montgomerie, 1868.
70 Royal Awards, 1868, 218.
71 Montgomerie, 1868, 168–169.
72 https://rajeshkochhar.com/googles-thoughtless-doodle-on-nain-singh-the-19th-century-camouflaged-trans-himalayan-explorer/.
73 Black, 1891, 144.
74 Black, 1891, 157.
75 The following is a sequence of the early International Geography Congresses: 1871 Antwerp; 1875 Paris; 1881 Venice; 1889 Paris; 1891 Berne; 1895 London; and 1899 Berlin.
76 Rockhill, 1891, 288.
77 Proceedings of the Asiatic Society of Bengal, 1863 (Mar.), 177.
78 Phillimore, 1958, 4, 137.
79 Accounts and Papers of House of Commons, 1851, 61, App. A, p. 23.
80 Dionne and Macleod, 1978, 59, note 34.
81 Records of the Geological Survey of India, 1880, 13, Part 1, 10.

4
ASTRONOMY, METEOROLOGY AND EARTH'S MAGNETISM

Sky as a geographical and navigational aid, timekeeping, weather, sea storms and tides were departments that concerned the English merchants and received attention. Geomagnetic and later solar studies were initiated not because the Company needed them but because the British science establishment insisted on them. By the 1840s, European scientists, mindful of the vast colonial territories under British control, were talking about coordinated international observing programmes. They also enlisted cooperation from Indian princely rulers who because of their personalized approach were easier to handle than the government.

India's, and the non-West's, first ever Astronomical Observatory was set up at Madras in 1787. It additionally undertook meteorological observations. As a result of a major reorganization of Indian observatories in 1899, the Solar Physics Observatory came up at Kodaikanal in Palni Hills in South India. At the same time, the Madras Observatory ceased its connection with astronomy and became a purely meteorological station.

When the Greenwich Observatory was established a 100 years previously, in 1675, it was a building without instruments. In India, instruments arrived first and arrangement for their permanent housing was taken up later. Over the years, surveying instruments were purchased from England or from the captains and crew of the European ships. When an officer died, his surveying instruments would be in great demand. In the early days, it was not the policy of the Company to supply instruments to its officers. But a small stock of sextants, quadrants, theodolites, clocks, telescopes, etc., was built up by purchases from England or within the country. Two celestial events, Transits of Venus in the 18th and 19th centuries, serve as benchmarks in the development of Western astronomy in India.

DOI: 10.4324/9781003466406-4

Transits of Venus

The transits of the planet Venus over the disc of the Sun that took place on 6 June 1761 and 3 June 1769 created great world-wide enthusiasm for astronomy. They gave a great fillip to the making and dispersal of scientific instruments. The transit observations made it possible for the first time to obtain an estimate of the distance from the Earth to the Sun and thereby scale the Solar System. However, more important than the scientific dimension was the geopolitical one. The transits became part of the rivalry between France and England who both sent expeditions to distant places as a matter of national pride. The 1761 Transit observation was badly affected by the ongoing Seven Years' War (1756–1763) between England and France. Also, because of the lack of experience by observers, "fruits expected from this observation... were but partially obtained." Great efforts were expended on the 1769 event, with both France and England agreeing not to molest the enemy scientific ships. Very cleverly, England made use of this understanding to outsmart France. Lieutenant (later Captain) James Cook reached Tahiti unharmed ostensibly to observe the 1769 Transit. Astronomy, however, was the least important part of his agenda. Following secret instructions from the British Navy, he proceeded towards New Zealand looking "for a Continent or Land of great extent." Nobleness of astronomy provided a convenient camouflage for many ignoble actions.

Le Gentil

The most luckless observer of the two transits was the Frenchman, Guillaume Joseph Hyacinthe Jean-Baptiste le Gentil (1725–1792), who holds the all-time dubious world record of the longest scientific expedition, and a failed one at that. He set sail for South India to observe the 1761 transit, but was thwarted by the ongoing British–French War. He decided to stay put in the East for eight more years to be able to see the 1769 transit which he could not because of cloudy sky.

The Royal Society deputed Reverend William Hirst, at the time chaplain of one of His Majesty's ships, to observe the 1761 transit. The Madras Government had earlier presented an English telescope to Mohammad Allah Cawn [Muhammad Ali Khan], the Nawab of Arcot. It was now borrowed back for the occasion.[1] Astronomical instruments were seen as symbols of a superior, science-driven culture and were presented as official gifts to native rulers as a show-off even when the latter had no use for them.

For the next transit, the Secretary of the Royal Society wrote to Madras on 22 January 1768:

> The honor of this Nation seems particularly concerned in not yielding the palm to their Neighbours, and the Royal Society intends to exert all its strength and influence in order to have this observation made... in various parts of the British Dominions.[2]

As it turned out, both the French and the English palms were left high and dry because of the cloudy skies over both Madras and Pondicherry.

Coromandel Coastal Survey

Burrow's proposal for the establishment of an observatory to assist in land survey had been turned down[44] (Ch 3; p. **163**), but astronomy had better luck on the East coast. As the sea traffic between England and India increased, the inherent limitations of the Coromandel Coast became abundantly clear. The Bay of Bengal is affected by monsoons for seven months in a year. Company ships that took barely six days between Calcutta and Madras in the winter months December–April could require 4–6 weeks at other times. The coast itself is rocky and full of shoals. Madras was not a natural harbour like Bombay was and did not provide safe landing to Indiamen which were often wrecked. A survey of the coast was thus literally a matter of life and death. Eventually, in 1785, a trained surveyor-astronomer Michael Topping (1747–1796) was sent out from England, passage paid and equipped with surveying instruments. With a view to providing reference meridian for his coastal survey and presenting the Court of Directors with a fait accompli, a private observatory was set up in his 11-acre garden house in Egmore in Madras in 1787 by a senior Madras official William Petrie[3] (d. 1816) who furnished it with his own instruments. That his initiative had official support can be seen from the fact that instruments lying scattered all over the Presidency were brought to Petrie's Observatory and into working condition.

William Petrie

Petrie arrived in Madras in 1765 as a civil servant and rose steadily through the ranks. He remained in India till 1812 when he left for Prince of Wales Island (Penang) to take over as Governor. He was in England during 1773–1777 and then again from 1780 till 1786. It was during one of these periods, presumably the second, that he acquired astronomical instruments. One of them was a pendulum clock made by John Shelton and similar to the one used by Captain Cook in his voyage. This clock is still ticking at Kodaikanal.[4] Petrie also gave the Observatory a 20-inch transit instrument.[5] He left for England in 1789 to return the next year. Before leaving, he offered his Observatory to the government. While urging the government to accept the offer, Topping reminded the Company Directors that they now had a chance of "affording their support to a science to which they are indebted for the sovereignty of a rich and extensive empire." The government took over the private observatory in 1790 and appointed Topping as its Director. The Observatory was provided with a campus and a building in 1792.[6]

Although the Company had grandiosely declared that the purpose of the Observatory was to "promote the knowledge of astronomy, geography, and navigation in India," it was clear that the main aim was to promote the Company's profitability. Science was only a part of the duties of the Company's officers. The value of various services can be gauged by the price placed on them. Topping's monthly salary as the "Company's Astronomer and Geographical Marine Surveyor" was a mere 192 pagodas. He got double this amount (400 pagodas) as the "Superintendent of Tank Repairs and Water Courses." An additional 100 pagodas per year per person (amounting to about 1200 pagodas) came from the superintendence of the Surveying School for the half-castes recruited from Male Military Asylum.[7]

Topping was succeeded by his erstwhile assistant, John Goldingham, who had arrived in India from Denmark. He retired in 1830. During his prolonged absence during 1807–1811, the Observatory was headed by Lambton's assistant John Warren. His most important contribution was the 1807 determination of the longitude of the Madras Observatory, which continued to be used in official maps till as late as 1905.

While the Observatory's scientific role as an adjunct to Trigonometrical Survey was coming to an end with Everest's 1830 reorganization of his Department, England still had use for the Observatory. The ever-expanding British colonial interests depended upon safe navigation, which in turn required familiarity with the southern skies. In 1826, state-of-the-art instruments (a transit instrument and a mural quadrant for measuring the coordinates of a star) were ordered and received in 1829. In 1831, Thomas Glanville Taylor (1804–1848), who was earlier an assistant at the Royal Observatory, Greenwich, took over as astronomer. Everest took the Court of Directors' permission to bring Taylor to Calcutta towards the end of 1831 for the Trigonometrical Survey work. Taylor's first task at Madras was to unpack the new instruments and put them in working order. Working laboriously with his new instruments, during 1831–1843, he prepared his famed Madras Catalogue of 11,015 stars, which in 1854 was described by the Astronomer Royal George Airy as "the greatest catalogue of modern times." The lasting value of Taylor's efforts can be seen from the fact that his catalogue was revised in 1901 by A. M. W. Downing, Superintendent of the Nautical Almanac, with financial assistance from the India Office and the Royal Society. Taylor's place in scientific history is assured by his Madras Catalogue, but his citation for the 1842 election as FRS introduces him as author of "5 Vols of astronomical observations at Madras," without explicitly mentioning his catalogue. He is credited with making "a Series of observations of the Magnetic Dip and Intensity at every twenty miles from Ongoli [should be Ongol] to Cape Comorin."[8] For the benefit of those who were to select candidates for the Society fellowship, it was essential to emphasize their scientific contribution towards advancing the colonial cause.

Captain William Stephen Jacob (1813–1862) held charge as Madras Astronomer from 1848 till his resignation in 1859. He brought with him a personal telescope: a six-inch aperture telescope on English mounting made by Lerebours and Secretan, Paris. Telescopes can have histories as interesting as those of human beings. Jacob's telescope was purchased by the government for £500 and served Madras well. Eventually, it was remodelled for solar work and sent to Kodaikanal where it is in regular use.

Major (later Lieutenant General) James Francis Tennant (1829–1915) took over as Astronomer in 1859, but remained in office only for a short period. Military officers were not spared for long civilian duties. A military career was far more rewarding and exciting than a low-paid dead-end appointment as Astronomer. Tennant was well-networked. Later, he became the President of the Royal Astronomical Society.

Pogson

Norman Robert Pogson (1829–1891) joined as Madras Astronomer in 1861 and worked for 30 long years till death, without taking leave. He was a neurotic and incapable of becoming part of a network. Those were the days when relatively small telescopes could produce impressive results. Because of Airy's destructive approach towards the Madras Observatory, driven by his personal aversion to Pogson, had he been given a free hand, Madras would have enriched world astronomy in a big way. Had he retired or passed away sooner, the Observatory could have been placed in more accommodating hands. As it is, his long tenure was a case of missed opportunities.

When he received Indian appointment, in a private letter, he rather pompously described himself as the "Astronomer Royal of India." But, he had reckoned without the Astronomer Royal of England, G. B. Airy, whom the Secretary of State for India consulted on all matters pertaining to the observatory. When the Sydney Observatory was established in 1858, Airy not only chose the first two directors but also laid down their scientific programme. Australian astronomy cut its umbilical cord with England in 1870 with the appointment of Henry Chamberlain Russell (1836–1907) as Director.[9] Such display of autonomy was not possible in India. If anything, Airy became more possessive about the Indian Observatories after loss of Sydney.

Pogson came to India with a solid scientific reputation. In 1856, he proposed a mathematical scale for defining stellar magnitudes, which in the course of about two decades, came to be universally accepted. This however did not benefit his career graph in any way. Before coming to India, he had already discovered three minor planets. He added another five from Madras. The first one was named Asia to commemorate the fact that it was the first astronomical discovery from the entire continent. All his seven daughters had names corresponding to minor planets discovered by him. He came to Madras with the hope that given the Observatory's low latitude, he would be able to carry out a Survey of the Southern Heavens on the lines of Professor Friedrich

Wilhelm August Argelander's (1799–1875) star catalogue known as Bonner Durchmusterung. He was also keen to continue work on his atlas of Variable Stars.

He asked for a European assistant, helpfully suggesting that a German was "likely to be obtained at a lower rate than an Englishman." The proposal was rudely turned down by the Secretary of State on Airy's advice. In a counter-offensive, Airy suggested that the Madras Observatory should be merged with Bombay, whose Director should report to the Astronomer Royal. Astronomical colonialism, however, was not acceptable to the British in India. The Madras Government rose to the occasion and pleaded for the continuation of the Observatory. The Madras Director of Public Instruction wrote to his Chief Secretary (16 January 1867): "Here I beg to call special attention to the fact that the views of Mr Airy are based simply upon the question as to what work is absolutely required to support the work done at Greenwich and other firstclass Observatories. I earnestly hope that the Rulers of India will take a higher and most extended view of matter, and consider what is due to this country [meaning the Europeans in the country]."[10] The Observatory continued, but Pogson was forced to take routine observations which he stubbornly refused to reduce and publish. He was permitted to appoint his son, Norman Everard Pogson, as an assistant at a monthly salary of Rs 150, the lowliness of which was justified on the ground that the appointee was a member of the astronomer's family and, therefore, not likely to incur any establishment costs. The son however committed suicide in July 1873,[11] and the appointment was given to Pogson's daughter, Elizabeth Isis Pogson.

Isis Pogson

Earlier, in 1867, Norman R. Pogson had been concurrently appointed as Meteorological Superintendent. In 1881, Meteorology was separated from Astronomy, and Isis was appointed as Meteorological Reporter. Her earlier post was now given to Pogson's second wife Edith. Isis is the world's first woman meteorologist. In 1886, she was nominated for the fellowship of the Royal Astronomical Society. The Council however decided that the use of the pronoun "he" throughout the Charter meant that women could not become Fellows.[12] She was eventually elected three decades later in 1920.

Workshop

If the Madras Observatory had managed to survive for 100 years against heavy odds, it was due to the workshop facility available to it. In 1859–1860, the Observatory purchased an excellent lathe by Holtzaffel. In September 1861, a German mathematical instrument maker, F. Doderet, was appointed at Madras to start workshops for the repair of levels, theodolites, etc. for the

Public Works Department. A workshop was set up at the Observatory. Doderet looked after the instruments, improvised them and made new ones out of the old ones. For the 1868 solar eclipse, he made handy telescopes out of the parts of the historical 1830 transit and mural circle. Poor observatories cannot afford the luxury of preserving their heritage.

Chintamani Ragoonatha Chary

Of all the Indian assistants in the 100-year history of the Madras Observatory, one name stood out. Chintamani Ragoonatha Chary [Raghunatha Acharya] (1828–1880) joined the Observatory as a supernumerary in 1840 when barely 12 years old and was given a regular appointment in 1847 on reaching the legal age. The last 17 years of his service were as the head assistant.

As Chary wrote in a letter:

> Mr. Pogson is mostly engaged in taking observations of variable stars, and in determining the places of minor planets with the equatorials; and I and other assistants are engaged in determining with the transit instrument the places of unknown stars in the southern regions, for the formation of a star catalogue.[13]

He consistently won high praise from his superiors for "rapidity in computing," "skill in the use of instruments," and "honesty in recording" of observations. The pointed reference to the last attribute suggests that it was not considered a common feature by colonial employers in their Indian staff. His 1867 discovery of a variable star R Reticuli is the first recorded astronomical discovery by an Indian. He was a prominent and useful member of the two expeditions fitted out to observe total eclipses of the Sun. The Madras Observatory sent various teams to different places for the eclipse of 18 August 1868. Chary was in the independent command of a party stationed at Vunputhy in the Nizam's dominion. His results were quoted in an important collation on eclipses which had occurred up to 1879.[14] For the 11 December 1871 eclipse, he was at the camp set up in the Coimbatore district. In 1872, he was elected a Fellow of the Royal Astronomical Society, on the basis of his publications in its journal and overall contribution. For 12 years, he edited the astronomical portion of the popular Almanac brought out by the Asylum Press. In late years, although he grievously deteriorated "in health, energy, and scientific usefulness," he was "merely allowed to hang on to qualify for maximum pension to make up the years he served as a supernumerary under the required age."

Indians in colonial service often saw their fellow countrymen through the glasses supplied by their employers and mentors. Thus, it was Chary's "ardent desire" to "study our own systems" and "to engraft on our own stock the reasoning and investigations in which we have been surpassed by more favored nation." He published an almanac, *Drigganita Panchanga*, with the help of the Nautical Almanac. In 1869, he ambitiously started work on an astronomical treatise which he called Jyotisha Chintamani, after his own clan name. Since he himself was "unversed in Sanskrit," he personally engaged the services of a Sanskrit scholar, who was also a good Siddhanti [a traditional mathematician-astronomer]. The project however had to be abandoned because of his failing health and his failure to raise funds. He also wanted an astronomical observatory to be set up, "where our countrymen should have easy access, learn the use of Astronomical Instruments, and be taught to make careful observations." He magnanimously offered to donate his own modern instruments, but there were no takers.

On the occasion of the 1874 transit of Venus, he brought out a pamphlet, the English version of which explains the phenomenon through a dialogue between a traditional pandit and a well-informed Siddhanti like himself. Pogson undertook the "scrutiny of the piece" and recommended it to Madras Government. The Deputy Accountant General of Madras, J. E. Cooke, arranged support for Chary "from quarters I could not have reached without his help."[15] Originally written in Tamil, it was translated into many languages: English, Telugu, Marathi and Urdu. There was subscription for more than 5000 copies from various sources. The Madras Government bought 1100 copies and Bombay 900. Other governments and departments, princely rulers, zamindars, college principles all asked for copies. Sir Salar Jung ordered 10 copies for himself and another 50 for the Kingdom of Hyderabad. To his European mentors, he was a proof of their success in improving the natives. His obituary believed to be written by his European superior, the Observatory Director Pogson patronizingly noted that Chary delivered a number of public lectures where he explained to the listeners "the true principles of science, as opposed to the ignorant superstitions and rough predictions of Hindoo astrologers and empirics of the old school." Chary's efforts to modernize traditional Indian astronomy, valiant as they were, failed to make any impression on his countrymen.

The type of details about native assistants which we are interested in now-a-days were not considered important by their British superiors. Official reports and obituaries give some information but it needs to be supplemented by non-English sources.

Chary was a Tamil Brahmin of the Iyengar caste. Many Iyengars used the caste name as surname. Chari [from Sanskrit Acharya] is also an indicator of the Iyengar caste. It is used as the last part of the first name or as the last name. Chintamani is a clan name. Marriages took place within the caste, but alliances within the clan were forbidden. Shankar Balakrishna Dikshit, the well-known Marathi historian of ancient Indian astronomy, included in his authoritative work published in 1892 a brief account of Chary, for which he consulted Madras pandits who had known Chary. According to Dikshit, Chary belonged to a family of astronomers and his father had been an assistant at Madras Observatory.[16] The person who fits the bill is C. Sashoo Iyengar, who joined the Observatory in 1837, rose to be the first assistant and died in 1863.[17] Another relative in the Observatory service was P. Raghavachari who was given an appointment in 1869 on the basis of a "General Test."[18] He retired in 1899.[19] While still in service he along with Chary's younger son was preparing the almanac. Dikshit in his original Marathi work calls him Chary's brother-in-law,[20] though it is not specified whether he was sister's husband or wife's brother.

Dikshit, whose work has been available in English since 1981, gives the precise date of Chary's birth which corresponds to 17 March 1828. Still, Rao et al.[21] have erroneously proposed 1822 as the "probable" year of birth, on the presumption that his joining the Observatory in 1840 must have been at the legal age. They failed to notice that official documents consistently make the distinction between Chary's joining the Observatory and joining the staff.

Lucknow Observatory (1831–1849)

In 1819 the Nawab of the rich province of Oudh (correctly, Avadh, corresponding to the eastern part of the present Uttar Pradesh) Ghazi-ud-Din Hyder, on the instigation of the British, declared his independence from the tottering Mughal Empire at Delhi and proclaimed himself the King. The second King (reigned 1827–1837) Naseer-ud-Din Hyder (who had a European wife) founded an Observatory at the capital city of Lucknow.

Although the Observatory belonged to the King, its scientific control was in the hands of the British, the astronomer's appointment being made by the Governor General. Major James Dowling Herbert (1791–1833) came to Lucknow with good credentials. He was at that time occupying the number two position at Calcutta as Deputy Surveyor General and Superintendent of Revenue Surveys (salary Rs 750 pm). He had earlier for a short period officiated as the Surveyor General, and his name had been mentioned to take over Everest's responsibilities as Superintendent of the GTS if Everest relinquished charge on grounds of health.

Herbert joined at Lucknow in December 1831 and promptly ordered the best available instruments for the Observatory. He died in 1833 and was succeeded by Lieutenant Colonel Richard Wilcox (1802–1848). The lure of high salary (Rs 1000) had again attracted a capable man to Lucknow. Since 1832, Wilcox had been an astronomical assistant at the GTS, with a salary of Rs 618 pm.

Wilcox joined at Lucknow in 1835 September. His place at the GTS was taken by Andrew Scott Waugh who subsequently succeeded Everest. Wilcox built the Observatory, put up the instruments, organized the plan of observations and brought the observatory into a state of high efficiency. The Observatory was ready for use in 1841. It was the best equipped in India, certainly better than Madras, and was in fact on par with Greenwich and Cambridge. Some of the observations were taken by the "Hindoo lads" which "will compete with those of any observatory."

The results from these excellent instruments were never published. Wilcox died in 1848 October; and the Observatory itself was abolished in 1849 by the King on the ground that the great outlay incurred in maintaining it had produced no advantage whatever to the state or to the people and learned of Oudh. It is reported that a memorandum to the King had asserted that "the Europeans and not Indians are benefited by this Observatory."

When Avadh was annexed by the British in 1856, there was a move by the Surveyor General, Sir Andrew Waugh, to use these instruments for an observatory at Calcutta. The Observatory was however ransacked in 1857. Lt James Francis Tennant of the Bengal Engineers was a part of the British force that recaptured Lucknow. He found that though the building itself was "unhurt," all the instruments had perished.

In the meantime, all the records of the Observatory, reduced as well as unreduced, were eaten up by insects. This is how a first-class observatory ended whose results could never see the light of day.

The maintenance of an astronomical observatory has never been an easy task. Instruments were expensive and needed to be handled by well-trained personnel. They required continual maintenance and periodic replacement. The Madras Observatory was the only astronomical success story in the 19th century. Astronomical beginnings at Trivandrum and Bombay were an embarrassment. Recognition and fame came their way only when they transferred to magnetism.

Just as Europe wished to learn about the natural history of the world and acquaint itself with the skies as seen from South India and southern latitudes, it also asked for data on meteorology and geomagnetism. There was a swelling of interest in the latter two in the 1830s. Setting up of magnetic observatories was seen as a matter of national pride and international duty.[22] Unlike astronomical observations which could be isolated, magnetic studies demanded simultaneous observations over wide areas for long periods of time.

Geomagnetic Studies

As far back as the year 1831, at the suggestion of the pioneering Russian magnetist, Professor Adolf Theodor Kupffer (1799–1865), the newly arrived Madras Astronomer, T. G. Taylor, "projected making a series of observations upon the magnetic dip and intensity in India," but could not procure the necessary apparatus here. He was "equally unfortunate in an application in England." In 1837, Taylor was able to arrange loan of a dipping needle and two intensity needles from naval officers. The former was the property of the Geographical Society of Bombay, while the latter had been employed in the magnetic survey of Ireland. He constructed some more intensity needles and set out to make observations upon the coast of India. He published his results in a 50-page paper in a Madras Journal in 1839.[23] His co-author was John Caldecott, Director of the recently established Trivandrum Observatory.

In 1836, Alexander von Humboldt wrote to the President of Royal Society, London, seeking its cooperation in establishing a network of magnetic observatories across the world, with "apparatus similar to his own … in order to obtain corresponding observations made at great distances at the same hours." The Royal Society was rather sluggish in responding. In August 1838, the British Association for the Advancement of Science launched a successful lobby which was aptly dubbed "the magnetic crusade" by its progenitors. Most members of this lobby were fellows of the Royal Society also, which finally, in 1839, wrote to the Directors of the East India Company for setting up magnetic observatories in various locations.

Accordingly, the Company decided to establish an observatory in each of the three Presidencies. Simla, Madras and Bombay were chosen as the sites but Bombay was later replaced by Singapore whose administration at the time was subordinate to Calcutta. Three officers of Engineers who were already "at home on furlo" were asked to train with the Reverend Professor Humphrey Lloyd at Trinity College Dublin. Lieutenant (later Major General) Samuel Edgar Owen Ludlow (1812–1888) of Madras Engineers was chosen for Madras and Captain John Theophilus Boileau of Bengal Engineers for Simla (Singapore was entrusted to Lieutenant Charles Elliot of Madras Engineers.) After the training, Ludlow was asked to go to Bristol to see the tide gauges being constructed there for the Company. Boileau supervised the construction and shipment of magnetic, meteorological and astronomical instruments meant for the three Observatories at Simla, Madras and Singapore. At these stations as well as at Trivandrum and Colaba in Bombay, work began in 1841 as part of a global programme, with uniform equipment. Their careers however developed differently.

Madras

The Madras Magnetic Observatory was established in 1841 and placed under Ludlow. In October 1847, it was made part of the Madras Observatory, shifted there, and placed under the charge of the Astronomer. A personal dip circle which Ludlow had been using was now purchased by the Observatory. Of all the magnetic centres, Madras probably was the most un-exciting.

However, the head native assistant, R. Ramanajooloo Naidoo, was singled out for praise by his European superiors in their own language: He

> was a rare instance of a native who delighted in his scientific occupation more for its own sake, than for the moderate pay it procured him, and who, at a time when higher education was not so easily attainable as it now is, managed to acquire a fair knowledge of mathematics, so far as spherical trigonometry, and an intelligent comprehension of all the processes, alike of observation and calculation, required in the discharge of his somewhat difficult duties. He died in 1880.[24]

John Caldecott

John Caldecott (1801–1849) was "bred an architect." Failing to find employment in England, he came to India as an employee of a commercial concern. India made him into a scientist. He arrived in Bombay in 1821 and began working at Apollo Cotton owned by members of a family known to the Caldecotts. During his stay in Bombay, he developed an interest in astronomy and built a collection of portable instruments. In 1829, he left for Alwaye (now in Kerala) where he formed a partnership firm, Owen, Caldecott & Co. In August 1831, he entered Trivandrum Government service with appointment as the Commercial Agent and Master Attendant at the port of Alleppey. He built an observatory at his Alwaye residence. "The British officer representing his Government at the Court of Travancore, under the title of Resident, has always had a weighty influence in the decisions of the Travancore Government." The current Resident, Colonel (later Lieutenant General) James Stuart Fraser (1783–1869), became an intermediary between the amateur astronomer and, Swati Tirunal Rama Varma II, Raja of Travancore from 1829 till 1846. The next two Kings are relevant from a magnetic point of view: Uthram Thirunal Marthanda Varma (ruled 1846–1860) and Ayilyam Thirunal Rama Varma (ruled 1860–1880). Fraser introduced Caldecott to the King in 1832 and in 1836 obtained the King's approval of Caldecott's proposal for the establishment of an astronomical observatory. In 1837, the King "named Mr. Caldecott his astronomer; and gave him powers to build the Observatory at Trevandrum [Trivandrum], and to furnish it with the best instruments that could be obtained from Europe." The Observatory began with Caldecott's own instruments and with some meteorological equipment.

Caldecott stayed in England for more than a year, from August 1839 till after September 1840. He became aware of plans for a worldwide network of magnetic observatories. Trivandrum was particularly suitable as a site because of its proximity to magnetic equator. He obtained the Raja's consent to buy a set of magnetic instruments from Grubb of Dublin to match those being provided for the other British and East India Company Observatories.

Caldecott and Boileau both were elected Fellow of Royal Astronomical Society on 10 January 1840. This was a prelude to bigger recognition by a more prestigious body. Caldecott became a Fellow of the Royal Society on 20 February 1840 and Boileau on 25 March 1840. The citation certificate said that Caldecott was "distinguished for his acquaintance of Astronomy, Terrestrial Magnetism, and Meteorology," and Boileau was "eminent as one who is attached to science and anxious to promote its progress." The honours were not so much a recognition of past accomplishments (which in Boileau were none), but in anticipation of future work. While Boileau lived up to the expectations, Caldecott fell far short. He will still be remembered as the founder of a new facility in a far-off place.

Caldecott attended the 10th meeting of the British Association for the Advancement of Science (BAAS) at Glasgow in September 1840 where he reported on his Observatory and on the hourly meteorological observations which had begun in June 1837 in pursuance of a suggestion by Sir John Herschel. He was also present at the dinner on the last day of the meeting where a toast was raised to the Rajah of Travancore for agreeing to create a geomagnetic facility.

Trivandrum

On return in 1841, Caldecott took up the task of installation of the instruments obtained from England. In the case of the astronomical ones, he obtained help from the Madras Astronomer T. G. Taylor who also trained a native assistant. Others were hired from Trivandrum. Caldecott's enthusiasm was no substitute for professional training. It was subsequently found that the astronomical apparatus had not been properly installed nor its errors determined. He went to England in 1846 to seek help from some scientific society to publish his observations, but in vain. He returned to Travancore in 1847. The King agreed to publish his results, but his death interrupted the process. The Observatory had no output to show for the first 15 years of its existence.

The golden age of the Observatory coincided with the tenure of John Allan Broun FRS (1817–1879) who served as Director from 1852 till 1865. He studied at the University of Edinburgh. In 1842, on the recommendation of his professor, he was appointed director of a "highly equipped" private observatory, established by Sir Thomas MacDougal Brisbane at his residence in Makerstoun, in response to the scientific world's recently awakened interest in "cultivating terrestrial magnetism." Broun worked here for eight years. Academically, he was well qualified to be a university professor, but since he steadfastly belonged to the Free Church rather than the official Church of Scotland, he would not be considered for an appointment. Through the influence of the powerful Company official Colonel W. H. Sykes, he received appointment at Trivandrum.

He discarded astronomy and focused on meteorology and magnetism. In 1855, he established an Observatory at Agustia Malley [Agastya Malai] the highest mountain near Trivandrum in the Western Ghats and rebuilt it in 1863. He obtained a complete set of hourly magnetic observations at Trivandrum from March 1852 to March 1865, and at Agustia from June 1855 to July 1858, and again during ten months in 1863. He also made a short series of hourly magnetic observations simultaneously at three different stations, including one which was as nearly as possible on the magnetic equator. In 1859–1860, he made a magnetic survey of the west coast, with stations extending from Bombay to Cape Camorin.

In 1865, he returned to Britain for medical treatment. The King closed the Observatory but accepted his request that a limited series of observations be continued by "the two most experienced native assistants," who would forward monthly reports and abstracts of observations to him. Finally, in 1874, he published the Trivandrum observations, by the order of the King. One of the fundamental discoveries he made was that the Earth loses or gains magnetic intensity not locally, but as a whole. He also found that solar activity causes magnetic disturbances. The Royal Society of Edinburgh awarded him Keith Gold Medal for 1859–1861. The Royal Society of London elected him a Fellow in 1853 and awarded him one of its Royal Medals, in 1878. On his death, Travancore sanctioned an annual pension of £75 to his widow.

Simla (1841–1846)

Boileau set up the Magnetic and Meteorological Observatory, Simla and began observations in 1841. "[i]n spite of repeated efforts by the Governor-General to have them discontinued on the grounds of economy," they continued till 1845 when the facility was abolished. It was located on Bentinck Hill, which was later occupied by the Viceregal Lodge. In a survey carried out during 1872–1874, the "slopes to the south are marked Boileaugunge (Boileauganj)." In 1844, Boileau prepared the design for Christ Church on the Ridge and raised money for its construction. It is not known when and by whom the name Boileauganj was given, and whether the commemoration was of the Church or the Observatory or both.

Colaba

The Colaba Observatory made a mark in the world through its geomagnetic researches. However, it was envisaged as an astronomical facility to begin with. It is a matter of mild curiosity that in 1806 William Taylor Money (1769–1834) set up an Observatory in the Marine Yard. He was a captain in the Company's Navy from 1793 till 1801 and the Superintendent of Marine at Bombay during 1803–1810. He was a British MP from 1816 till 1826.

From 1818 till 1826, he served as the Company Director representing ship-ping interests. He requested the support for his Observatory but it was not forthcoming. On the eve of his return to England, in 1815, Money, the retiring President of the Bombay Literary Society, presented his personal transit instru-ment to it to serve as the nucleus of an astronomical observatory. The Society approached the government for support which was readily given. The Society was given a grant of Rs 2000 as also land at the Fort's southwest ravelin facing the open Esplanade. A building was constructed and "some valuable instru-ments" were purchased, presumably second hand from European officers. The Observatory opened in 1818 under the charge of a watchmaker Roger Francis Hereford. He however died in 1820. It was then decided to ask the govern-ment to take over the Observatory which was done. It came about not in re-sponse to any felt need, but out of consideration for the Literary Society whose members formed "a select circle of high placed Europeans."[25]

John Curnin was chosen as Director of Bombay Observatory on the recom-mendation of the eminent Sanskritist, H. T. Colebrooke. Curnin arrived in 1823 and decided to shift the Observatory from the Fort to Colaba, then a separate island. He was entrusted with the design as well as the construction of the buildings. To make the Observatory operational, he wrote down the specification of the instruments he wanted and sent the list to the Company. The instruments were received by early 1827, but Curnin declared these to be substandard and not worthy of use. His assessment was endorsed by a Committee of Engineers formed to examine the instruments. The instruments made for Madras, Lucknow and Trivandrum were all made by reputed mak-ers such as Dollond and Troughton, but the Colaba lot was made by inferior makers, the Gilberts, who were the Company's official instrument makers.

Curnin rudely sent back the instruments within five months of their re-ceipt, that is, in August 1827. His criticism of the instruments may have been acceptable but not his condemnation of the system. He openly charged the instrument maker and the Company librarian, the well-known Sanskrit scholar Charles Wilkins with lack of integrity. His covering letter "teems with invectives, and imputes motives... for which there is no shadow of a foundation."[26] He was dismissed in 1828 end.

George Buist, who held temporary charge of the Observatory during 1842–1845, wrote sympathetically about Curnin:

Had he chosen to sit quietly down, as four-fifths of men would have done, with the means provided him for the performance of the duties assigned to him, and thought of no more than what was required by the regulations of the service and permitted by the implements at his disposal, he might have been to the hour of his death [as] the Company's Astronomer at Bombay, with an income abundantly ample to have provided for his own enjoy-ments, and for the wants of those he might have left behind him.

Personal dimensions apart, his exit marked the demise of astronomy at Bombay.

A "portion of instruments were returned to Bombay" in 1835, but remained unpacked for five years. The same year the Elphinstone Institution was constituted formally in 1835 and Arthur Bedford Orlebar (1810–1866) arrived as Professor of Natural Philosophy. His association with Colaba occurred in two phases. First, he was assigned the Observatory as his residence and then made its director. The transit instrument was put up at last, in 1840.[27] A magnetic observatory was erected the next year. Of all the magnetic facilities created in India, Colaba turned out to be the most durable. And yet formation of such a facility was an accident and pre-required the presence in India of England-trained magnetists.

The instruments that came to be in use at Bombay were originally intended for Aden. But the officers, "who had engaged to superintend them" died. "The Royal Society considered that Bombay would be an eligible station," and the instruments were put under Orlebar's charge on 10 March 1841. The instruments however were not accompanied by "any directions and instructions" with the result that Orlebar found himself "not only without guidance as to the nature of the building, but also as to the parts and objects of many of the instruments which were of course quite new to me." Boileau, from Simla, sent Orlebar a copy of the Royal Society's instructions. However, before they could reach Orlebar, Caldecott passed through Bombay, on his way from England to Trivandrum, and gave sufficient information to enable Orlebar to commence work, which began in November or December 1841, but regular series began only in 1846.

In 1864, it was felt that the Observatory work was not being carried out satisfactorily. A committee of enquiry was appointed which submitted its report in 1865. As a result, the Observatory was provided with its first full-time Director, Charles Chambers, FRS, who held office for three decades, from 1865 till death in 1896. At the same time, the Observatory was supplied with a "complete set of self-recording magnetical and meteorological instruments on the Kew pattern." These instruments were brought into use in 1871–1872 and a continuous series of observations was begun.[28] Colaba now entered upon an era of real scientific activity both in regard to the collection of accurate data and to their discussion.[29] Even routine observations taken over a long period with the same instruments become scientifically significant. "The complete record, for instance, of the monthly values of the magnetic moment of one of the standard magnets, extending over nearly forty years, is probably unique." Chambers was succeeded by Nanabhoy Ardeshir Framji Moos (1859–1936), who has the distinction of being the first Indian Director of the Colaba Observatory. He was a Parsi. The relationship of the British with the Parsis was different from that with other Indians. He held office from 1896 till

1919. His long uninterrupted tenure gave stability and direction to the Observatory for the next quarter of a century.

His father, Ardeseer Framji Moos, a class fellow of Dadabhai Naoroji, was an important Parsi and Bombay citizen of his time. In his 1871 book *Journal of Travels in India*, he described himself as Merchant; Justice of the Peace; Formerly Superintendent of the Elphinstone Institution Central School, Lower Department, and Assistant Professor of Chemistry and Natural Philosophy, Upper Department, etc.[30] This was not the occasion to mention that he quit the Rs 40 per month Elphinstone job to take up a better paying appointment in the telegraph department. Subsequently, he became the Secretary of Bombay Royal Mills at Rs 1200 per month. Later, he joined family business.[31] In 1888, Nanabhoy's sister, Bai Bachoobai Moos (1850–1946) founded a girl's school in South Bombay, now known as Girton High school. Nanabhoy received his schooling at the Elphinstone School and, after matriculation at 16, joined the College of Engineering, Poona, earning his degree in 1878. He joined the Bombay Municipal Engineering Service, but later moved to his alma mater at Poona to teach engineering. Moos obtained his BSc with distinction in 1886. He was awarded a bursary of £20 on the basis of a competitive written examination and went to Edinburgh for higher education.[32] On his return to India, he held a series of appointments, including that of a professor of physics at the Elphinstone College, Bombay.

Concurrently, with Colaba directorship, he was appointed the (ex-officio) Director of Time Communication to the Harbour, "for superintending the working of the Time Ball arrangements," under the supervision of the Bombay Port Trust. For this work, he was paid an additional Rs 150 per month. The Directors of all Observatories were required to drop time ball every day (at 1 P. M.) to provide correct solar time to ships. The paid appointment for time announcement was a new initiative.[33]

The growing urbanization of Bombay proved detrimental to the Observatory. Horse-drawn tram service was introduced in 1874. Early in 1900 it was decided to replace the horse by electricity. Since this posed a serious threat to the magnetic work, Moos boldly decided to move the observatory to a more suitable site at Alibag, about 30 km to the South on the same longitude. After securing duplicate records at the two stations in 1904 and 1905, the magnetic work at Colaba was finally closed in 1906, and Alibag established as a magnetic observatory.[34]

Moos's great opportunity came with the plan for putting together and discussing the complete series of observations of the old Bombay Observatory; and the two volumes of "Colaba Magnetic Data, 1846-1905" are a monument of conscientious and successful labour. They form an indispensable part of the equipment of a magnetic library.[35]

Nizamiah Observatory, Hyderabad

Nizamiah [Nizam's] Observatory, Hyderabad, represents a successful experiment in international programme made possible by equation between the nobility and royalty of an Indian princely state on the one hand, and between the nobility and English astronomers on the other, with British India playing no role. The Observatory occupies a special place in the early 20th century world history of astronomy by virtue of its belated but dedicated participation from 1914 till 1946 in the International Astrographic Catalogue or Carte du Ciel programme.

The Observatory was established in 1901 by Nawab Jafar [Zaffer] Jung (1866–1907) at his estate in Phisalbanda. The nawab was no ordinary nobleman. He came from the Paigah family which ranked next only to that of the Nizam. His mother was a daughter of Asaf Jah V so that Asaf Jah VI, who ruled from 1869 till 1911, was his maternal uncle. Jung's father, Sir Khurshed Jah, was head of one of the three branches of the extended Paigah family. When he died in 1902, Asaf Jah VI, guided by family relationship, nominated Zafar Jung (instead of his elder half-brother) to be the new head of his branch. He was also appointed the minister for military affairs in the Nizam's Government.

Jafar Jung was educated at Nizam College and, in 1883–1884, sent to England for a year, in the company of a Maulvi (Syed Mahmood) and an Englishman (one Mr Stevens). There, he received instruction from a private tutor and enrolled as an officer in Queen Victoria's life guards. Before returning to Hyderabad, he visited Paris and other places on the Continent.[36] Three years later, in 1887, he was again in England, this time on official assignment. He was a junior member of the delegation which included an even more illustrious Paigah, Sir Asman Ali Jah, and which represented the Nizam at Queen Victoria's Jubilee celebrations.[37] It is noteworthy that shortly before the Jubilee there had taken place an international astronomical congress at the Paris Observatory which decided on Carte du Ciel and Astrographic Catalogue covering the whole sky through a collaborative effort of suitably located observatories the world over.

On 29 September 1901, Jung wrote to the Nizam that he proposed to establish an astronomical observatory seeking permission to name it after the Nizam. He also obtained an undertaking that the government would take over the Observatory after his death, and his "heirs will cease to have any connection with it."[38] That the details of the arrangement had already been worked out can be gauged from the fact that the Nizam's permission came the very next day. After Jung's death, the Observatory was placed under the finance department in 1908. The Nizamiah Observatory officially takes 1908 as the year of its founding.[39] Since the Observatory was named after Nizam from the very beginning, and because of continuity in its history, it would be more appropriate to take 1901 as its year of establishment.

The question of choosing its director dwelt on Sir George Casson Walker, ICS, financial secretary to the Nizam from 1901 till 1911.[40] On the recommendation of Herbert Hall Turner (1861–1930), Arthur Brunel Chatwood (1866–1915) was appointed the director. He held office from 1908 till 1914. Turner was the director of the Radcliffe Observatory, Oxford, and deeply involved in the international astrographic catalogue programme. As early as 1889, the Santiago Observatory, Chile, was assigned the sky zone, –17 to –23 degrees, but not much progress had been made. As Turner recalled in 1918, "[I]t was then thought to be desirable to assign half the zone to Hyderabad, and Mr Chatwood was sent out to Hyderabad to put it in order."[41] Immediately on arrival, Chatwood wrote to the Nizam asking for permission to participate in the Catalogue and requisite funding to carry out the task. The Nizam gave his approval on 27 July 1908, and the International Congress formally assigned the sky segment to Nizamiah, on 20 April 1909. Hyderabad's participation in the Catalogue was a great relief to the European astronomers. Not only did they get a suitably located observatory to look at the southern skies but also at no expense to them.

Chatwood was more of an engineer than an astronomer. For many years he was engaged in his father Samuel Chatwood's well-regarded works, Chatwood Patent Safe and Lock Company, where in later years he was involved in "designing and erecting security structures, hydraulics, and other machinery."[42] As preparation for his overseas appointment, Chatwood "accepted a modest and temporary post" at the Radcliffe Observatory. To enhance Chatwood's professional prestige, Turner got him elected a fellow of the Royal Astronomical Society. Chatwood shifted the Observatory from Phisalbanda estate to a suburb, Begumpet.

Instruments

Jung expended considerable effort and money in equipping his observatory. In 1901, he acquired an 8-inch aperture telescope by T. Cooke and Son. It had been made on order for the South African land surveyor and amateur astronomer, Josias Eduard de Villiers (1843–1898), who wanted it for his planned Sea Point Observatory, Cape Town.[43] He however unexpectedly died in a train accident. The telescope was "afterwards sold to Messrs. Lawrence and Mayo and sent to Hyderabad – 1901."[44]

In 1903 or 1904, Sir Howard Grubb supplied an 15-inch "clear aperture achromatic telescope of the same form, dimensions, & construction as those we specially made for the Internat[ional] Survey of the Heavens & supplied by [should be 'to'] the British, Colonial, and foreign observatories." It was priced £1450. In addition, two domes, large and small, were also supplied, no doubt for the two Nizamiah telescopes.[45]

In about 1890, Grubb also made extremely precise 13-inch photographic refractors (astrographs) for the International Photographic Survey. Only seven were made, so that at this late stage even if Jung had wanted one, it might not have been available. He settled for a relatively inferior 8-inch aperture astrograph from T. Cooke and Sons.

Keeping in mind the requirements of the Catalogue, Chatwood took up work on the astrograph on priority basis and installed it in 1909. However, some parts had to be sent to England for repairs so that the instrument became usable only in late 1914. The Astrographic Catalogue work can be taken to have begun on 9 December 1914 when the first usable plates were taken by Chatwood's successor.

Chatwood's accomplishments did not go beyond installation. He resigned in 1914 and the appointment went to Turner's protégé, Robert John Pocock (1889–1918) who held office from 1914 till his sudden death, due to pneumonia, in 1918. In the meantime, the Osmania University was set up in 1917 and the control of the Observatory was transferred to it in 1919. Pocock was succeeded by T. P. Bhaskaran who held office till 1946. The Catalogue continued right through his tenure.[46]

Grubb Telescope

It was noted in a 1934 publication by Mudiraj that Zafar Jung "engaged the services of an English astronomer, by name of Grubb."[47] It seems certain that the man referred to is Sir Howard Grubb's son George Rudolf Grubb (b. 1878). He obtained a degree in engineering in 1899 from Trinity College, Dublin. The next year he was in Spain assisting Spanish and Irish teams with the installation and adjustments of their instruments for observing the total solar eclipse of 28 May 1900. Sir Howard Grubb was the leading member of the Irish team and source of many instruments for its use.[48] The well-known chemist, James Emerson Reynolds and Rudolf Grubb (in that order) filed for a US patent on "Improved Production of Films on Plate-Glass or other Transparent Bodies." The application was signed in Dublin on 18 September 1901. It will therefore be wrong to say that he moved to India in 1900.[49]

The *Deccan Chronicle* in 1904 published a photograph that shows Jung flanked by two Europeans, a young man and an older man flanking Nawab Zafar Jung with the Grubb telescope in the background. It is titled "Nawab Zafar Jung with astronomy experts." The younger one may well be Rudolf Grubb, but the two need to be identified with certainty.[50] It is likely that Rudolph was sent by his father to Hyderabad to set up the telescope, and he decided to stay in India. The other possibility is that he had already come to India on his own, and the father gave him the Nizamiah assignment.

The 15-inch Grubb telescope was not immediately installed at Begumpet after removal from Phisalbanda. Astronomical optics was a rarity in India.

The Kodaikanal Observatory borrowed the Grubb lens in 1916 and returned it seven years later when the telescope was finally commissioned in 1922.[51] One of the assistants at Nizamiah was M. K. Bappu whose son M. K. Vainu Bappu became the Director of the Kodaikanal Observatory and then the Indian Institute of Astrophysics, Bangalore.[52]

Modernization of the Observatory was carried out of the wheat loan PL 480 rupee funds held by the USA. A 48-inch (1.2 m) reflector was ordered from J. W. Fecker of Pittsburgh and commissioned at a new site for Japal-Rangapur Observatory, in 1968. This is the only major telescope in India ever sourced from USA. In 1963, the historic Begumpet site was surrendered, and the Nizamiah Observatory shifted to a new building in the University campus. In course of the time, both the Nizamiah and the Japal-Rangapur Observatories became non-functional.

While bland facts about the Phisalbanda, or the Jafar Jung phase, are known, they need to be placed in context. Published accounts give the impression that Hyderabad's participation in the Astrographic Catalogue was thought of only after Zafar Jung's death. This cannot be true, because the requisite instruments had already been purchased by Jung. Who was his scientific advisor? When exactly was the Nizamiah's association with the Carte envisaged? These intriguing questions can be answered only when relevant archives are located in Hyderabad, England, or elsewhere, and closely examined.

Solar Physics

India's astronomical fortunes revived with the advent of the new field of solar physics. India was ideal for extensive photography of the sun, which was not possible in cloudy Britain. Also, it was then believed that a study of the Sun will help predict the failure of the monsoons. In 1878, solar photography was started at Survey of India, Dehradun, and photographs were sent to England for analysis. A solar observatory was established by the Imperial Government at Kodaikanal in 1899 which still exists as part of the Indian Institute of Astrophysics, Bangalore.

By the middle of the 19th century, physical astronomy, as distinct from positional astronomy, had already taken some shape, thanks to the advent of solar spectroscopy and photography. There were a number of solar eclipses in quick succession and visible from India: 1868, 1871 and 1872. These eclipses brought observers from Europe to India, and gave fillip to solar instrumentation and studies the world over. In 1868, the French astrophysicist Pierre Jules Cesar Janssen discovered helium from Guntur. During his post-eclipse stay at Simla, Janssen created the first spectro-helioscope, which facilitated the daily examination of the sun.

Then came the 1874 Transit of Venus. The scientists' agenda for it ran deep. What was advertised was the brief passage of Venus in front of the solar disc; what was planned was a long-term study of the disc itself. British (and European) solar physicists wanted photographs of the sun for each day of the year. Since this was impossible in Europe's weather conditions, data was needed from the colonies.

The British Association for the Advancement of Science passed a resolution asking the Government of India to make arrangements for observing the event and to provide instruments which were afterwards to be transferred to a solar observatory. Such was the prestige enjoyed by science and scientists in Europe at the time that the British Empire, as the owner of the most of the world's sunshine, agreed to help, though partially. The 1874 transit eventually led to regular solar physics studies in India, even though the exercise took 25 years. The initiative came from the influential British scientist of the time, Sir Norman Lockyer.

To sum up in advance, the step-wise developments were as follows.

- Observation of the 1874 event.
- Creation of interim facilities for collection of data and its transmission to Europe.
- Permanent facility in India.

The 1874 Event

It is noteworthy that the Survey of India (and not Madras Observatory) was asked to observe the 1874 transit of Venus. More than 100 photos of the sun were taken at Roorkee with a photoheliograph made by Dallmeyer and sent to the Astronomer Royal George Airy. Photos from all over were reduced by Captain G. L. Tupman who wrote: "There is only one really sharp image in the whole collection, including the Indian and Australian contingents, and that is one of Captain Waterhouse's wet plates taken at Roorkee."

Dehradun Observatory (1878–1925)

Lockyer used his equation with Lord Salisbury, the Secretary of State for India, for making arrangements for solar photography in India. Salisbury wrote to the Viceroy on 28 September 1877:

> Having considered the suggestions made by Mr. Lockyer, and viewing that a study of the conditions of the sun's disc in relation to terrestrial phenomenon has become an important part of physical investigation, I have thought it desirable to assent to the employment for a limited period of a person qualified to obtain photographs of the sun's disc by the aid of the instrument now in India.

From the technical details given in the letter, it is clear that it was drafted by Lockyer himself.

Accordingly, starting from early 1878, solar photographs were regularly taken at Dehradun under the auspices of the Survey of India and sent to England every week, more out of a sense of duty than enthusiasm. The larger of the two photoheliographs fell into disuse, and when Lockyer visited the facility in 1898, he was stung by on-the-spot discovery that "the dome has been taken possession of by bees." The arrangement was discontinued in 1925, and the equipment was sent to Kodaikanal.

St Xavier's College Observatory, Calcutta (1879)

Sunny India caught the attention of astronomers in the continent also. The Italian Transit-of-Venus team led by Professor P. Tacchini of the Palermo Observatory stationed itself in Bengal, its chief instrument being the spectroscope, "an instrument not recognized in the equipment of any of the English parties." A co-opted member of the Italian team was the Belgian Jesuit Father Eugene Lafont (1837–1908), the popular professor of science at the elitist St. Xavier's College. Lafont, no researcher himself, was an inspiring educator and science communicator. Tacchini suggested to Lafont "the advisability of erecting a Solar Observatory in Calcutta, in order to supplement the Observations made in Europe, by filling up the gaps caused in the series of solar records by bad weather." Lafont used his influence with Europeans, Anglo-Indians (half-castes), rajas, zamindars and Indian men of note, and soon collected a substantial sum of Rs 21,000 through donations, including Rs 7000 from the Lieutenant Governor of Bengal. A 9-inch refractor by Steinhill of Munich was purchased and housed in a spacious dome constructed for the purpose. No research or teaching use was ever made of this facility. This is unfortunate. If the experiment had succeeded, observational astronomy might have become part of Indian education system. As it is, astronomy has largely remained decoupled from college/university teaching.

Takhtasinhji's Observatory Poona (1888–1912)

It was a Government Observatory, named after the principal funder, Maharaja of a princely state, Bhavnagar. It was India's first modern astrophysical observatory. Unfortunately, it was created for an individual and did not last long. The original plan was to establish a spectroscopic laboratory at Elphinstone College, Bombay for use by students. The initiator of the proposal was a lecturer in the College, Kavasji Dadabhai Naegamvala (1857–1938), who obtained a seed money of Rs 5000 from the Maharaja of Bhavnagar and a matching grant from the Bombay Government for establishing a spectroscopic laboratory for use by the students. While in England in 1884 for buying the equipment, he was persuaded by the Astronomer Royal and Lockyer to build a spectroscopic observatory instead. Thus, Indian educational needs were sacrificed at the altar of European scientific requirements. Instead of a permanent educational facility, a temporary research centre was created for the benefit of European solar physicists.

Lockyer equipped Poona as a satellite facility. Its chief instrument was a 16½-inch aperture silver-on-parabolic glass Newtonian made by Grubb. A six-inch Cooke equatorial purchased by the government for the 1874 transit observation from India had been loaned to Lockyer's Observatory in South Kensington.

Not surprisingly, the relationship between Poona and South Kensington was non-symmetrical. It was marked by the latter's sense of superiority. Whenever Lockyer found fault with data collection at Poona, he did not write directly, but formally complained to Naegamvala's superior, Dr Giles, the Director of Public Instruction. Yet, when the Kodaikanal Observatory was being planned, Lockyer suggested Naegamvala's name for the directorship. The position was however offered to an Englishman, Charles Michie Smith, a non-descript physics professor at Madras, who was supported by the Astronomer Royal. Lockyer and he constituted two independent centres of power in England, and Kodaikanal came under the latter's sphere of influence. Naegamvala took observations till the very last date of his employment, 11 January 1912. The Observatory was officially abolished on the day of his retirement and all equipment was sent to Kodaikanal.

Kodaikanal Observatory (1899)

If the 1874 transit of Venus was important for solar physicists, so was the severe famine of 1876–1877 in the Madras Presidency. Monsoons fail at times, but the severity of famines was particularly high in the colonial period because of the large-scale export of food grains from India to Britain in utter disregard of local requirements. Astronomers of course would not worry about avoiding famines, but in predicting monsoon behaviour. In 1879, Lockyer presented a report to the Indian Famine Commission claiming that famines were correlated with sunspot minima. There is no doubt that Lockyer and many others genuinely believed at the time in a correlation between solar activity and terrestrial weather. But it is also a fact that the practical benefits to be derived from a study of the sun were exaggerated to gain government support.

In 1881, the Government of India's Chief Meteorologist Henry Francis Blanford reported to the Famine Commission that no such simple sunspot–monsoon correlation as suggested by Lockyer existed. The government however decided to go ahead with the Solar Observatory. It was however decided to wait till the end of the tenure of Pogson. This happened in 1890.

It was decided in 1893 to establish the Kodaikanal Observatory with Charles Michie Smith (1854–1922), Madras Astronomer and a protégé of Astronomer Royal William Henry Mahoney Christie (1845–1922) as its director.

In 1895, the plans for buildings and instruments were approved by the London-based Indian Observatories Committee, chaired by Lord Kelvin. The formal government sanction followed as a matter of course. The foundation stone of the Kodaikanal Observatory was laid in 1895. The Observatory finally became operational in a 100-acre estate atop Nadingipuram Hill in Kodaikanal in 1899.

In 1907, a spectroheliograph was installed by George Evershed who chose to come to Kodaikanal to work in solitary splendour. Using it, he discovered what after him was designated the Evershed Effect. This was the only time the Observatory ever had a state-of-art equipment. Routine work carried out at Kodaikanal (as at Colaba) with the same instruments for a very long time-line has become valuable for the world community of solar physicists.

Kodaikanal Observatory has remained at the same site since its establishment and has been in continuous use. It fulfils all conditions for inclusion in UNESCO's list of world astronomy heritage sites.

False Point Super-cyclone in the Bay of Bengal, 1885

A cyclone crossed the Orissa coast on 22 September 1885. Known as the False Point cyclone (after the name of the harbour where it hit land), it ranks as one of the severest cyclones in the recorded history of Bay of Bengal. It generated storm surge as high as 7 m and wind speeds of 250 km per hour. There is no official casualty figure but contemporaneous accounts suggest that about 10,000 people lost their life. The damage due to the cyclone was minimal thanks to the scientific acumen of a 22-year-old Indian meteorologist who, though placed on the lowest rung of official hierarchy, boldly issued the red alert on his personal responsibility without caring for green signal from his superiors.

Ruchi Ram Sahni (1863–1948) was the first Indian to be appointed to a scientific post in the India Meteorological Department which was at the time headquartered in Simla. In September 1885, the Met Chief Henry Francis Blanford as well as the first assistant, both Europeans, were away to Calcutta, leaving the lowly Indian second assistant in charge. While preparing the daily weather report, which normally was an un-exciting affair, Sahni was struck by the input from Diamond Harbour which showed an unusually rapid fall of atmospheric pressure. He sent an urgent telegram to the observer there asking him to send a fresh report of the latest readings. This report confirmed the original suspicion that a big storm was approaching. Sahni then asked him to remain in place till further orders and to keep sending half hourly reports on the weather. Next, Sahni asked two or three of the other neighbouring stations to do the same. In the meantime, he educated himself on the previous big storms by reading their description. Convinced of the veracity of his findings, he boldly made his forecast public. The timely warning was a great help to the ships.

Dutifully, Sahni sent a long telegram to his chief at Calcutta explaining what he had done and on what grounds. Seriously perturbed and upset at the news, Blanford at once ran to Alexander Pedler and asked him if he knew of anything of a big storm in the Bay. Pedler was professor of chemistry at the Presidency College Calcutta and also the provincial meteorological reporter for Bengal. In the latter capacity, he used to get copies of all reports that were sent to Simla. Pedler however had not even looked at the reports and knew nothing of the storm. On Blanford's suggestion, Pedler sent out orders to the affected stations to repeat the telegrams they had been sending to Sahni. By this time the storm had very much increased in intensity and had invaded the coast. Blanford and Pedler were now convinced that Sahni had been correct in his judgement and the orders that he had issued were quite justified. Pedler went on to write a well-cited 80-page scholarly paper on the cyclone. Predictably, the lengthy paper does not refer to the circumstances of its prediction. True to pattern, we know of Sahni's forecasting of the storm from his own memoirs; the colonial-time records do not mention his name.[53]

Notes

1 Philosophical Transactions of the Royal Society, 1761, 52, 397.
2 Love, 1913, 3, 591.
3 https://rajeshkochhar.com/william-petrie-d1816madras-civil-servant-1765-1812-and-governorpenang-1812-1816/.
4 Kochhar, 1987.
5 Chary, 1874, vi.
6 All original buildings are long gone, but some stone remnants of the Observatory can still be seen. The campus now houses the offices of India Meteorological Department.
7 Kochhar, 1991.
8 Taylor & Caldecott, 1839.
9 Bhathal, 2009.
10 Madras Director of Public Instruction to Chief Secretary, 16 January 1867, No. 100.
11 He committed suicide on his father's refusal to let him marry the girl of his choice; Personal communication from Ethel Richards, 1988. Ethel is grand-daughter of Pogson's son William Norman.
12 Bailey, 2016, 1.20.
13 Astronomical Register, 1876, 13, 71.
14 Ranyard, 1879.
15 Chary, 1874, ii.
16 Dikshit, 1981, 2, 181–182.
17 Pogson, 1887, xv.
18 Report for the Madras Observatory for 1897–1898, p. 1.

19 Report on the Kodaikanal and Madras Observatories for 1899–1900, p. 1.
20 Dikshit, 1981, 2, 182.
21 arXiv:0908.3081v1.
22 Morrell &Thackray, 1981, 354.
23 Taylor & Caldecott, 1839, 254.
24 Jacob, 1884, III. http://indicatorloops.com/caldecott.htm.
25 The Society was formed in 1804 and became the Bombay Branch of Royal Asiatic Society of Great Britain and England in 1829.
26 Phillimore, 1954, 3, 435.
27 Markham, 1871, 21.
28 Letter dated 29 May 1896 from the Meteorological Reporter, John Eliot, to the Secretary, Revenue and Agricultural Department (No. 410-S), p. 6.
29 Unaker, 1936, 862.
30 Moos, 1871, cover.
31 Ramanna, 1992, 719.
32 Unaker, 1936, 863.
33 Krishnan, 2013, 70.
34 *Nature*, 1911, 88, 113.
35 *Nature*, 1936, 138, 430.
36 The above biographical details are taken from Mudiraj, 1934, 67–68.
37 *The Times*, London, 20 June 1887, p. 6.
38 Sanwal, 1983, 1.
39 Sanwal, 1983.
40 The designation is taken from *The India List and India Office List for 1905* (London: Harrison and Sons), pp. 637–638. He is variously described as financial adviser to the Nizam or assistant finance minister.
41 *Observatory*, 1918, 41, 428.
42 Proceedings of the Institution of Civil Engineers, 1916, 201, Part 1, p. 403.
43 Warner & Hurly, 1976. I thank Ian S. Glass for bringing this reference to my notice.
44 I thank Alison Brech, Vickers Collection, Borthwick Institute for Archives, University of York, Heslington, UK for her help.
45 On 11 March 1903, Grubb sent detailed specifications of instruments being supplied to an un-named "Superintendent" of "Nizam's Observatory." This information comes from the primary source material, not noticed before: MS 2076/2, Science Museum Library, Wroughton, Swindon.
46 Sanwal, 1983.
47 Mudiraj, 1934, 68.
48 Transactions of the Royal Irish Academy, 1902, 32, 272.
49 Biographical Encyclopedia of Astronomers, 2007, 1, 447 (Springer). I thank Mary Kavanagh for help.
50 https://commons.wikimedia.org/wiki/.
   File: Nizamia_obsevatory_Hyderabad,_Nawab_Zafar_Jung_with_astronomy_experts.jpg.
51 Bhaskaran, 1923, 497.
52 Kochhar, 2014.
53 https://rajeshkochhar.com/a-historical-super-cyclone-in-the-bay-of-bengal-the-punjab-connection/.

5
NATURAL HISTORY

Portuguese and Dutch India, 16–17th Century

In the 16th century, the health needs of sailors, merchants, administrators and missionaries who went to distant lands needed to be addressed. It became necessary for them to acquaint themselves with new medicinal plants and plant-based remedies. At the same time, Europe was interested in new medicines and exotic remedies from America and Asia for its new and old diseases.

The early success of its oceanic voyages brought contrary pulls to bear on Europe, with the practical needs of the hour standing in contradistinction to the age-old religious authority, sectarian antagonism, and the recovered Greco-Roman medico-botanical tradition. Old authorities still held sway. Between 50–70 CE, Dioscorides wrote his Materia Medica which contained about 500 plants. Galen (129–c. 210 CE) Greek physician, writer and philosopher remained a dominant influence on European medical theory and practice from the Middle Ages until the mid-17th century.

Even as botanical knowledge from Spanish America and Portuguese India broadened European horizons, there was reluctance to admit to the limitations of Galen and Dioscorides. Europe, in addition, lacked the maturity to appreciate the native American healthcare systems. In the course of time and in stages, American and Asian streams were merged, and the extant knowledge was systematized.

Books on new medical materials were published in Portuguese and Spanish for the benefit of merchants, physicians, apothecaries and lay persons. For the same reasons, these works were translated into other European vernaculars. They were rendered into Latin as well, the language of the learned. The vernacular and the learned streams were not antagonistic, but mutually supportive. When a work in one language became available in

DOI: 10.4324/9781003466406-5

TABLE 5.1 Landmarks in Botanical Studies in America and Asia, 1511–1693

Year	Landmark
1511–1530	America. De d'Anghiera (1457–1526) published information on some plants from America.
1526–1536	America. Oviedo (1478–1557) describes more than 250 American plants and animals.
1533 and 1545	Europe. University of Padua appoints Francis Bonafede as professor of simples (medicinal plants), and opens Europe's first garden for "the rebirth of the materia medica of the ancients."
1552–1577	America. Franciscan friars sent accounts of the Aztec system of healthcare and herbs to Europe. Codex Barberini (1552) ignored; Florentine Codex (1577) confiscated.
1555	America. Andres Laguna (c. 1510–1559) mentions drugs not found in Dioscorides' Materia Medica.
1563	India. Garcia d'Orta publishes *Colloquies*.
1565–1574	America. Monardes (c. 1493–1588) publishes his three-part *Historia Medicinal*, describing the use of about 100 American drugs, including tobacco.
1567	Europe. Clusius publishes the Latin abridgement of d'Orta's Colloquies.
1572	Asia. John Fragaso publishes Discursos, extending d'Orta.
1574, 1579	Europe. Clusius translates Monardes into Latin.
1576	America. Hernandez prepares a massive well-illustrated manuscript on Mexican plants on Royal orders. Belatedly used in various ways including academic.
1578	Asia. Christobal Acosta's *Tracado*, based on d'Orta.
1582	Europe. Clusius combines d'Orta, Monardes, and C. Acosta, in Latin.
1590	America. Jose de Acosta publishes *Historia Natural*.
1651	Europe. Hernandez enters the academic mainstream. Lyncean Academy, Rome, publishes a richly illustrated encyclopaedic work with the short title *Rerum* using his extant text as the nucleus.
1678–1693	India. Van Rheede organized the 12-volume *Hortus Malabaricus* incorporating traditional knowledge, published in Latin from Amsterdam.

others, very often it was not as a mere translation but as a critically revised and enlarged edition. There was thus a certain collectivity in the European efforts. This trait of sharing scientific knowledge, even while fighting over technology, territory, and commerce, was seen later in other fields such as astronomy and map-making.

Botanical studies in the Americas proceeded independently, with a 50-year lead over Asia.

Making use of secondary sources, Pedro Martir d'Anghiera (1457–1526) included the account of some American plants in his famous *Decades*, published over 1516–1530. Gonzalo Fernandez de Oviedo y Valdes (1478–1557), known simply as Oviedo, who spent a considerable number of years in America published in 1526 a smaller work, *The Sumario*, and followed it up in 1535 the longer and more fully illustrated *Historia*. In these, Oviedo described American plants and animals on the basis of first-hand knowledge.

European academe responded to new developments, but defensively. In 1533, Padua University appointed Frances Bonafede as Europe's first-ever lecturer in simples (that is medicinal plants). On his initiative, the senate of the Republic of Venice established Europe's first botanic garden in 1545. Originally known as the garden of simples, its object was explicitly stated to be "the rebirth of the materia medica of the ancients."[1]

> About 1550 a doctor in England was called before the College of Physicians for impugning the authority of Galen. He recanted, acknowledged his heresy and was pardoned.[2]

When the Hellenist and physician Andres Laguna (c. 1510–1559) published his Spanish translation of and commentary on Dioscorides' *Materia Medica* in 1555, he mentioned drugs which he could not fit into it. With passage of time, it slowly became clear that non-Europe grew medicinal plants not known to old European authorities.

Monardes

Europe was more enthused by commercial concerns than purely academic considerations. Seville-based Spanish practising physician Nicolas Bautista Monardes (c. 1493–1588), slave trader and importer and grower of American medicinal plants, published his most significant work *Historia medicinal*. It was published in three parts under varying titles. The first two parts were published in 1565 and 1569 and all three together in 1574. He commented on the use of about 100 American drugs, including tobacco.[3] The Latin translation of the first two parts was prepared in 1574 by Clusius. The English translation of the entire work was entitled *Joyful News out of the New Founde Worlde* and published in 1577.

Bezoar

The sense of desperation in healthcare and fascination with the exotic both combined to popularize remedies which today would be called bizarre, like the bezoar stones, which Monardes discussed at length. The name bezoar is a corruption of the Persian *bad-zuhr*, meaning antidote.[4] These stones, obtained from inside the animals, were invested with magical remedial powers. Monardes affirmed that little stones found in the heads of sharks when crushed and administered as a powder would dissolve the stones in the kidney and bladder. As a trader, he maintained that the stones from the West Indies were far superior to those from the East because for ten real ones from the latter source, "we receive hundred which are counterfeits."[5] It is not surprising that fakes were being made. These stones cost a fortune. A genuine stone was valued at 50 gold crowns in Calcutta, while another was bought for 130 crowns.[6]

Hernandez

Propelled by Monardes' success, the Spanish King Philip II in 1570 sent Francisco Hernandez (1515–1587) on a field trip to Mexico where he remained for seven years. The version of his work that Hernandez submitted to his King, in about 1577, comprised 893 pages of text and 2071 pages of paintings. It discussed more than 3000 Mexican plants. This massive work was over the years variously used; European trading companies borrowed from it for the manuals they wrote for sailors and overseas officials, while learned academies paid attention to its intrinsic scientific value. Years later, in 1651, the Lyncean Academy, Rome, published a richly illustrated encyclopaedic work with the short title *Rerum* which used the available Hernandez' text as the nucleus but went beyond it by adding extensive learned commentaries. The publication was a significant development. So far, interest in the New World's natural history has largely been driven by utilitarian considerations or personal scholarship. But now natural history was being supported as an intellectual discipline for its own sake. *Rerum's* section on plants was prepared by the great botanist Fabio Colonna (also written as Columna) and won praise from Linnaeus.[7]

During 1552–1577, Franciscan friars in Mexico working with local physicians sent accounts of the Aztec system of healthcare and herbs to Europe. Europe of the day however was not mature enough to appreciate the work. *Codex Barberini* (1552) was ignored and *Florentine Codex* (1577) was confiscated. In contrast, local informants from India came to be appreciated.

Garcia d'Orta

Garcia d'Orta (1501/2–1568) came to India in 1534 and remained there till his death.[8] Before taking up a discussion of his work, it would be appropriate to examine the details of his life, because his intellectual attitude seems to have been moulded by his family background. Orta's parents were Spanish Jews who migrated to Portugal in 1492 when Jews were expelled from Spain. Forced in 1497 to choose between exile and conversion, the family nominally converted to Christianity. D'Orta was fortunate to find a patron in Dom Fernao de Sousa, "of a noble family descended from a natural son of King Alfonso III by a very beautiful Moor, daughter of the Cadi of Faro."[9]

D'Orta studied at the Spanish universities of Salamanca and Alcala, from 1515 to 1523, although it is not certain where he went first. After graduating from the university, he practised in his home town, Castelo de Vide, till 1526 when he came to Lisbon where he remained for the next eight years. He secured a university chair in 1530 and was even elected a member of the university council in 1533. In March 1534, he sailed for Goa in the fleet commanded by his lifelong friend, patron, and protector, Martim Affonso de Sousa (c. 1500–1571) who was Captain Major of the Indian Ocean during 1534–1538 and then served as the Governor General of the Portuguese Asia 1542–1545. It is believed that the major reason for his leaving Portugal was the increasing pressure being felt by the New Christians. It was probably due to Sousa's influence that d'Orta was permitted to sail as his personal physician despite the law enacted in 1532 prohibiting any New Christian from leaving Portugal. A supporting reason would have been the opportunity to learn about new plants and cures.

In Goa, d'Orta served as a physician to the governors of Goa and also to Burham Nizam Shah, the Sultan of Ahmednagar. He grew many medicinal herbs in Goa. In 1554 or 1555, the Viceroy of Goa granted d'Orta the lease of the islet of Bombay (part of Bombay as it came to be) where he maintained a house and a garden.[10] In addition to maintaining an extensive medical practice, he was also a trader, chiefly in Materia Medica, jewels and precious stones, and a ship owner. He knew personally all the plants within his reach from which drugs were derived. For the rest, he made sustained efforts. He met Persians, Arabs, Malays and traders from all over Goa. He was on friendly terms with learned Muslims and Hindus and conversed familiarly with ordinary Asian traders, shopkeepers and physicians in his quest for knowledge. Additionally, he paid correspondents and agents who sent him plants and seeds from elsewhere.[11] He acknowledges the assistance of "his intelligent Konkani servant girl Antonia," but gives no other information about her.[12]

The celebrated Portuguese poet Luis de Camoes (1524–1580) spent time in Goa twice. He first arrived in 1554 for a compulsory two-year service in the Indian Ocean and again in 1561. He would probably have met d'Orta during his first visit also. But we are told that during the later visit he passed many agreeable and instructive hours in d'Orta's house, admiring his collections and examining his extensive library, finding in both materials for the last two cantos of *Os Lusiados*. While in Goa, Camoes composed an ode *"Aquele unico exemplo"* to Goa's Viceroy, the Count of Redondo. It was written in support of d'Orta's petition to the Viceroy requesting permission for the publication of the former's treatise.[13]

Thanks to Camoes' poetical support and d'Orta's own equation with the Viceroy, d'Orta's book was published in 1563, with the ode included. This was the first time Camoes was getting published. But, it could not have helped Camoes much because very few people ever saw the book. D'Orta's book in

Portuguese whose title in brief translates as *Colloquies on the Simples, Drugs and Materia Medica of India* was first written in Latin and then translated by d'Orta himself so that it could reach a wider readership in Portuguese Asia.[14] D'Orta's was the third book to be printed in Goa and India and the first on a non-religious subject. What set it apart from other publications of the time was the extent of its errata. The body of the book consists of 57 drugs and simples colloquies, mostly on drugs of vegetable origin but also including items like ivory, diamonds and the bezoar stones. Among other things, it describes the effects of *bhang* (cannabis) and furnishes Europe with the first account of the symptoms and treatment of a case of Asian cholera.[15] In addition, there is much interesting matter, for example, the fights between the cobra and mongoose,[16] and the etiquette of chewing betel nut.[17]

His book is in the form of a dialogue between two persons. One of them, the questioner, is a fictitious character, Dr Ruano, who had studied at d'Orta's alma mater, Salamanca, and is very much a man of the school, erudite and ready with quotations. Ruano is probably what d'Orta was in his younger, bookish days. The answerer is the maturer d'Orta, traveller and observer, perpetual learner and pluralist, who rejects received wisdom in favour of empirical knowledge: "For me the testimony of an eye-witness is worth more than that of all the physicians, and all the fathers of medicine who wrote on false information." In a similar vein, he tells Ruano, "Do not try to frighten me with Dioscorides or Galen, because I merely speak the truth and say what I know."[18] It is of interest to see what d'Orta had to say on tamarind. Tamarind is a produce, special to India, as can be seen from the name itself. The name is derived from the Arabic/Persian *Tamar al Hind*, or Indian date, which was coined by traders. Tamarind was sent out from the Indian west coast to Cairo from where it was taken to Alexandria and then Venice for use in Europe. It was not known to the ancient Greeks. It is mentioned by Yuhanna bin Masawayh (777–857), the celebrated Persian-Christian physician who attended on four Caliphs at Baghdad. He is Ruano's authority on tamarind: "Mesue, who is so much admired by his Arabian imitators, says that they (tamarinds) are from the wild palms of India."[19] No doubt, Masawayh's description was based on a paraphrase of tamarind's name. But, as Orta explained, "It is not a kind of date, nor has it the form of a date tree, except that both have stone." Mesue, declared Orta, "does not know what he is talking about."[20] Describing tamarind first hand thus provides Orta with an opportunity to debunk old authorities, because as he says elsewhere, "even I, when in Spain, did not dare to say anything against Galen or the Greeks."[21]

As soon as d'Orta died, in 1568, his hidden Judaism caught up with him and his family. His sister Catarina was arrested as a Jew the same year and burned at stake the next year. Garcia himself was posthumously convicted of Judaism. His remains were exhumed and burned publicly in 1580.

D' Orta's reception in Europe

Europe was introduced to d'Orta by Charles de l'Ecluse, or Carolus Clusius (1526–1609), a physician and well-known translator and synthesizer of his time, Clusius came across a copy of the *Colloquies* in Lisbon in 1564, and recognizing its worth decided to translate it into Latin, not in its entirety but by omitting parts that would appear to be "insignificant" to European readership. Further, he re-arranged the selected matter and added valuable notes.[22] Clusius' version achieved great popularity in European universities, ran into five editions in Clusius's lifetime and "is the form in which d' Orta's original work was chiefly disseminated for the next two centuries."[23] It was not d'Orta's book but the Clusius version of it that was translated into European languages. Antoine Brigant's translation into Italian appeared in 1576 and went into many revised editions. The French translation, by Antoine Colin, came in 1619. Second-hand translations meant that d' Orta's historiography which he consistently hammered in his book went unnoticed in Europe.

In 1872, the Brazilian historian Francisco Adolfo de Varnhagen (1816–1878) reprinted d'Orta's book, with an introduction that he wrote himself. "It contains many lacunae and imperfections, is without notes, and only attempted the identification of one plant, which is quite wrong."[24] The standard edition of d'Orta's work, edited and annotated by an accomplished botanist, Count Ficalho, appeared as late as 1891 and 1895 in two volumes. It was translated into English in 1913 by Clements Markham. The most reliable biography of Orta is by Augusto da Silva Cavalho, published in Portuguese in 1934 and summarized by Charles Ralph Boxer from whom much of the above information is taken.

D'Orta became relevant for Spain when it entered Asia with the colonization of the Philippines in 1565 and hoped to participate in the spice trade. In 1572, King Philip II's physician Juan Fragoso published his *Discursos* in Spanish, based on the *Colloquies*. Fragoso selects a few plants from d'Orta, arranges them alphabetically and gives a succinct account of each. What makes the book particularly valuable is that it lists earlier writers on Asian flora and points out discrepancies between d'Orta and them. Fragoso was translated into Latin in 1600.[25] The next influential author on Asian flora was a Portuguese converted Jew, Christobal Acosta (c. 1514–1594), who spent many years in the East. He met d'Orta in Goa before 1550 and again visited it in 1568, a few months after d'Orta's death. He even served as a physician in the Royal Hospital in Cochin. His *Tractado* was published in Spanish in 1578. The work describing 69 plants and other sources of drugs and medicines is based on d'Orta's but goes beyond it. The great merit of Acosta's works is that they include well-drawn full-page illustrations of 46 plants with roots. "His work completed what the learned Portuguese, Dr. Orta, began." Not content with translating from Monardes and d' Orta,

Clusius combined their work with that of Acosta in 1582, providing Europe with access to information on Asian and American flora in one volume, and brought out a final edition in 1605.

Hortus Malabaricus

A hundred years after d'Orta, Europe was introduced to the richness of flora of the Malabar region of Western Ghats in South India under the auspices of the Dutch East India Company. Hendrik Adriaan van Rheede tot Drakenstein (1636–1691), was born into a Dutch family of noblemen, and in 1680 took the title *Lord of Mijdrecht*. He joined the Dutch East India Company as a soldier, came to Batavia (Jakarta) in 1657 and rose through the ranks. He participated in the campaigns to subdue the Portuguese in South India. He was appointed commander in Jaffna in 1665, and of Dutch Malabar in 1670, with Cochin as his headquarters. Persistent differences with the Governor of Ceylon, Rijcklof van Goens (who subsequently became the Governor General of the Dutch East Indies), led to his departure from Malabar in 1677 for Batavia. In 1678, he left for the Netherlands. In 1684, he again sailed east as the leader of an enquiry, under the designation Commissioner General of the Western Quarters of Asia. He died in Bombay in 1691 and was buried in Surat.

The trigger for van Rheede's botanical excursions was utilitarian. In 1669, Batavia requested the Ceylonese Government to investigate the availability of medicinal plants there, because medicines from the Netherlands were not only expensive to import but also ran the risk of deterioration during transit. Van Rheede, stationed in an area of rich biodiversity, was hopeful of self-sufficiency in medical supplies.[26]

Van Rheede set up a laboratory at his residence in Cochin, where the chemist Paulus Meysner distilled oil from roots of wild cinnamon which was used with favourable results in the Dutch hospital in Cochin. The High Government however disapproved of the laboratory on the grounds that "the knowledge of the distillation of oil from cinnamon would be detrimental to the market in Europe if results of the research became generally known in Europe." The laboratory was finally closed in 1678.[27] Even when an enlightened colonial administrator took an initiative for development, he was not permitted to proceed by his superiors.

Van Rheede's medical and botanical advisor was the Discalced Carmelite physician-missionary Father Matthews of Order of St Joseph. Within the Company, van Rheede's friendship with Father Matthew and the favours shown to the Carmelites came to be used as a "vicious weapon" against him.[28] Van Rheede took up an ambitious project to document the flora of Malabar, a 900-km long, 70–200-km wide tract extending from Goa to

Kanyakumari [Cape Comorin]. He was not a botanist himself. This was an advantage because he could provide disinterested leadership. Untypical of the times, he was scrupulous in recording the names of Indians who actually carried out the project and gave them due credit. Thanks to his personal interest, organizational abilities, high administrative position, perseverance, social position in Europe, ability to rise above prejudices and sectarianism, and capacity to raise resources all combined to make his mission very successful.

The 12-volume *Hortus Malabaricus* was published during 1678–1693 from Amsterdam describing 742 species of plants, supported by 792 copperplate engravings. The first three volumes published during 1678–1682 carried the title *Hortus Indicus Malabaricus*. Van Rheede enjoyed the support of the King of Cochin and other kings, enabling him to receive cooperation from local sources. He assembled a large, about 25-strong, team. Field information came from the members of the Ezhava community of toddy-tappers, who were "adept both at tree climbing and plant identification." Some of them worked as Vaidyars, traditional physicians with an extensive, time-tested knowledge of the medicinal value of plants. Van Rheede's team was headed by a Vaidyar named Itti Achuden (also spelt Achudem). The team also included three Konkani Ayurveda experts, described as Brahmins, Appu Bhatt, Ranga Bhatt and Vinayak Pandit who were asked to provide information from their traditional Sanskrit text, *Maha Nighantu*, a pharmacological glossary that lists 400 medicinal plants from different parts of India.

The task of sketching the plants was initially taken up. Achuden's primary source was an old family manuscript, presumably on palm leaf, which had been expanded from generation to generation. Unfortunately, it is no longer extant. The Hortus manuscript was first prepared in Malayalam and then translated into Portuguese, Dutch and finally Latin. Neither the final nor any intermediary manuscript is extant. The *Hortus* thus is the only record of Malabar botany as it stood in the 17th century. Van Rheede may have taken an extended view of botany, but for the record he emphasized utility. In the preface to the third volume, he wrote that the Dutch Company "would be able to save those expenses which it spends on transporting medicaments" to India.

In the traditional Indian setting, knowledge residing in Ezhavas would not have impressed the ruling classes. Upper castes would also have refused to collaborate with low castes. Since the initiative came from a high-ranking European who enjoyed support from the local king, all fell in line. Thus, documentation of traditional botanical knowledge became possible only because Europeans were involved.

The set of the first three volumes was reviewed in England in 1682. The reviewer described it as "excellent Work giving accounts of the most rare and strange Trees and Shrubs of the most fruitful and flourishing country of Malabar in the East Indies."[29]

The German-Dutch botanist Karl Ludwig Blume (1796–1862) who worked in Java from 1817 to 1826 honoured Achuden by naming a genus *Achudemia* after him.

Ceylon

A university-educated German physician Paul Hermann (1646–1695) was given an appointment in Ceylon in 1672 as chief medical officer to its garrison. In addition, he was directed also to undertake an exploration of the island's medicinal flora. He remained in Ceylon till 1677. During his stay, he collected plants and prepared a *Hortus* siccus (dry garden) or herbarium and drew living plants. From 1679 till his death, Hermann served as professor of botany at Leiden University and also the director of the Hortus botanicus Leiden.

While in Ceylon, Hermann prepared two herbaria; one he kept for himself, the other he gave to the Amsterdam botanic garden. His own description of plants was published by his student, William Sherard (c. 1658–1728), as *Musaeum Zeylanicum* in 1717. The Amsterdam herbarium became the basis for *Thesaurus Zeylanicus* published by the Dutch botanist Johannes Burman (1706–1779) in 1737. Finally, returning to Hermann's own herbarium, Linnaeus published his *Flora Zeylanica* in 1747.[30] The latter was the first book on tropical plants based on the Linnaeus' classification scheme.[31] The Hortus introduced the world to cardamom and popularized its Malayalam name *elettari*. Cardamom was displayed at the International Exhibition of 1862.

England

Characteristically, England of the day was interested in plants of medical or commercial value but not in scientific botany. In 1673, the royally chartered Company of Apothecaries (later named Society) began cultivating a medical garden in Chelsea. It had an important part to play. Herbal cures from distant lands were in great demand, but the prescribing physicians were inclined to keep all the details secret lest their own earnings be adversely affected. Public cause demanded that descriptions of plants be properly documented and faithful illustrations prepared. James Petiver (1663–1718), a successful apothecary and dedicated naturalist who from 1709 onwards served as the demonstrator at the Chelsea garden, called for and received plants from all over, exchanged specimens within Europe, maintained a natural history museum and published the descriptions sent from the field along with his own "Thoughts and Discoveries." His informants included captains of ships and European surgeons working in the colonies. The career of Samuel Browne (d. 1698), appointed a surgeon in Madras in 1688, was rather controversial, but England gratefully remembered him as a supplier of dried plants which now form a part of the British Museum. He sent Petiver a packet of 46 specimens collected at "Unanercoonda," about 12 miles from Madras. The seeds were distributed to various gardens (including the Chelsea) where they were raised. Browne's observations and Petiver's remarks were published in *Philosophical Transactions* in numerous papers during 1700–1702. *Cassumunar* roots had been used in England since 1672, as a cure for epilepsy, but "whence it came, and how to come by it," nobody would tell. Identification became possible only when Browne's plant collection was carefully examined. The druggists could now order the herb from India.[32] Linnaeus made several visits to the Chelsea garden during the 1730s. The Dutch and the British colonial collections provided him with material for his binomial system of taxonomy (1735). Thus, medical and economic botany seamlessly led to scientific botany. A Linnaeus or a Darwin would not have been possible without European colonial expansion.

Notes

1 Conrad et al., 1998, 301–303.
2 Parker, 1915, 730.
3 Huguet-Termes, 2001, 365.
4 Elgood, 1951, 369.
5 De Asua & French, 2005, 106–107.
6 Kunz, 1915, 204.
7 De Asua & French, 2005, 95.
8 Markham, 1913, vii
9 Markham, 1913, viii.
10 Da Cunha, 1900, 97.
11 Boxer, 1963, 9.
12 Markham, 1913, ix.
13 White, 2008, 266–68. I thank Landeg White for giving me a copy of his translation of Camoes' Goa ode. For an earlier loose translation of some parts, see Markham, 1913, xi, note.
14 Boxer, 1963, 14.
15 Markham, 1913, 154–157.
16 Markham, 1913, 337.
17 Markham, 1913, 195.
18 Markham, 1913, 60.
19 Markham, 1913, 424.
20 Markham, 1913, 425
21 Markham, 1913, 275.
22 Flückiger & Hanbury, 1879, 760.
23 D' Cruz, 1991, 1594.
24 Markham, 1913, xi.
25 Lach, 1994, 436.
26 Desmond, 1992, 20.
27 Heniger, 1986, 38.
28 Heniger, 1986, 40.
29 Philosophical Transactions of the Royal Society, 1682, 13, 100.
30 Pethiyagoda & Sudasinghe, 2017, 7.
31 Desmond, 1992, 50.
32 Philosophical Transactions of the Royal Society, 1700, 22, 580.

6

NATURAL HISTORY

Missionary and Colonial India, 18–19th Century

Different sets of Europeans found India useful in different ways. The merchant-rulers wanted medical plants for their own use and for export. They tried to cultivate commercial plants in India that grew outside their worldly possessions and made efforts to find substitutes for drugs and simples that were imported from the Americas. The ever-expanding scientific community in Europe was excited about the opportunities the ecology of the vast landmass of India offered in natural history studies. Finally, Christianity enthusiasts in Europe viewed European rule in India as a godsend for propagating the Gospel in the East. These seemingly diverse interests converged at various levels. As in philology, Christian missionaries were pioneers in scientific natural history also. While colonial officials in India wished to make money and return to Europe, most missionaries came for good. They constituted a valuable resource for naturalists in Europe, especially in Germany. European interests in their fieldwork brought them scientific recognition as well as the much-needed cash. As a tool of trade, they learnt local languages and interacted with the population at large. They became a bridge between the tacit knowledge of fishermen and others on the one hand and the European scientific mainstream on the other. Above all, they introduced British medical men in India to systematic botany which then was institutionalized.

While d' Orta and van Rheede had worked on their own initiative, things changed in the second half of the 18th century. Now, individual European naturalists and institutions wanted not only specimens from India but also bits of tacit knowledge resident in the local population. The European India was ready and willing to oblige, but mainly as a collaborator rather than a courier. We shall focus on India-based Europeans who built a scientific

DOI: 10.4324/9781003466406-6

reputation for themselves; there were of course others who merely served as suppliers to Europe.

Tranquebar (1706)

Emulating the English Society for the Propagation of the Gospel in Foreign Parts (SPG) which at the time focused on America, King Friedrich IV of Denmark, the only Lutheran monarch in Europe, decided to set up a mission[1] at Tranquebar, which had been a Danish enclave since 1620. It lay on the Indian east coast some 300 km south of Madras, within the Kingdom of Tanjore. The Danish Lutheran Church remained aloof from the King's project with the result that no Danish missionaries could be found for the task. The King then turned to his court chaplain Franz Julius Lütkens (1650–1712) who through his Pietist connections enrolled two fellow Germans, Bartholomew Ziegenbalg (1682–1719) and Heinrich Plutschau (sometimes spelt Plutscho), who together arrived in Tranquebar in 1706, marking the beginning of the mission. Throughout its existence, the mission was manned by German missionaries mentored and sent by the University of Halle professor August Hermann Francke (1663–1727) who in addition ran an orphanage which later became part of the Franckesche Stiftungen (Franckish Foundations). Tranquebar was a major development for Europe. Letters, diaries, and essays of the missionaries were published in a periodical, *Hallesche Berichte*, brought out over a long period extending from 1710 to 1772 and from 1776 to 1810. These publications were even sold at book fairs. Parts of them were translated into English, Dutch, French, and Latin.[2] The mission was closed in 1825.

The mission was not set up in response to any felt need. Neither Danish commercial or political interests nor Danish hands in India had any use for it. If the King had not so wished, the mission would not have come up. Had it closed down shortly thereafter, nobody would have been surprised. And yet, it went on to initiate cultural encounters of various types and at different levels, some of which turned out to be of great consequence. The irrelevance of Denmark and Germany in the larger Indian geopolitical context enhanced their value in the cultural domain. The Tranquebar Mission was co-opted by England. For more than 100 years, the English Society for Promoting Christian Knowledge (SPCK) worked in India through, and in collaboration with, the Lutherans. On the closure of the Tranquebar Mission, SPCK transferred its activities to SPG.

In 1760, Tranquebar became home to another mission, the Moravian Mission, which was established with the permission of the Danish King. It was meant to serve as a base for religious activity in Nicobar. It failed in its religious mission and was closed in 1803, but it did leave behind its scientific impact. The older mission has been known variously as the Tranquebar

Mission, the Lutheran Mission, or the Danish-Halle Mission. The two missions were theologically antagonistic but became collaborators in natural history field work.

Europe looked up to Tranquebar for botanical and other natural history samples. Missionaries were well educated and able to collect information from local people whose language they knew. They could be contacted directly. Since they were perpetually short of money, remuneration received for service to European science was a major consideration. Collection of specimens from all over the world was a necessity for scientists and their institutions. Gift and exchange of natural history specimens were a common practice which benefited science and yielded diplomatic advantage.

Just as the Indian kings and feudal lords routinely became patrons of dance, poetry, and arts, it became fashionable for European royalty and nobility to collect natural curiosities. Many brilliant but impoverished young men cut their professional teeth on cataloguing private collections which in addition brought them patronage, social connections, and cash. During 1735–1738, Linnaeus worked as the curator of the private botanical garden of George Clifford III, a director of the Dutch East India Company. He was given a salary and free board and lodge. Clifford also sponsored his visit to London. Later, in 1751, Linnaeus was asked to begin work on a full-length description of the natural history collection of his King Adolf Fredrik and Queen Lovisa Ulrike. The Queen had a magnificent and unrivalled collection of Indian butterflies and other insects as well as shells. The task was an education for Linnaeus because he was obliged to create a system of classification of shells. He became quite free with the King and the Queen to the extent that he was among the privileged few to play blind man's buff with the Queen and the courtiers. On such occasions, it was considered a serious breach of etiquette for anyone to touch the Queen, but Linnaeus when he became the blind man could see a little and deliberately caught her. Linnaeus took no note of her reproof and clapped the Queen on the head, declaring that those who play a game must abide by its rules.[3] The opportunity for social rise acted as a great incentive for aspiring scientists.

Samuel Benjamin Cnoll

The first active European man of science in Tranquebar was the Halle-educated medical doctor Samuel Benjamin Cnoll (1705–1767) who served at the mission from his arrival in about 1732 until his death in 1767. Johann Heinrich Pott (1692–1777), a chemistry professor at the University of Berlin, wrote to Cnoll enquiring about borax which was an import item into Europe. His description was published in Latin in the journal of the Royal Prussian Academy of Sciences of which Cnoll was made a member. Cnoll's account must have been found very useful because a German summary was published in Copenhagen in 1753. Finally, the complete text was published in German in 1756 and French in 1759. This was an early example of Europe's desire to benefit from India's knowledge base. Tranquebar however was unable to educate Europe on zinc and saltpeter because they were not locally available.[4]

Scientific enquires from Europe included Biblical natural history. The German scholar Johann David Michaelis (1717–1791), who had been educated in Halle and was now a professor in Göttingen, wanted to satisfy himself if the large animal behemoth mentioned in the Old Testament could be an elephant as had recently been suggested. He was curious to learn about the elephant's habitat, food, and reproductive habits. Obligingly, the missionaries forwarded the questions to their acquaintances in India and Ceylon and themselves spoke to the head of the mahouts in the Kingdom of Tanjore. Michaelis also wanted to know the maximum number of people an elephant could carry. The considered answer from India was 28, smaller than figure 32 mentioned in the Bible[5] (the behemoth is now identified with hippopotamus). The Bible so far has been treated as a revealed text. It was now being subject to scientific scrutiny. In a way, the demolition or at least the weakening of the old order, be it religious, social, or classical, was as significant a development as scientific curiosity in Europe about the East and the New World.

During 1732–1744, Tranquebar sent as many as nine herbarians to Europe, all commissioned by influential quarters. Some of them were meant to replace earlier shipping damaged during the voyage. Dr August Johann von Hugo (1686–1760), personal physician to the Hanover-born English King George II, commissioned a herbarium from Tranquebar in 1732. It arrived in 1735 in a damaged condition; therefore, two more were ordered and received in 1737 and 1740. The undamaged ones are preserved in the University of Gottingen as *Plantae Malabaricae*. It is the largest existing pre-Linnaean botanical collection from the Coromandel Coast.[6]

> [i]t consists of 12 volumes with herbaria sheets containing around 660 individual plant specimens (including doublets), the majority of them with name tags of paper and palm leaf stating the plant's Tamil name in Tamil script and Latin transliteration-a total of about 465 individual Tamil names.

Linnaean botany was introduced into India at Tranquebar, at the Moravian Mission rather than the Danish-Halle. Because of the proximity to Tranquebar, Madras pioneered organized natural history studies, but the advantage was short-lived. Very soon Calcutta became the main centre of activity.

Johann Gerhard König

Dr Johann Gerhard König (1728–1785) arrived at the Moravian Mission in 1768 and remained in India till the end, though not with the Mission. König was born in the Duchy of Courland, now in Latvia, and was originally trained as a pharmacist in Riga. In 1748, he took an appointment in Denmark. During 1757–1758, he studied natural history in Uppsala as a student of Linnaeus with whom he maintained correspondence. In 1759, König was appointed to the Royal Frederick's Hospital in Copenhagen as a surgeon and pharmacist, being by special permission allowed to study medicine at the University. In 1764, he became amanuensis to Georg Christian Oeder, curator of the newly launched Flora Danica project. His first mission as amanuensis was in 1765–1766 to investigate the flora of Iceland which at the outset was a part of the double monarchy of Denmark and Norway. It would seem that König's proximity to Linnaeus did not go well with Oeder, and König was left with no alternative but to move out. He came to India to pursue his vocation as a naturalist. His dissertation, dated 1773, was submitted in absentia under Professor Friis Rottboel.[7]

König was unable to fund field trips from his meagre mission income. In 1774, he accepted the post of naturalist to the Nawab of Arcot.[8] It is not known whether the initiative came genuinely from the Nawab himself or as is more likely he was persuaded by his European friends to employ König. The appointment allowed König frequent excursions to the hills and even a voyage to Ceylon. Payments to König by the Nawab were irregular[9] such that in 1778 he took employment with the Madras Government as the Company's first-ever natural historian.[10] He held the post till his death in 1785 (the designation was interchangeably used along with botanist and naturalist. The post would be abolished in 1828). During 1778–1780, he was sent to Thailand and the Straits of Malacca to bring economic plants such as cardamom and gamboges for cultivation in British territories. One of his first acts on return was to transmit a number of useful plants of these regions to St Helena.[11] He also brought information on tin ore and minerals. For himself, he collected substantial information on Thai orchids.

Indian botany was greatly supported by Sir Joseph Banks (1743–1820), a well-known botanist, influential scientist, and a friend of King George III. He became the (informal) director of the Royal Botanic Gardens at Kew in 1773 and the president of the Royal Society in 1778, both of which positions he held till his death.[12] Banks' secretary Daniel Carl Solander (1736–1782) who had also studied in Uppsala was König's "learned Friend and Fellow disciple."[13] Banks declared that König had repaid the Company "a thousand-fold over in matters of investment, by the discovery of drugs and dying materials fit for the European market." König bequeathed his manuscripts and herbarium to Banks.[14] König dutifully sent his results to his friends in Europe and Banks. Linnaeus wrote to a friend, John Ellis, on 20 December 1771, that "König had found a lot of new things in Tranquebar."[15] There are three shells in the Linnaeus collection marked Tranquebar, without mention of the sender's name.

König's Pupils and Associates

Two Lutheran Missionaries became König's direct pupils and collaborators. Christoph Samuel John (1746–1813) arrived in 1771 and Johan Peter Rottler (1749–1836) in 1776. Both became valuable informants for German natural science which duly acknowledged their contribution. König also instructed the Company surgeon Dr William Roxburgh (1751–1815) who went on to find scientific botany in British India. Much later, after König's death, two other names became well known: a local boy, Johann Gottfried Klein (1766–1821), and a German, Dresden-educated, Dr Benjamin Heyne [Heine] (1770–1819), who arrived in Tranquebar in 1792 as a Moravian and was taken into Company service in 1793.

Johann Klein's father, Jakob Klein (1721–1790), was a Lutheran missionary who came to the Danish Mission in 1746 and remained here till the end. Junior Klein was born in Tranquebar, went to Copenhagen to study medicine and returned in 1791 as the mission doctor.[16] His 30-page dissertation dealing with the treatment of venereal disease in India was submitted to the University of Copenhagen and published in 1795. He is the first India-born modern botanist.

In Tranquebar, there were two missions, two Kleins and two Königs. The resulting confusion has a long history but that is no reason to perpetuate it. The Moravian Mission and the Royal Danish Mission have very often been treated as one and the same thing.[17] J.G. König's only connection with the Danish Mission is that he was for a while its medical adviser. But he was not a part of it. As it happened, an ordained priest, Rev. Johann Friedrich König (1741–1795) came to the Danish Mission in 1767 and remained there till death.[18] The accounts of the two Königs have been hopelessly intermingled. Confusion is not a recent phenomenon; it was noticed as early as 1861![19] Similarly, by confusion with his father, younger Klein has at times been made a member of the botanist König's original band, although by the time Klein became professionally active, König was already dead.

The Moravians entered into a contract with Banks to send him plant specimens on payment. Accordingly, as many as 500 specimens were sent between 1775 and 1778.[20] König-led naturalists formed themselves into an informal society to pool their resources in general and to honour the Bank's contract, in particular. Presumably, the name United Brethren was first given to the core group comprising the Moravians and the Lutherans to highlight the fact that though theology pulled them apart, natural history served as a unifying force. König and his collaborators assiduously collected plants throughout the Indian peninsula and in Ceylon, and at least in the initial stages, named them jointly. In such cases, *nob.*, short for the Latin *nobis* (meaning us), was appended to the given name.[21] "Nomenclature has always been regarded by systematic botanists as practically the most important department of their science, of which classification is the framework, and in no other department of knowledge so much careful attention been paid to it."[22] The specimens were transmitted to Europe, many of which were published in different works, sometimes under the names given by the donor, sometimes under a new name.[23] The fact that India-based European naturalists decided to give names to plants themselves shows their level of confidence and knowledge. What the India-based European botanists lacked by way of access to current scholarship and publications was more than made up by the novelty of the material in their hands.

In the early years in India, John's income was so low that he and his wife lived in extreme poverty. To earn some extra amount, "John went out and collected shells and such like curiosities" which he sold to European collectors. This way, "he made some hundred dollars which enabled him to pay off his debts."[24] He set up the missionary garden in Tranquebar where he introduced many plants from other parts of South India and also from Ceylon.[25] He found a recurring if controversial way of supplementing his income. In addition to the mission school, he ran a private school for a better class of people, namely the half-caste children whose European fathers were anxious to see them well educated. These pupils in turn served as assistants for field work. In the afternoon, after school time, he took the children to the garden and occupied them with gardening and collecting plants and insects.[26]

John became a dependable informant for German naturalists. In 1792, Johann Reinhold Forster (1729–1798) wrote to the missionaries in South India asking for information on poisonous snakes and traditional antidotes. John collected the information and sent it to Forster. Similarly, John was of great assistance to Berlin-based Marcus Elieser Bloch (1723–1799) who emerged as the pioneering authority on fishes with his well-illustrated 12-volume *Natural History of Fishes* published during 1785–1799. Bloch wrote that

> his assertion respecting the generation of some fishes, that the eggs are retained in the mouth till the young are hatched, has been confirmed by Mr. John, in his last letters from Tranquebar, who says it is a fact known to the fishermen there.[27]

Indian fishermen's common knowledge became a European research finding. Bloch named three fishes in John's honour. He similarly honoured Rottler and Klein.

John was useful to German scholarship in other ways also. For 35 long years, John served as a valuable source of information on Indian languages to Halle-based Professor Johann Christian Christoph Rüdiger (1751–1822).[28] Rottler was in contact with various professors in Europe: Johann Christian Daniel von Schreber (1739–1810) in Erlangen, Carl Ludwig Willednow (1765–1812) in Berlin, and Martin Hendriksen Vahl (1749–1805) in Copenhagen. A well-propagated misinformation needs to be set aside. On 30 April 1795, the German

Academy of Sciences Leopoldina conferred the degree of doctor and magister of philosophy on Rottler and John. This was done on the recommendation of its President, van Schreber. At the time (and till 1904), the Academy did not have a permanent address and the location of its President served as the seat of the Academy. The 19th-century accounts give wrong and conflicting accounts about the award. In 1837, it was erroneously said to have come from the University of Erlangen.[29]

At the close of 1795, Sir Hugh Cleghorn (1752–1837), the first colonial secretary to Ceylon, was deputed by the government to make a general tour of the island. He engaged Rottler "at a very moderate expense" to accompany him as a Tamil–English interpreter and naturalist. Rottler stayed back for some time to "render his assortment more complete." Rottler's Ceylonese collection was subsequently incorporated into the general herbarium at King's College London.[30] Indian flora reached Canada also. Sir Thomas Andrew Lumisden Strange (1756–1841), the chief justice of Nova Scotia during 1789–1797, served as the first chief justice of the Madras Supreme Court during 1801–1817. In 1802, Rottler and Klein presented a collection of 168 plant specimens to Strange which he in turn passed on to King's College, Windsor.[31]

In 1803, Rottler was transferred to Madras. He is the first India-based botanist to publish in European journals. In 1830, as part of his missionary duties, Rottler began work on his Tamil–English dictionary which was partly published in his own lifetime in 1834. An interesting feature of the dictionary is that it

> contains a very extensive list of the vernacular names of South Indian Plants, with the technical names by which they were known attached, not a few of them were of his own choosing; and this list will be found to be of very considerable help to Botanists in identifying the plants prescribed in the earlier letters on Indian Botany.[32]

He bequeathed his herbarium to the Vepery Mission. Put up for sale in England, it reached King's College London which in 1872 presented it to the Royal Botanic Garden, Kew.[33]

In 1834, while paying tributes to the Tranquebar missionaries "for their dedicated exertions towards the advancement of Botany," Wight and Arnott rather defensively added in the very first paragraph of their preface that these studies were merely a recreation for the missionaries turned botanists; their more important duties were "instructing the natives of India in the wisdom of the west, and of thus fitting them to become partakers of the promise of the Gospel."[34] The authors would have found it difficult to substantiate their pious assessment. In fact, botany became a compensation for the missionaries for their failure on the evangelical front. Referring to the later decades of the 18th century, pastor Johannes Ferdinand Fenger wrote in 1863 in his *History of the Tranquebar Mission*:

> During these very sad times, the missionaries tried to be useful to science. Botanical and other scientific remarks are most frequent in their accounts of their journies [sic] which were published at Halle. They were in many ways connected with learned men, more especially with such as were interested in Natural History, both in Europe and India. The botanical collection of Dr. Rottler, John's conchological and Klein's ornithological and entomological collections were of great importance. Eight different learned Societies voluntarily elected them as members.[35]

TABLE 6.1 Naturalists, Madras Presidency, 1778–1828

No	Person	Tenure as Naturalist	Remarks
1	J.F. Konig (1728–1785)	1778–1785	[1]
2	Patrick Russell (1727–1805)	1785–1790	[2]
3	William Roxburgh	1790–1793	[3]
4	Benjamin Heyne	1802–1819	[4]
5	William Sommerville Mitchell	1819 Oct.–Nov.	
6	George Hyne (1800–1826)	1821 Jan.–Jun.	
7	James Shuter (1775–1826)	1822–1826	
8	Robert Wight (1796–1872)	1826–1828	[5]

[1] Founder of Linnaean botany in India;
[2] Initiates Russell's viper named after him;
[3] Transfers to Calcutta Botanic Garden in 1793. Considered the Father of Indian botany;
[4] Earlier superintendent of the Madras Presidency's pepper and cinnamon plantations at Samulcottah; also a geologist. Entrusted with the departments of botany, mineralogy, and natural history in the Mysore Survey;
[5] Wight & George Arnott Walker-Arnott (1799–1868) publish *Prodromus Florae*.

TABLE 6.2 Superintendents of the Calcutta Botanic Gardens

Person	Tenure	Remarks
Robert Kyd	1787–1793	[1]
Roxburgh	1793–1813	
William Carey	1813–1814	
Francis Buchanan	1814–1815	
Nathaniel Wallich	1815–1816	[2]
James Hare (d. 1831)	1816–1817	
Nathaniel Wallich	1817–1846	
Hugh Falconer	1847–1855	[3]

[1] Founder of the Calcutta Botanic Garden;
[2] Temporary charge;
[3] Earlier, 1832–1842, Superintendent, Saharanpur Botanic Garden.

Patrick Russell

Physician and naturalist, Patrick Russell (1727–1805), was among the few of his time who ventured out of Britain after completing their medical education. With an MD from Edinburgh, he came to Aleppo in Syria in 1750 to live with his elder (half-) brother who was a physician to the English Factory. On his brother's return to Scotland in 1753, Patrick took up his appointment and held it till 1771. During outbreaks of bubonic plague in Aleppo, unlike other Europeans who remained aloof and unconcerned, Russell at considerable personal risk ventured out to treat the native patients and understand the disease. An appreciative Pasha gave him the privilege of wearing a turban, a rare honour for a foreigner.

While in Aleppo, Russell carried out a "comprehensive investigation of the practice and spread of inoculation in the Ottoman Empire." By interviewing women in harems, their bedouin servants, and many merchants from as far east as what is now Iraq, Russell established that inoculation was used almost everywhere outside the bigger cities such as Constantinople and Aleppo, where it was "proscribed" by the Turks.[36]

On return, Patrick set up a medical practice in London in 1772 and was elected FRS in 1777, for "being well skilled in many branches of Natural knowledge." He is among the very few who had established scientific credentials before coming to India. His younger brother Claud Russell joined the Madras Civil Service in 1752 but was ordered to England in 1777. He was rehabilitated later and appointed Chief-in-Council at Vizagapatam, on 24 July 1782. Since Claud's state of health at the time was precarious, Patrick decided to close his practice and come with him to India. One of Patrick's first tasks after arrival was calling on König in Tranquebar. In Vizagapatam, Russell did not confine his attention to the vegetable kingdom alone but eagerly collected, figured, and described the fishes and the serpents in the Carnatic plain which stretches along the coast of Coromandel.

In 1785, Russell was appointed as a Naturalist in succession to König. He remained in office till 1789. On appointment, Russell was asked to catalogue the economically useful plants of Madras and publish König's scientific notes. It was however not sufficient that the Company naturalists worked for the government. They must be of help to the scientists in Europe also. Payment to Russell was made contingent on his writing an annual report for the Royal Society.[37] Far-sightedly, he suggested to the Madras Governor that information on all economically useful Indian plants be collected.

He proposed that letters should issue from the highest authority, inviting the gentlemen, particularly of the medical department, resident at the different stations, to transmit every information in their power concerning such useful plants, accompanied with specimens of each plant, including the leaf, flower, and fruit, with a view to publication.[38]

Russell's plan, with a list of the plants he had selected to begin with, was approved by the Court of Directors which requested Banks to oversee the project. Russell left in 1789, but the project continued.

Russell's greatest contribution was his initiation of a study of snakes. This was a subject of great importance because a visit to tropical lands also meant an encounter with snakes. He wished to educate the people on the distinction between poisonous and non-poisonous snakes so that a snake bite did not always cause fear and anxiety and harmless snakes were not killed out of ignorance. Harmless snakes have teeth in both upper and lower jaw while the poisonous snakes do not possess upper teeth. It may not be prudent to check the teeth while the snake is still alive. Keeping this in mind, he prepared detailed descriptions of various snakes towards the end of 1787. His write-up and figures were published by the government and widely distributed. His major publications came out after his return to Britain.

The Company took up the expense of publication of coloured figures of the snakes along with their descriptions by Russell. He published the first volume of his book *An Account of Serpents collected on the Coast of Coromandel* in 1796, while the second volume was published in four parts during 1801–1809. He named red sand boa *Eryx johnii* in John's honour, while his own name was assigned to the viper species. Different combinations, based on different specimens, were tried: *Coluber russelii* (Russell's snake) in 1797, *Vipera daboia*, in 1803, *Daboia russelii* in 1842, and finally *Vipera russelii* in 1890.[39] Daoia comes from the Hindi word, daboya, meaning one who lurks.

Russell also took note of folk practices and subjected them to scientific scrutiny. He acquired numerous samples of *tabasheer*, found in the hollow stem of the bamboo and said to be "possessed of extraordinary virtue." The samples sent to The Royal Society were analyzed by James Louis Macie who published his results in 1790. Tabasheer was almost pure silica.[40] While tabasheer was a mere curiosity, the so-called Tanjore pill merited serious consideration because it was presented as a remedy for the bite of venomous and rabid animals. The pill contained arsenic, and the medical opinion on it remained divided.[41]

William Roxburgh

After Russell, there came a man of outstanding merit and long service. Edinburgh-educated William Roxburgh has been called the Father of Indian Botany. He was probably an illegitimate son of an influential family in Scotland. He was able to overcome the disadvantage of birth, thanks to the social patronage received from the Boswells of Auchinleck and the professional patronage from Professor John Hope and Sir John Pringle (1707–1782), President of the Royal Society during 1772–1780.[42] He began his career as a surgeon's mate on Company ships and joined the Madras medical service as an assistant surgeon in 1776. In 1781, he was appointed surgeon to the garrison at Samulcotta [Samalkot] in what was known as Northern Sircars. Located at the edge of a hilly region, 27 miles from one of the mouths of the Godavari River, Samulcotta is endowed with "a very interesting Flora," and was the site of an old Mughal garden. Now, Roxburgh established a Company garden and began to develop a collection of living plants which he studied for their economic value. In the task of collecting, sorting, and naming his material, Roxburgh received direct help from König. In 1786, he reported the significant discovery that "the Pepper Plant was a native of the Hills in the Rajamundry Circar." During 1787, Roxburgh procured 400 slips of the pepper vine from the Rampa hills, and within 12 months raised upwards of 40,000 plants.[43] He cultivated coffee and worked on a number of topics including various dyes including lac and caducay gall and the culture and manufacture of silk and various grasses. He spent considerable time and energy on the study of *Swietenia febrifuga* as a possible substitute for cinchona.[44]

Within the overall ruthlessness of the Company, there was individual thoughtfulness which was listened to. Although Roxburgh could not have pointed to the Company how its policies caused famines in India, he suggested that coconut trees be planted on canal banks and street side. He also advocated the cultivation of the sago, date, palmyra, plantain, jack, breadfruit, and opuntia, all of which possess food value.[45] He also experimented with teak, which would become a priority in the Calcutta garden. In addition to the Company garden that he supervised, Roxburgh set up a private garden of his own. He carried out private trade in collaboration with Andrew Ross, former mayor of Madras, from which he made a considerable fortune for himself.[46]

He was appointed Madras Naturalist, in 1790, but left three years later, in 1793, to take over as the first full-time salaried superintendent of the Calcutta Botanic Garden.

Benjamin Heyne

Following Roxburgh's departure to Calcutta in 1793, Benjamin Heyne, who was already at Tranquebar and had been strongly recommended to Roxburgh by Reverend C. S. John, was appointed superintendent of the Madras Presidency's pepper and cinnamon plantations at Samulcottah. His own major interest however lay in geology. He wrote on diamond and copper mines and on garnets as well as on iron smelting industry. In 1795, he submitted voluminous reports on diamond mines in Malavelly and the iron smelting industry in Ramanaikpetta near Ellore. The next year he wrote on copper mines at "Agrcondula in the District of Innacondah," which had been neglected or abandoned for two centuries. He also wrote on garnets and the geology of the "Boggleconda Hill" near Innacondah.[47] In 1798, Heyne in a letter gave a glimpse of how he carried out his botanical work: "In this country a man who is Botanically inclined cannot do without people to collect plants...As Plants were daily brought in, I ordered the Painter to draw only the outlines with Indian ink, and colour only one flower, fruit, and leaf; by doing which I get a great many more plants drawn."[48]

Mysore Survey

The British conquest of Mysore in 1799 made it a successor to the well-run Mysore state. Its territories now extended from the east coast to the west. From a scientific point of view, this was an exciting development because the new lands presented different flora and geology. Post-Tipu, the first task for the Company was the compilation of maps from whatever "meagre and unsatisfactory material" was already extant. Next, the Governor General ordered a thorough and systematic Mysore Survey. It was to comprise two components. The mathematical survey would fix the external boundaries and also lay down the "Country in detail" through primary triangulation. The physical survey would deal with botany, mineralogy, medicine; diseases, weather, rains, soil, agricultural produce, animals, revenue, population, etc. The survey was placed under the overall charge of Colin Mackenzie, while Francis Buchanan was appointed to investigate "the state of agriculture, arts, and commerce, in the dominions lately acquired from Tippoo Sultan." The departments of botany, mineralogy, and natural history were entrusted to Benjamin Heyne.

For his Mysore Survey establishment, Heyne drew on Samulcotta. It included a European painter; two local painters; two plant collectors who were "natives accustomed to this service," and three peons and harkaras for preserving and carrying minerals, plants, and other objects of natural history.[49] Bangalore already had a beautiful garden, known as Lal Bagh. It was placed under Heyne's charge to be appropriated as a botanical garden and "as a depository for useful plants sent from different parts of the country." The Governor General's directions were explicit and materialistic:

A decided superiority must be given to useful plants over those which are merely recommended by their rarity or their beauty, to collect with care all that is connected with the arts and manufactures of this country, or that promises to be useful in our own: to give due attention to the timber employed in the various provinces of his route, and to collect with particular diligence the valuable plants connected with his own immediate profession [medicine].[50]

In 1802, Heyne was made independent of Mackenzie's survey and given the appointment of Madras Naturalist which he held till his death in 1819.[51] In between, for about two years 1812–1814, he was in Europe on furlough. In 1813, he passed on a considerable number of plant specimens to the German botanist Albrecht William Roth (1757–1834) who published an account of 200 of them in *Novae plantarum species praesertium Indiae Orientalis*, from Berlin in 1821.[52] In 1814, in keeping with the general trend of officers serving in India, Heyne published his *Tracts, historical and statistical, on India*. Though much of the material in the book is of a scientific nature, there is a near-mandatory essay "On the propagation of the Christian religion in India, and on the moral character of the Hindoos."

There were two little-known short-term successors to Heyne. William Sommerville Mitchell held the appointment for less than two months (October–November 1819) followed by George Hyne (1800–1826) who remained in office (January–June 1821).[53]

James Shuter

Hyne's successor was the Irishman James Shuter (1775–1826), who obtained MD from Edinburgh in 1800 and went to Madeira in 1809 where he remained for 10 years. He did noticeable work in geology and botany. He returned to England in 1819 on his way to India. On 1 June 1819, he was elected Fellow of the Linnaean Society from a London address.[54] He was appointed as assistant surgeon at Madras on 14 June 1821 and a Naturalist a year later, on 12 July 1822.[55] He returned to England on sick leave in January 1826 but died on 12 October.[56] Shuter officially bought Klein's collection after his death from his estate. On orders from the Madras Governor Sir Thomas Munro, Shuter prepared a Materia Medica, which Munro personally presented to the University of Edinburgh, in 1826. A "portion of many seeds and some of the roots" were handed over to Robert Graham (1786–1784), professor of botany, "with every prospect of their vegetating."[57] Kew has a herbarium from him which he brought on express wishes of Sir William Jackson Hooker (1785–1865).[58] He has been described as a protégé of Sir George Abercrombie Robinson, Director of the East India Company from 1808 till 1829.[59] It appears likely that he was sent out not so much as a researcher but as a courier. Even a mediocre India-based European naturalist was of great use to European naturalists as a supplier of specimens and illustrations drawn by his draughtsman.

William Hooker was a professor of Botany at Glasgow University from 1820 till 1841 and the first official director of Kew Gardens from 1841 till 1865. His son Sir Joseph Dalton Hooker (1817–1911) joined the Geological Survey of Great Britain as a botanist, in 1846. Next year, he was nominated by his father to travel to India to collect plants from the Himalayas. He was the first European to collect plants from the Himalayas. He remained in India for three years. He served as the assistant director of Kew Gardens from 1855 till 1865 when he succeeded his father as a director. He retired in 1885. Thus, for almost half a century, the Hooker father and son dominated English botany.

Robert Wight

Shuter's successor, Robert Wight (1796–1872), was a botanist of great fame, who already had an MD before he came to India. He was the last one to hold the Madras Naturalist's post and saw the focus shift from scientific botany to the economic. Wight came after obtaining his MD. Coming from a well-connected Scottish family that had seen better days, Wight was educated at Edinburgh University, where in 1818 he wrote a 14-page dissertation in Latin with the translated title "On the nature of fevers dissected with a scalpel" (that is, by surgical investigations). It is said that he joined a ship as a surgeon and made many voyages including one to America. He came to Madras in 1819 as an assistant surgeon in a regiment of which his elder brother James subsequently became a colonel. Wight had had no particular training in botany. Earlier botanists were all gone that there was no one to induct him into the discipline. He educated himself with the help of books which he managed to obtain: Willdenow's *Species Plantarum* (published 1797–1806), Persoon's *Synopsis* (1805–1807), and Lichfield's translation of Linnaeus' *Genera Plantarum* (1787). Wight hired local plant collectors and set out to prepare specimens. In 1823, he sent a collection to Dr Robert Graham, a professor of botany at Edinburgh who however did not respond. It has been defensively said that the consignment was lost at sea[60] but the fact of the matter is that Graham did get the specimens but chose to ignore them.[61]

The Madras Government decided to make use of his earlier anatomical training. Tipu had maintained a cattle breeding establishment named Amrit Mahal at his capital Seringapatam for military purposes. In 1824, the establishment was placed under Wight's charge. His staff comprised an Indian draughtsman, two senior medical pupils, and an Indian doctor. Wight, however, resigned the job for reasons of health and was replaced by Dr A.E. Best. In July 1825, Wight was given a new posting, as assistant surgeon to a different regiment, but this was short-lived.

In 1826, he was appointed to the vacant post of Naturalist. In this position, he undertook a nine-month collecting tour of South India. Next, he planned an extensive two-year tour that would have taken him to "all the richest botanic districts in the south of India including the Malabar coast." He hoped to collect and describe as many as possible of the plants that figured in van Rheede's *Hortus Malabaricus* and make drawings of all the little-known useful plants mentioned in Buchanan's Travels in Mysore, Malabar, and Canara. But that was not to be.[62] Munro's successor as Governor, Stephen Lushington, was a man of limited vision, who additionally held a personal grudge against Wight. In February 1828, the governor abolished the post of naturalist on grounds of economy, dismissed the valuable collections built over the years as mere curiosities, and dispatched them to the India Office, London. These included, apart from Wight's own collection, older specimens that Russell had collected or Wight had bought from Rottler. The collection also included 150 botanical drawings (now at Kew).[63] Wight was sent back as surgeon to a garrison stationed in Nagapattinam. Disappointed but not disheartened, he continued his botanical work in his spare time and with his own resources. The value of his work lies in the fact that his field area in South India was different from the one earlier covered by König and others. Wight now established a valuable collaboration with William Hooker in Glasgow, who published his work in *Botanical Miscellany* during 1830–1832 and as thanks sent books to Wight in India. While the worth of research reported from distant India was immediately recognized, the name of the author rang no bell; in the first three articles, Wight's first name was wrongly given as Richard.

Wight spent three valuable years 1831–1834 in Britain on furlough, while maintaining his establishment in India. He brought with him a herbarium of 4000 species (weighing two tons) and about 100,000 specimens of plants of the presidency of Madras. He distributed his duplicates, established himself in professional circles, and initiated a very fruitful collaboration with his school and university friend and William Hooker's protégé, George Arnott Walker-Arnott (1799–1868). This collaboration resulted in the publication in 1834 of *Prodromus Florae Peninsulae Indiae Orientalis*, containing descriptions of plants found in peninsular India. Wight's stay in Britain partially overlapped with that of Wallich who spent four years, 1828–1832, on leave but with full salary. Wallich was in fact on an important public relations exercise for the Company. He was entrusted with the onerous task of cataloguing the plant specimens owned by the Company and distributing the duplicates to interested parties. Many specimens had been collected under Wallich's own superintendence while others were older. Where botany stood in 1830 in India, Calcutta and Madras combined, can be seen from the list of the Company herbariums: (i) Herbarium collected by Patrick Russell, mostly in the Circars, (ii) an extensive herbarium from the peninsula collected by Klein, Heyne, and Rottler, (iii) a very extensive herbarium collected in various parts by Francis Buchanan, (iv) a small herbarium of Roxburgh, (v) a herbarium collected by George Finlayson (1790–1823), surgeon and naturalist to the Crawford Trade Mission sent out to Siam and Cochin China (Viet Nam) by the Bengal government in 1821; (vi) a most extensive herbarium collected in various parts of the peninsula by Wight; and (vii) a special collection forwarded by Wallich to the Company's museum.[64] The enormity of the exercise can be gauged from the fact that Wallich distributed 250,000 specimens in 641 parcels to 66 individuals and institutions.[65] In this dispersion, he was aided among others by Augustin Pyramus de Candolle (1778–1841) from Geneva and Professor Kunth from Berlin. The Company's primary collection, the Wallichian herbarium, was given to the Linnaean Society in 1832, which in 1913 transferred it along with later additions to Kew Gardens, but only after a well-wisher, Sir Frank Crisp, reimbursed the Society the cost of the mahogany-faced cabinets which housed the specimens.[66]

The Company's dispersal of plant specimens and the transfer of its herbarium to a learned body were well-timed. They came at a time when the Company's 1833 Charter was under discussion. An Edinburgh journal wrote in 1831:

> Duplicates of these plants have been liberally issued by the Company to botanists of all nations, who have been encouraged to examine and publish them. Under the auspices of our merchant princes of Leadenhall Street, several splendid works of botanical illustration have already appeared, of which Dr Wallich's *Planta Asiatics Rariorcs* is the chief. Such powerful exertions in behalf of science are the proudest boast of a Company which, maligned as it has been, will still remain one of the most stupendous exhibitions of British power.[67]

In a similar manner, the Company endeared itself to European Orientalists by making old Indian manuscripts available to them.[68]

On return to India, in 1834, Wight was posted in Bellary (now in Karnataka) in a medical capacity. His regiment's march to Palamcotta, near Cape Comorin, gave Wight a chance to botanise. Finally, in 1836, Wight, thanks to the Scottish network he had activated during his long furlough, was relieved of his medical duties so that he could now spend full time on botany. He was transferred to the revenue department to "enquire and report on the cultivation of cotton, tobacco, senna and generally of all Indian products."[69] The last 11 years of Wight's Madras career, 1842–1853, were spent working on cotton at Coimbatore. The work on economic plants so far had focused on Indian species. But now the plan was to introduce new varieties from the USA and export raw materials to by-now industrialized Europe. The project was more or less a costly failure but it does tell us about the British priorities of the time.

Lithography

Once freed from his peripatetic medical duties, Wight mastered the art of lithography and set out to publish illustrations of his plant specimens. He simultaneously began work in 1838 on the hand-coloured *Illustrations of*

Indian Botany and the un-coloured *Icones Plantarum Indiae Orientalis*. The Illustrations appeared in two volumes published in 1840 and 1850 and contained 182 plates, of which all except the last one were coloured. The *Icones*, carrying a total of 2101 un-coloured plates, was published in six volumes over an extended period of 15 years, 1838–1853. The government partially subsidized the enterprise by ordering 50 copies of each publication. Wight selected about 200 Nilgiri plants from his *Icones*, had them coloured, and issued as *Spicilegium Neilgherrense* (1846–1851) Wight could claim with justifiable pride that "the Indian Flora can now ... boast of being more thoroughly illustrated than any other country under British sway, Great Britain alone excepted."[70] Wight's contributions were handsomely acknowledged by Sir Joseph Dalton Hooker and Thomas Thomson in their celebrated 1855 publication *Flora Indica* as being "the most important" "not only to botany, but to natural science, which have ever been published in India, and they have been of the greatest service to us throughout our labours."[71]

Calcutta (1787–1846)

The initiative for the Calcutta Botanic Garden came from Lieutenant Colonel Robert Kyd (1746–1793), secretary to the military department in Calcutta and a horticulture enthusiast who cultivated a private garden of his own. On 15 April 1786, Kyd suggested to the government that plants of the Sago tree growing in the Malay peninsula be brought and grown all over British possessions.[72] He followed this up with a broader proposal, couching it in a mercantile idiom he knew the Company would understand. He suggested "establishing a botanical Garden, not for the Purpose of collecting rare plants...but for establishing a stock for the disseminating such articles as... may tend to the Extension of the National Commerce and Riches."[73] The letter was accompanied by a long list of plants he wanted for the garden including Dacca cotton, indigo, Sarasparilla, teak wood, pepper, cardamom, gum copal, asafoetida, nutmeg, clove, tea green, China lacquer, and papia. The Court of Directors consulted Banks who supported the proposal and emphasized the need for the reciprocal exchange of plants and seeds between Calcutta and the West Indies. The Company accepted Kyd's proposal on 31 July 1787, seeing "a great source of wealth" for itself in the cultivation of cinnamon, which would break the Dutch world monopoly. Accordingly, a botanic garden was established on 300 acres in Sibpur on the banks of Hooghly, with Kyd as its honorary superintendent, and his private garden was merged with it.[74]

Speaking in 1899, Sir George King (1840–1909), who had been the Superintendent of the Garden during 1871–1897, rather uncharitably described Kyd as a "gardener rather than a botanist." Under his successor, Roxburgh, the Calcutta Garden moved beyond horticulture and utilitarianism. For Roxburgh, there was continuity between Samulcotta, Madras, and Calcutta. In September 1790, Roxburgh sent from Madras a consignment of drawings to Sir Joseph Banks in London. Roxburgh included descriptive notes with the pictures, mentioning how the plants were used in India. By 1794, he had sent around 500 drawings to Banks, who decided that some of the most economically important would be good subjects for engraving and publishing. The final product of the monumental effort was the *Plants of the Coast of Coromandel*, with a preface by Russell, which was published by the Company. The first volume appeared in 1795, the second in 1798, and the third in 1819 after Roxburgh's death. The work featured 300 drawings with accompanying notes.

In 1805 when it seemed that Roxburgh's illness would render his post vacant, Banks reminded the Company that the superintendent of the garden should be

> capable of communicating advantageously to the learned world such discoveries in the animal, the vegetable and the mineral kingdoms as are made from time to time in the extensive regions of the east to the intimate advancement of natural knowledge.

This was a significant observation that the Company accepted. By this time, the British Government had a say in the Company affairs and scientists in the British Government. The Calcutta Botanic Garden was no longer a mere Company depot, but an international research centre.

After Roxburgh's departure in 1813, the garden remained leaderless for four years. Roxburgh handed over charge to William Carey who held it till April 1814. In 1814 itself Carey published from his Serampore mission press a catalogue of the plants growing in the garden, under the title *Hortus Bengalensis*, with financial support from the government. This was an important development because Europe at large learnt about the garden from it. Carey's own 12-page introduction sums up the progress of the garden up to that time. At the beginning of Roxburgh's term, the garden had about 300 plants. By the time he left in 1813, the number of plants drawn and described by him stood at 1963.[75]

Nathaniel Wallich

Francis Buchanan was appointed the superintendent in 1814 but he left in 1815. It would be another two years till the garden got a permanent director. Nathaniel Wallich's (1786–1854) association with the Garden began under the shadow of war. Wallich was educated in Copenhagen under Professor Martin Vahl (1749–1804). But since he was a Jew (his original name was Nathan Wolff), he could not have been employed in Denmark itself.[76] Wallich arrived in the Danish enclave of Serampore as a surgeon in November 1807.

When in 1808 the British annexed Danish territories in India in continuation of developments in Europe, he was among the prisoners of war taken. He was released, on 1 January 1809, on Roxburgh's intervention to be employed at the Calcutta Garden.[77] An official letter dated 30 June 1809 says:

> Dr Wallich, a Danish prisoner, has been appointed to assist Dr Roxburgh, but without any additional allowances. In the event of his pursuing his researches in the interior of the country he is to be granted Rs 200 per month for travelling charges.[78]

Wallich was absorbed into the medical service in 1814. The same year he proposed to the Asiatic Society the establishment of a museum which blossomed into the Indian Museum. He held temporary charge of the Calcutta Garden from 24 February 1815 till 20 April 1816 when James Macadam Hare (1775–1831) of the Bengal Medical Service and Apothecary General took charge. Eventually, Wallich was given the regular appointment from 1 August 1817 which he retained for 30 long fruitful years till his retirement in 1846.

Wallich's tenure "constitutes the most prominent era in the botany of India." At his suggestion, the government allotted an area, five miles in circumference, for the Garden, and employed upwards of 300 gardeners and labourers. Subordinate gardens were formed in remote parts of the Indian possessions; collectors were sent out to discover new, and especially useful, plants; and the British residents were invited to send the vegetable productions of their respective districts to Calcutta, both in a living and dried state. In 1816, following the war with Nepal, Britain appointed a Resident, Edward Gardner, in Kathmandu. Four years later, in 1820, Wallich came over and spent more than a year assiduously collecting specimens for more than a year in the vicinity of the capital. Since the interior was closed to the Europeans, he arranged for local collectors. He was thus able to add a fair knowledge of the alpine flora to the abundant information on the temperate and tropical regions that he obtained by his personal exertions. Before returning, he trained a number of collectors, who continued, during a long series of years, to transmit dried specimens from Nepal.

One Mr Blinkworth, an active collector, explored Kumaon, and Mr Gomez contributed extensive collections from the rich province of Sylhet and from the neighbouring Khasi hills, while Wallich himself visited Penang and Singapore, thus adding knowledge of the Malayan flora to that of the rest of India. In 1825, he examined and collected the plants of the kingdom of Oude [Avadh] and the province of Rohilkhand, the valley of Dehra, etc. His last mission was to Ava. The number of species in Calcutta by 1828 was estimated to be 8000–9000. While Wallich was away in Europe, the acerbic Victor Jacquemont, the French traveller and letter writer, had to say about him in 1829: "A Danish botanist, of mediocre talents, who passes here for the first in the world, is the director of this establishment; he has certainly the best income of any savant in existence."[79]

Saharanpur Garden (1817)

Next in importance to Calcutta, there stood the Saharanpur Garden which was a revival rather than a creation. A 40-acre public garden aptly called Farhat Baksh [delight giver] was established at Saharanpur in 1779 by Rohilla Fauzdar Zabita Khan who assigned the revenue of seven villages for its maintenance. His son Ghulam Qadir who pitilessly blinded the hapless Mughal Emperor Shah Alam in 1788 continued the arrangement. The Mahrattas after him reduced the quantum to two villages.[80] Saharanpur passed into British hands in 1803. In 1816, George Govan (1787–1865) who had joined as civil surgeon at Saharanpur the previous year wrote a letter to the Governor General strongly arguing for the revival of the old, now dilapidated, garden. In particular, he advocated the cultivation of chocolate, sarsaparilla, guaiacum, cassia, liquorice, vanilla, and "various species of cinchona furnishing the Peruvian bark." His advocacy of tea cultivation anticipated later developments. He very sensibly pointed out that tea could not be unique to China and should grow in conditions similar to those in tea-growing parts of China.[81] The Governor General agreed that "considerable advantages would result not only to Science but to the interests of the Honourable Company from the proper management of the Botanic Garden at Saharanpur." Govan's appointment as Superintendent was sanctioned on 13 June 1817.[82] Govan's tenure however was short. In 1821, he left India on sick leave and Saharanpur for good. When he resumed duty, it was as a geologist. Like in Europe, natural history served to decrease the distance between the aristocrat and the commoner. In 1827, at the newly founded hill station of Simla, Lady Amherst and the Governor General Lord Amherst liked to go out every morning after breakfast with Dr Govan "walking or rather scrambling up the mountains… in search of plants." Victor Jacquemont who met Govan at Simla in June 1830 described him as a "rigid Scot, a good man but a poor botanist."[83] History however has chosen to ignore Govan rather than be harsh on him. Jacquemont was generally appalled at the good time and high salaries many people less gifted than him were enjoying under British auspices.

John Forbes Royle

In Govan's time, the Saharanpur Garden was an independent entity, but after him, it was placed under the control of the Calcutta Garden. Many Saharanpur superintendents in fact rose to head the latter. In 1823, the Saharanpur charge was handed over to the civil surgeon John Forbes Royle (1798–1858). Kanpur-born Royle was educated at Edinburgh and Addiscombe with a view to a career in the army like his father, but thanks to his pupilage of Anthony Todd Thomson (1778–1849), he became interested in botany, obtained his diploma, and came to Bengal in 1819 as an assistant surgeon. In 1823, he was appointed the superintendent of the now 400-acre Saharanpur gardens which position he held till 1831. In addition, he had hospital duties: accouchier [obstetrician] to the civilians' wives and body surgeon to the convicts.[84] Scientifically, the Calcutta and Saharanpur gardens were complementary; commercial plants which would not grow in the former had a chance in the latter. Royle successfully sent collectors to Kashmir under the guidance of shawl dealers when they were returning home.[85] Royle returned to England in 1831 bringing duplicates of all his collections with him. After a long spell of leave, he retired in England in 1837. The same year he took the MD degree from Munich. In 1833, he published the first part of his *Illustrations of the Botany and Other Branches of the Natural History of the Himalayan Mountains and of the Flora of Cashmere*. The second part, containing the plates, came out in 1839.

On the opening of King's College London in 1836, Royle was appointed a lecturer on *Materia Medica*, the post he filled till 1856. On the basis of his course material, he published in 1837 *An Essay on the Antiquity of Hindoo Medicine: Including an Introductory Lecture to the Course of Materia Medica and Therapeutics, delivered at King's College*. From 1847 to 1857, he was a reporter on economic products for the East India Company. In a lecture delivered at the Society of Arts in 1854 during the war with Russia, Royle drew attention to India as a source of various fibrous materials used in the manufacture of cardage, clothing, etc. The lecture was expanded into a valuable book *On the Fibrous Plants of India*, published the next year. He took an active interest in the cultivation of tea in the East Indies. Royle's life sums up a capable European botanist's professional career driven by India: a collection of live plants and specimens in India; enrichment of herbariums in Britain; and advancement of the Company's commercial interests. Royle was succeeded by Hugh Falconer (1808–1865), who made a name for himself by the discovery of the Shivalik fossils.

Hugh Falconer

Falconer first studied at the University of Aberdeen, "aided by the resources" of an elder brother who was a merchant in Bengal. In 1830, he obtained his MD from Edinburgh and was almost immediately appointed assistant surgeon in Bengal. Since he had not yet reached the required age of 22, he came to London to assist Wallich in the distribution of the herbarium. At the same time, he studied the collection of fossil mammalia from the banks of the Iravati River which had been brought by John Crawfurd during his mission to Ava and which was now housed in the museum of the Geological Society of London.

Falconer joined Bengal Medical Service in September 1830 and met Royle in April 1831 in Saharanpur when his official duties brought him there. On Royle's recommendation, Falconer was speedily appointed to officiate as Superintendent of Saharanpur Garden during his leave of absence. When Royle left for England in 1832, Falconer succeeded him.

Thus, at an early age of twenty-three, did he find himself advanced to a responsible and independent public post, offering to a naturalist the most enviable opportunities for research; so fertile was the Indian service then in chance to rise for any young officer who chose to make the exertion.[86]

Fossil Fauna

In 1847, Falconer became the superintendent of the Calcutta Garden and also a professor of botany in the Medical College there. The British desire for exploration and increased revenue indirectly led to the epoch-making discovery of fossil fauna in the Shivalik hills. The story deserves to be told in some detail because it brightens a particularly dark period in Delhi. As early as 1351 CE, Firoz Shah Tughlaq cut through a hill with the help of 50,000 men to dig a West Yamuna (or Delhi) canal. In 1568, Akbar ordered that it be excavated deeper and wider. East Yamuna, or doab canal, was constructed in 1626 during the reign of Shah Jahan. Both these canals had ceased to flow by the middle of the 18th century.[87] The British Indian Government took up the task of restoring these two old canals. After a preliminary survey in 1810–1811, work on the Firoz Shah canal was begun in 1817 and the doab canal in 1822, Saharanpur being the head of both. Sir Proby Thomas Cautley (1802–1871), in charge of the doab canal, had already discovered fossil bones, but their real nature had been overlooked. Falconer was aware of a report by Firoz Shah's historian Farishta where he described the unearthing of three-yard-long bones of giants while digging the east canal. Towards the end of 1831, Falconer and Cautley discovered bones of crocodiles, tortoises, and other fossil remains in the tertiary strata of the Shivalik hills. Cautley was able to follow the lead by discovering more fossils by blasting the hills.[88] On 16 November 1834, the superintending engineer, Lieutenant (later Sir) William Erskine Baker (1808–1881), received a present of a fossil of an elephant's tooth from the Raja of Nahan. Promptly, he sent a sketch to the Secretary of the Asiatic Society Calcutta. On hearing this, Dr Falconer made enquiries and had a fragment of a similar tooth presented to him also:

I got a hint where they [the teeth] came from and on going to the spot. I reaped a rich harvest. Only conceive my good fortune. Within six hours [on 20 November 1834] I got upwards of 300 specimens of fossil bones.[89]

These discoveries proved that in the remote past, a sea occupied the valleys of the Indus and Ganga. In 1835, Falconer and Cautley discovered the remains of the giant Miocene fossil tortoise, "which by its colossal size realized the mythological conception of the Tortoise which sustained the Elephant and the World together on its back."[90] In simpler words, if the existence of such fossils was known in ancient times that may explain the concept of Vishnu's incarnation as a tortoise (kurma) which carries the weight of the whole earth.

Colonial researchers carried out their work, "far distant from any living authorities or books on Comparative Anatomy to which they could refer." "[I]n the surrounding plains, hills and jungles," "they slew the wild tigers, buffaloes, antelopes, and other Indian quadrupeds," and preserved their skeletons. "They also obtained specimens of all the reptiles which inhabited that region."[91] Falconer's 1868 biographer smugly noted that "the white man had to draw on local means in all emergencies;" "but the intelligence, docility, and exquisite manual dexterity of the natives, backed by their faith in the guiding head of the European, furnished an inexhaustible fund of resource." To construct a barometer for mountain exploration, broken tumblers were melted and blown into a tube; mercury was distilled from cinnabar purchased in the bazaar; and "a brass scale was cast, shaped, and even graduated, by a native blacksmith, under the superintending eye of the [European] amateur."[92] In 1837, both Falconer and Cautley were jointly awarded the prestigious Wollaston Medal of the Geological Society of London.[93]

The discovery of Shivalik fossils was an extraordinary find. It emerged as a corollary of a giant government undertaking, namely the digging of canals, and burst on the scientific scene. There can however be no doubt that no matter what the driving force for field studies in India, recognition by the British scientific power centres was coveted and solicited.

In 1842, Falconer left for Europe on sick leave and remained there till 1847. He brought with him his natural history collections amassed during ten years of exploration. These included 70 large chests of dried plants from Kashmir, Afghanistan, Tibet, Punjab, Himalaya, plains of what is now western Uttar Pradesh, and from the neighbourhood of Darjeeling, Assam, and Sylhet. His collections from Kashmir and Little Tibet were particularly valued, him being one of the first botanists to visit these areas. His collection also included 48 cases containing five tons of fossil bones, together with geological specimens, illustrative of the Himalayan formations from the Indus to the Gogra, and from the plains of the Punjab across the mountains north to the Mooztagh range.

Cautley had already (1840) deposited his collection with the British Museum, the transportation costs from India being paid by the Indian Government. Falconer's collections were divided between the East India House and the British Museum. There were other fossil collections in the university museums in Oxford and Edinburgh. In July 1844, the presidents of various learned societies sent a memorial to the Court of Directors pointing out the desirability of having the specimens in the various collections prepared, arranged, and displayed and also of publishing an illustrated work to convey to the men of science a "knowledge of the content of Sewalik Hills." They further suggested Falconer's name for carrying out this work. Since the Company does not seem to have been too enthused with the idea, the President of the British Association for the Advancement of Science along with the presidents of other societies asked Her Majesty's Government for support. The government responded promptly by making a grant of £1000 to prepare the materials in the British Museum in a paleontological gallery. In December 1844, Falconer was entrusted with the work. The Company now fell in line, treating Falconer on duty. Both the Company and the British Government agreed to buy 40 copies. Nine of the envisaged 12 parts of the illustrated work titled *Fauna Antiqua Sivalensis* were published within three years. In June 1847, on Wallich's retirement, Falconer was appointed superintendent of the Calcutta Botanic Garden and a professor of Botany at Medical College. He would have liked to work on the Shivalik fauna in London on his Indian salary. But the Company refused to extend Falconer's stay in London, compelling him in December 1847, under the threat of loss of pension, to return to his duties in India. Falconer tried to resume the work in 1856, on his return to England after retirement, but eventually, the work was completed in 1868 after his death.

The Industrial Revolution brought home the realization that coal was more important than diamonds. The colonial quest for coal led to studies in Indian geology.

From Coal to Continental Drift

Early British India did require some coal for use by its arsenal for casting ordnance. This coal was imported from England. As early as 1774, attempts were made to replace sea-coal with Indian coal, but the experiment was not a success. The initiative came from a Bengal civil servant, the Rhode Island–born American royalist, Suetonius Grant Heatly[94] (1741–1793), who arrived in 1766 as a writer and by 1774 was the commissioner of Chhota Nagpur and Purnea. The area included the hilly Ramgarh country [Ramgur or Ramghur] where the Subarnrekha River runs for some miles through a coal mine. Being a trader and ruler at the same gave certain advantages to the English. In 1842, Heatly captured the Rajah, extracted from him "a knowledge of the existence of coal," and obtained government permission to work on it.[95] The enterprise however failed. Heatly and his partners felt that "they were unfairly dealt with, owing to the strong interest made by the coal contractors at home."[96]

As England industrialized, it needed its coal for itself. At the same time, demand in India also increased with the result that England could not supply it to India in sufficient quantities year after year. In September 1808, the Governor General, Earl of Minto, asked the Military Board to examine "the practicability of substituting Bheerbhoom coal for sea-coal."[97] It was however only in 1814 that the government decided to sponsor the quest for better quality coal. As a first step, it contacted Matthew Smith, an eminent shipwright of the day based in Calcutta, who had been using coal from the nearby Pachete area for his forge.[98] He recommended William Jones (d. 1821), known as Guru Jones, and better remembered as the architect of the Bishop's College Calcutta. Jones was rumoured to be a younger son of an Irish Duke, who left home after a family quarrel. He trained with the firm of Boulton and Watt, but refused employment[99] and instead chose to come to Calcutta, in 1800.[100] His father and brother died, and he became the heir to the title, "but if he knew of the change in his fortune he made no claim."[101] Jones would have led a prosperous life if he had been interested in trade rather than in engineering. For the first ten years, he was described as a mechanic, but in 1810 he was dignified with the designation manufacturer. In 1811, he was listed as the proprietor of a canvas manufactory in Howrah. The same year the expedition for the capture of Java was delayed because of the want of cartridge paper. Jones rose to the occasion and set up a small paper manufactory from which he furnished all the paper that was required. The government however had no interest in promoting manufacturing capabilities in India, and Jones' factory was closed "as soon as the object of the expedition was accomplished."[102]

In 1814, the government hired Jones at a monthly stipend of Rs 600 "to examine the country lying in a northwestern direction from Calcutta with a view to the discovery of mines of coal of good quality."[103] The result of his mission was that he re-discovered some of Heatly's old workings and more importantly discovered the Raniganj seam.[104] The site did not have any earlier name. It was called Raniganj after the Rani of Burdwan.[105]

Jones obtained a patta or deed of lease from the Burdwan Raj for the Raniganj coal mine and 133 bighas of land. In 1817, he arranged for a government loan of Rs 40,000 at 6% interest from the government as working capital. He mined and sold coal, not from quarries but from pits.[106] Jones thus became the first person to bring Indian coal to the general market. He was a pioneer, and like most pioneers, a commercial failure; "either he did not succeed in extracting it profitably, or, as is more probable, he failed in other speculations."[107] After his dissociation from Raniganj, he took up the construction of the Bishop's College in Shibpur, Calcutta. During the superintendence of the building, he caught a fever and died in September 1821.[108]

On his death, an agency house, Alexander and Company, which had stood security for Jones cleared the loan. The house itself failed in 1832 and placed the mine for sale. In 1834, the zamindar, dewan, and banian, Dwarka Nath Tagore established Carr, Tagore and Company which after hard bargaining acquired the lease for a mere 70,000 rupees. In 1843, the Raniganj mine was amalgamated with the independent entity of Naraincoory mine, under the name Bengal Coal Company, giving Dwarka Nath a near monopoly of the coal industry. The biggest buyer of the coal was the government which in 1840 had nine steam vessels out of which four were Ganga boats.[109]

Alexander Laidlaw

As soon as Kumaon was annexed, the government thought of exploiting its mineral wealth. However, the first geological appointment in British India was an imposition from the very top, with disastrous results. A London magazine reported in 1816 that the directors had handpicked Alexander Laidlaw to go to India "for the purpose of exploring their mineralogical productions— a task for which he is eminently qualified,"[110] his lack of "liberal education" notwithstanding.[111] The Governor General, Earl of Moira,[112] had no option but to rationalize: He wrote in 1817: "We have been duly sensible of the want of professional enquiry into the mineral produce of the hill country lately acquired by us. The remedy [that is, Laidlaw] now offers itself." Laidlaw was attached to Captain William Spencer Webb (1784–1865) in his survey of the Kumaon region. Laidlaw's pay was commensurate with the legendary mineral wealth he was to explore: "a salary of Rs 600 plus Rs 200 for bill carriage, and free issue of instruments and stores, to say nothing of an advance of Rs 2500 in cash."[113] Laidlaw was to seek "indications of metallic veins" in the tracts which Webb was surveying. Moira however cautioned: "To copper or iron I would not point Mr Laidlaw's attention, as I think the working either might injuriously affect important articles of British export." The idea was to add trade items to the Company's list, but not to offer competition to England. Mr Laidlaw did not pay attention to these instructions and was dismissed. He was debarred from Company service and asked to leave the country. Laidlaw paid no attention to these orders either and continued to live quietly in Kumaon where he died in Pithoragarh on 6 August 1836.[114]

At the time of the reorganization of GTS in 1818, it was decided to appoint a surgeon and geologist to the survey. The post was offered to the Glasgow-educated Dr John Ross (1788/9–1818) who had been strongly recommended to the Governor General by Sir Alexander Crichton (1763–1856), physician to Emperor Alexander I of Russia.[115] Ross however died soon thereafter, and the appointment was offered to university-educated Henry Wesley Voysey (1791–1824) who joined in December 1818. Strictly speaking, much to his disadvantage, Voysey never became a Company servant. He continued to be a part of a King's regiment which was to boot not based in India. So pressing was the Company Government's need to attach a naturalist

to the geodetic survey that while on duty in Cape of Good Hope, he was induced by a high-ranking Indian civil servant to come to Calcutta in anticipation of an appointment.[116] Voysey wrote a report on the stone used in the
construction of the Taj Mahal which he visited in 1822. Far more to the point
was his report on one of the diamond mines in Banganpalle (now Andhra
Pradesh), which he visited in January 1821.

Coal Committee

The introduction of steam machinery in manufacturing as well as in river and
ocean navigation brought home the realization that the Company should be
looking for coal in India rather than diamonds. A six-member committee for
investigating the coal and mineral resources of India was appointed in 1835
with Dr John McClelland (1805–1875) of the Bengal Medical Service as its
junior member and secretary. Its report submitted in 1838 largely dealt with
coal. It "added nothing to the previously existing knowledge of the Geology
of the field,"[117] but neatly summed up the work done so far, which had been
sporadic and isolated. The time had now come for a systematic coal survey.
England had already done so. In 1832, Sir Henry Thomas de la Beche[118]
(1796–1855) suggested that the maps being prepared by the British Ordnance
Survey be coloured geologically. This was the starting point for the Geological
Survey of Great Britain (then called Ordnance Geological Survey) which was
instituted in 1835 with de la Beche as its director. The same year a Museum
of Economic Geology was established under Beche, and a chemist, Richard
Philip (1778–1851) attached to it in 1839. The same year Beche hired David
Hiram Williams (c. 1812–1848) as an assistant to survey the coal fields in
South Wales.

During 1841–1843 McClelland entered into correspondence with eminent
British geologists Sir Charles Lyell (1797–1875) and Sir Roderick Impey
Murchison (1792–1871) expressing a desire for a scientific examination of
the coalfields of India.[119] On de la Beche's recommendation, David Hiram
Williams (1812–1848) took up an appointment as the Geological Surveyor in
the Service of the East India Company, on 5 February 1846. He hoped to earn
money for the sake of "our little ones,"[120] but never saw his family again.

The Company's professional directions to Williams were explicit:

> you will direct your principal attention to those localities which promise
> to afford supplies of coal, and which are so situated with respect to water
> carriage, as to give a real commercial value to the coal which they may
> produce.[121]

European professionals in India believed that their own financial considerations, the Company's commercial interests and Europe's scientific agenda

would all converge. Williams hoped that the survey of Indian coalfields "will eventually turn out both in an economic point of view and a branch of the Geological Survey of Great Britain."[122]

The geologists travelled on elephants that had been trained to pick up fossils. In his *Himalayan Journals*, Sir Joseph Dalton Hooker described his 1848 field trip with Williams:

> Our elephant was an excellent one, when he did not take obstinate fits, and so docile as to pick up pieces of stone when desired, and with a jerk of the trunk throw them over his head for the rider to catch, thus saving the trouble of dismounting to geologise.[123]

During one of his field explorations, Williams fell off from an elephant, and again from a precipice, and caught jungle fever from which he never recovered, and died in 1848. As a stop-gap arrangement, the charge was first handed over to McClelland and then to the deputy surveyor general Thuiller. The Court of Directors offered the Geological Surveyor's post to Thomas Oldham (1816–1878), who was at the time a professor of geology at Trinity College Dublin as well as the local director of geological survey. He however refused to accept the offer till the Company provided him with two assistants of his choice, increased his salary to £1000, and paid "travelling costs, etc."[124] Partially accepting his demands, the Company offered him a package comprising a salary of £1200 and one assistant.[125] Accepting the offer, Oldham joined his post in India on 5 March 1851 and held it till 1876. In 1856, the survey was constituted as a government department under the formal name Geological Survey. Under the Survey, geological explorations continued uninterruptedly and moved from merely the economic to the manifestly scientific. "The Ramghur-coal field ...is not rich in coal, and what does occur is not of the best quality. But like the adjoining field of the Bokaroh valley, it offers many points of very high interest to the geologist."[126]

What began as a simple quest for coal ended in providing evidence for the continental drift hypothesis and an addition to geological terminology. Trinity College Dublin-educated Henry Benedict Medlicott (1829–1905) left the British Geological Survey to take up an appointment in the Geological Survey of India in 1854. He served at Roorkee Engineering College from 1854 till 1862 when he returned to the Survey. Finally, he succeeded Oldham as the superintendent in 1876 and held office till April 1887, three years beyond the age of superannuation. In 1872, in an administrative report, he used the term Gondwana system for coal-bearing formations in the Satpura basin. The term was generalized to Gondwana System in 1876, by the Bohemia-born palaeontologist, Otokar Feistmantel (1848–1891), who worked at the Geological Survey of India. The term Gondwanaland was coined by Austrian geologist Eduard Suess (1831–1914). It however has since fallen into disuse, because

Gondwana itself means land of the Gonds. Gondwana is now widely accepted to denote a hypothesized supercontinent in the southern hemisphere.

Origin of Geological Survey of India

We have seen that Williams took charge as Geological Surveyor in 1846, and Oldham was appointed as his successor in 1851. When his contract was renewed six years later, the same designation was used.[127] The term Geological Survey of India was employed in a descriptive sense till in 1856 it was given a specific meaning as a government department. Regrettably, most publications, including the official ones, make the date of Oldham's appointment the date of the beginning of the Geological Survey of India. The Government of India even brought out a stamp in 1951 commemorating the Survey's centenary. The counting is wrong. The year 1851 has no particular significance. Either the Geological Survey should be taken to begin in 1856 when it was formally so constituted, or in 1846 when Williams was appointed Geological Surveyor. It is relevant to note that the Survey of India takes its roots back to the 1767 appointment of Rennell as Surveyor General of Bengal. Apart from the Medical Service, the Survey of India and Geological Survey were the only other services in British India under the Company rule.

Tea

Till the mid-19th century, Europe entirely depended on China for its tea. In 1823, the Royal Society of Arts offered a "gold medal or fifty guineas to the person who should grow and prepare the greatest quantity of China tea of good quality, not being less than 20 lbs. weight, … and should import the same into Great Britain." "These offers, opportune as they certainly were, seem to have been in advance of their time, for they produced no response."[128] At the time, the East India Company enjoyed a monopoly over China trade and saw no reason to encourage competition. It was only when the China monopoly was ended in 1833 that the Company Government launched official efforts to grow tea in Assam (and elsewhere). Assam tea was delivered to London in 1838. The next year a Committee of the House of Commons commended the work of Charles Alexander Bruce, superintendent of tea plantations in Assam. As a consequence of this, the gold medal offered 17 years earlier by the Society of Arts was awarded to Bruce in the session 1839–1840, "for his meritorious services in discovering the indigenous tea tracts and cultivating and preparing tea in Assam."

Unhappy at the honour bestowed on Bruce, Lieutenant Andrews Charlton launched a rather acrimonious campaign in Calcutta demanding recognition as a tea discoverer for himself. In 1841, a newspaper in far-off Australia, the Sydney Gazette, declared that the "undivided voice of society has always conferred this honour on Lieut. Charlton," implying that Bruce was not part of that society. The President of the Agricultural and Horticultural Society of India, Sir Edward Ryan, who was also the Chief Justice of Calcutta, announced his decision to abstain from the meeting saying that if he attended he would vote against Charlton. The gold medal was awarded to Charlton at a Society meeting held on 7 September 1841. He was carefully described "as the first person to establish, to the Satisfaction of the Tea Committee and its Secretary, that the Tea Tree was indigenous in Assam." The meeting was chaired by the Vice President, C. K. Robison, who declared that if Charlton was to be honoured so must be Captain Francis Jenkins on whose orders Charlton was acting. The next meeting held on 9 November 1841 awarded a gold medal to Jenkins "for bringing to a successful result the inquiry in regard to the establishment of the tree plant in Assam." The resolution was carried by 12–11 votes. Charlton pointed out that to facilitate the medal, Jenkins had presented the Society with a donation of 500 rupees out of which a medal of 100 rupees could easily be "coined out."[129] The grace and decorum which one normally associates with award functions of learned societies were missing in this case.

1810s

British army officers posted in Assam noticed tea as early as the 1810s. An 1843 publication noted that "[I]n 1815, Colonel Salter was well acquainted with the tea of Assam, that was brought to the Rungpore market in a manufactured state"[130] (Rangpur, present-day Sibsagar, was the capital of the Ahom kings. It is not to be confused with another Rangpur in Bengal). An otherwise authoritative work published in 1935 says: "What appears to be the earliest mention of indigenous India tea is to be found in a report made in 1815 by Colonel Latter, of the British forces in India, in which he told how the Singpho hill tribes of Assam gathered a species of wild tea, ate it with oil and garlic, after the Burmese manner, and also made a drink from it."[131] It seems both authors are referring to the same Colonel, with Latter being a misprint for Salter. In 1818, Edward Gardner, the Company's Resident in Nepal, sent flowers and ripe fruit of the plant to Wallich who simply forwarded them to Sir Joseph Banks.[132]

1830s

The next official in the tea story was Lieutenant Andrew Charlton of the Assam Light Infantry who arrived in Assam in 1830 and cultivated the tea plant in his own garden in Jorhat. In October 1831, he brought to Calcutta a small number of plants which he presented to the Agricultural and Horticultural Society through Dr John Tytler.[133] On 21 January 1832, he sent a letter to Tytler concerning a tea tree growing in the vicinity of Suddiya. A paragraph from the letter was published in the Transactions of the Society. Charlton's claim to priority over tea discovery is based on this para.

Bruce next contacted Scott's successor, Captain (later Major General) Francis Jenkins (1793–1866) who held the post till retirement in 1861.[134] Bruce submitted him a report on the localities where the plant grew and the different modes of preparation employed by the natives. The report dated 26 March 1833 was forwarded by Jenkins to the Political Secretary in August or September 1833.[135]

On 24 January 1834, the Governor General, William Bentinck, constituted a Tea Committee which guided and coordinated subsequent developments. The Committee had 12 members out of whom two, Radhakant Deb and Ramcomul Sen, were Indians, but they hardly played any role. The most influential member by virtue of his office was Nathaniel Wallich, the Superintendent of Calcutta Botanic Garden. To begin with, Wallich (and following him the Committee) held that Assam did not produce true tea. Even if it did, it was not suitable for domestication. If eventually, Assam became a flourishing commercial tea centre, it was despite the topmost botanist of British India.

On 3 March 1834, the Committee Secretary, George James Gordon, issued a circular asking for information on where tea grew or could be grown. At the same time, convinced that the solution to India's tea problem lay in adapting China seeds, the Committee dispatched Gordon, accompanied by the Reverend Charles Gutzlaff to China who returned with seeds in 1835. Jenkins responded to Gordon's circular, by sending, on 7 May 1834, specimens of the tea plant, but without flowers or seeds. Wallich pronounced them to be the leaves of the Camellia. Persisting that genuine tea did exist in Assam, Jenkins asked Captain Charlton at Suddiya to send him tea leaves, flowers, and seeds as soon as the season permitted. The consignment reached Wallich on 8 November 1834. On 8 February 1835, Wallich recalled Gordon from China saying that having "maturely weighed the subject of the new discovery in Upper Assam in all its bearings," the Committee have concluded that "[T]he genuine tea grows there" and that

> it is therefore useless and unnecessary to import from China at a great expense and great risk what may be had, as it were on the spot, to any extent almost in a state of perfect freshness and strength for vegetating.[136]

Assam tea had finally won recognition in Calcutta.

On 13 March 1835, the Governor General deputed Wallich along with the botanist William Griffith and the geologist John McClelland to report on "the subject of the growth of tea shrubs in Upper Assam." The deputation has often been called Tea Commission, although the term does not occur in official records. At times in place of the Tea Commission, the term Tea Committee has been used which is worse because an official Tea Committee was already in existence. Bruce was asked to assist the deputation. On 11 February 1835, he was appointed in charge of nurseries to be developed in Upper Assam, at Sadiya and other places, at a salary of Rs 150 per month.[137] In 1836, he was appointed Superintendent of Tea Plantations. This was a whole-time appointment necessitating resignation from the charge of the gunboats and severance of connection with private business.[138] In August 1836, his late brother's Assam-born son Captain R. Bruce resigned as head of Purandhar Singh's [Poorunder Sing] militia to join as his uncle's assistant.[139] Assam was moving from gunboat to commerce.

Wallich's tea education progressed in stages. On receiving Charlton's samples, he gushingly wrote to the Tea Committee on 6 December 1834: "I humbly submit that a more interesting and more valuable fact has never before been brought to light in Indian Agriculture than has been established beyond all dispute by Lieut. Charlton." The letter was no doubt written in the first flush of excitement and was suppressed. Charlton later used it to bolster his case for the Calcutta discovery medal. Wallich would have learnt that Charlton was acting on orders from Jenkins. On 24 December 1834, Wallich modified his stand and asserted in the name of the Tea Committee that

> We have no hesitation in declaring this discovery which is due to the indefatigable researches of Capt. Jenkins and Lieut. Charlton to be by far the most important and valuable that has ever been made in matters connected with the Agricultural or Commercial resources of this empire.[140]

In Calcutta, Wallich would not have known of the Bruce brothers. He would have become aware of them only when he visited Assam. Finally, on 15 March 1836, he went on record to say: "It was Mr. Bruce and his late brother who originally brought the Assam tea into public notice many years ago when no one had the slightest idea of its existence."[141] It is this testimonial which influenced London's decision to medal to Bruce. All members of the deputation agreed that Assam tea was genuine, but could not produce a unanimous set of recommendations. Dr Griffith was convinced that "a wild plant is not likely to give as good produce as a one that has been cultivated for centuries,"[142] meaning that Chinese-domesticated plants were preferable to wild Assam plants. Gordon was again sent to China in 1836 and for many years Chinese tea seed was imported regularly. Gordon also brought Chinamen to work as tea cultivators. Experimental cultivation was carried out at various places including Kumaon, Garhwal, Nilgiri Hills, and Upper Assam. Later, Harold Hart Mann (1871–1961), the Chief Scientific Officer of the Indian Tea Association, described the China tea seed as "the curse of the Indian tea industry."[143]

Besides these experimental plantings of the Chinese variety, Bruce started a nursery devoted solely to the indigenous variety at Sadiya, in 1836. He continued searching for new tracts of the wild tea. In 1837, he found several new ones in the Matak country, near Sadiya, and by 1839 he had located 120; the most extensive was in the Naga hills, but there were large numbers in the Tippoom and Gubru hills. "The wild tea," he said, "may be traced from tract to tract, thus forming a chain of tea tracts from the Irrawaddy to the borders of China, east of Assam."[144] It became clear that the China variety or China–India hybrids were commercially unimportant and Assam tea was in a position to hold on its own.

Bruce was not a scientific man. He did not possess a knowledge of botany or horticulture, but he walked through hundreds of miles of pathless jungles looking for tea plants, removing on the way the "prejudices" of the native chiefs and actually persuading them "to aid him in his labors."[145] The success of a tea enterprise required "the establishment of friendly feelings in the minds of the rude tribes amongst whose villages the indigenous tea is found, towards the British name generally." Bruce's "extraordinary talent for conciliating the goodwill" of the local population was appreciated. The Governor General sanctioned 500 rupees for the purchase of cheap arms by native chiefs of his choice.[146] As long as the local population stood apart, it was called rude. But once they agreed to aid British commercial interests, they were said to be moving towards civilization.

A moment's thought will convince anybody that only Bruce and not Charlton could have been the European discoverer of Assam tea. Since senior Bruce was a private individual during 1823–1824, he could enter Burmese territory and notice tea. But a serving Company army officer could have entered Burmese Assam only after it was conquered. Bruce knew in Assam that he was dealing with tea while Calcutta needed to be convinced that Assam indeed had tea. Credit for Charlton and Jenkins arises from the fact that they acted as a bridge between the Assam outpost and the Calcutta citadel and prised open Calcutta's closed scientific mind. Had the Tea Committee not existed and had the Governor General put his faith in Bruce, the journey of Assam tea from the forest to the tea table would have been smoother, quicker, and less expensive.

In 1837, Bruce sent 46 packets of tea to Calcutta, but because of defective packing, most of the tea was damaged. Only a small fraction was sent to England where it was well received.[147] Eight chests of Assam teas were auctioned in London in January 1839.[148] The next consignment was a considerable improvement on the earlier one. Of the 95 boxes, 10 were distributed free of charge while the remaining 85 were sold by public auction on 17 March 1840.[149] In March 1840, the government handed over two-thirds of its experimental gardens in Assam to the newly formed Assam Company, free of charge for 10 years. It is a measure of the recognition of Bruce's work that the Company immediately employed him as the superintendent of the northern division.[150] Belatedly, but more substantially, sometime before 1864, the Indian Government gave a land grant to Charles Bruce for his "discovery" of tea, and "his subsequent services in fostering the cultivation of the shrub and manufacture of tea."[151]

In 1866, as much as 96% of tea imported into England came from China, and only 4% from India. Twenty years later, in 1886, China's share had fallen to 59% and India's had risen to 38%. The remaining 3% of the imports came from Ceylon. In 1903, the imports from China had reduced to 10%; India's share was now 59% and Ceylon's 31%.[152]

There was commonality in colonial approaches to cinchona and Assam tea. In both cases, there was much high-sounding trumpeted organized activity, while the problem was finally solved at the individual level: Charles Bruce in Upper Assam and Charles Ledger in Peru, respectively.

1820s

The first Anglo-Burmese war during 1824–1826 brought the British to the source of tea. Names of two Scottish brothers are associated with the discovery (for Europe) of Assam tea. In 1823, a free trader, Robert Bruce (d. 1825), carrying a large assortment of goods for sale moved beyond British Indian territory into Upper Assam which was held by the Burmese. He visited Rungpore and formed an acquaintance with a Singpho chief. Being "addicted to botanical researches," he soon discovered that the tea plant was growing on the hills in a state of nature. Through a written agreement, the chief agreed to furnish Bruce with some plants (it has been said that Bruce's intermediary was a local man Mani Ram Dewan).

His younger brother, Charles Alexander Bruce (1793–1871) came to the East in 1809 as a midshipman. Later, he went as an officer of a troop ship against Java. At the breaking out of the Burmese War, he offered his services to David Scott (1786–1831), Agent to the Governor General on the North East Frontier of Bengal from 1823 till his death.[153] Scott appointed Charles Bruce to command gunboats with his headquarters at Sadia [Suddeah, variously spelt]. After the capital had fallen to the Company forces, the Singpho chief handed him, in 1824, several hundred plants, and a considerable quantity of the seed as promised earlier to his brother. Robert the elder Bruce died in 1825 and the tea mantle fell on his younger brother.

Bruce had no direct access to Calcutta and operated through Assam-based high officials. He grew some plants in his own garden at Sadiya,[154] and distributed others, the most important recipient being David Scott. On 2 June 1825, Scott, writing to Wallich from Dekkow Mookh, sent him some leaves and seeds of a plant which the Burmese and Chinese stated to be wild tea. Two years later, on 26 July 1827, Scott wrote to Wallich from Gauhati sending him a small box containing seeds said to be those of the Tea Plant.[155] Wallich was the Empire's arbiter on all matters botanical. Unfortunately, the Wallich of the 1820s had convinced himself that true tea grew only in China. No doubt, Wallich could not have identified the plant merely on the basis of leaves and seeds that Scott had sent him. However, if he had had an open mind, he could have specifically asked for fruits and flowers. This he did not do. The impression went around that the expert opinion was that the Assam sample was not true tea, but camellia. The time for Indian tea had not yet come.

Forestry

The Company rule in India was bad for forests. Shipbuilding, railways, and rank commercial exploitation all depleted Indian and Burmese forest wealth at an alarming rate, compelling the government to initiate conservation measures in its own framework. A large number of surgeons, mostly Scottish, came to India, in Company service. India made many of them into botanists and foresters.

In 1828, John Malcolm, Bombay Governor during 1827–1830, unilaterally established an experimental botanic and agricultural garden at Dapooree [Dapoorie, Dapuri; now Dapodi] near Poona and presented it to the Company as a fait accompli. It was located on the 70-acre grounds of the estate Malcolm had purchased as his personal residence. The property was eventually sold off in 1865 and the garden closed. The Scottish surgeon, Charles Rush (1797–1845), served as the garden superintendent from 1828 till 1838. He was the first European in India to write on cotton. The Scottish surgeon Alexander Gibson (1800–1867) arrived in India in 1820 and made a name for himself by successfully introducing vaccination in Khandesh. Opportunities and challenges made him a botanist and forester. He succeeded Rush in 1838. Dapuri's shortcomings were obvious. "Dapuri is a nasty dry soil, bad quality, and no water." It was dismissively described as the "Governor's cabbage garden." Gibson felt it could be left in the care of a gardener. In 1839, Gibson shifted and most of the botanic activity was shifted to a new 38-acre site, Hewra in the "Jooneeer" valley, with plenty of water.[156] A subsidiary garden was established at Neergora. Also, "trees which are affected by the heat of the plains" were reared in "the cultivated portions of the Hill Fort of Sewnere."[157] He introduced and cultivated foreign trees and plants, which were imported from countries as far away as South America, Australia, and Europe. He also set up a laboratory at Hewra for extracting oils. In 1852, drugs grown at Hewra and manufactured in the laboratory were sent to England for the "forthcoming Exhibition of Indian Products."[158]

The garden led to bigger things. In 1840, Gibson was asked to inspect the forests and report on them. As England needed more and more and bigger

and bigger ships for commercial and naval purposes, shipbuilding was transferred to Bombay to protect England's own oak. This in turn told on the region's forest wealth. First, forests in Gujarat and Konkan were depleted and
then the axe fell on Malabar teak. Appreciating his concerns for protecting
forests, in 1847, the government appointed him to the more important post
of Conservator of Forests, Bombay Presidency, which position he held till
1860. His was the first such appointment anywhere in the country. He held
charge of vaccination till 1840 and concurrently held charge of Dapooree
and forestry. Gibson was succeeded by Nicholas Alexander Dalzell (1817–
1877) who held office till 1870 when he returned to Scotland. His career
graph was unique. He had been a student of divinity rather than botany or
medicine, but always interested in botany. India gave his interest a chance to
blossom. In 1841, he visited Bombay and was appointed assistant commissioner of customs. He became a forest ranger of Scinde [Sind] in 1858 before
succeeding Gibson. India's forest policy was laid down by the Governor
General, Lord Dalhousie, in 1855. The policy was enshrined in 1865 and
later acts enabled the colonial government to declare more and more land as
reserve forests, without paying any attention to the rights of the tribals and
other forest dwellers.

Apart from Gibson, two names are associated with scientific forestry, the
German university-educated Dietrich Brandis and the Scottish surgeon-
turned-botanist Hugh Francis Clarke Cleghorn (1820–1895) both of whom
worked in unison.

Hugh Cleghorn, up to 1864

Dr Hugh Francis Clarke Cleghorn (1820–1895) was the grandson of Hugh
Cleghorn (1752–1837) and the son of Peter Cleghorn (1783–1863) who was
a barrister and for some time Registrar and Prothonotary in the Madras
Supreme Court. Madras-born Cleghorn studied medicine in Edinburgh and
arrived in 1842 as an assistant surgeon in the Madras Military Medical
Service. He retired in 1869 and returned to Scotland.

Immediately upon arrival, he started taking an interest in matters associated with botany and forestry. In 1848, Cleghorn left for Britain for health
reasons and remained on furlough till 1851. He utilized this time to meet
like-minded people and plead for forest conservation. In 1851, at its
Edinburgh meeting, the British Association for the Advancement of Science
set up a committee to report on "the probable effects, in an Economical and
Physical Point of View, of the Destruction of Tropical Forests." The committee comprised members familiar with India: Dr. Hugh Cleghorn, Professor
Forbes Royle, R. Baird Smith, and R. Strachey. The last two were from
Bengal Engineers, while Royle was now at King's College, London. The com-
mittee report was published in the British Association Report for the 1851

Ipswich meeting (Cleghorn et al. 1852). Royle asked for and obtained Cleghorn's aid in preparing a Catalogue of the Raw Products in the Great Exhibition of 1851, "a task which occupied him ninety days." This connection served Cleghorn well. He returned to Madras in 1851 carrying a letter of introduction from Royle to Sir Henry Eldred Pottinger (1789–1856), Madras Governor during 1848–1854. In 1851, Cleghorn was appointed a professor of botany and *Material Medica* at Madras Medical College which had recently been upgraded from a medical school. He remained at the College till 1856.

In 1855 he was invited to meet Lord Harris, Governor of Madras during 1854–1859, at his residence, the only other person present being Sir Arthur Cotton. Railways were being planned in the Presidency; the first line running between Madras (Royapuram station) and Arcot would become operational in 1856. Since wood would be required for sleepers, the Governor was advised to consult Cleghorn. The meeting turned out to be eventful indeed. Cleghorn prepared a report on forest conservancy which was approved. Accordingly, the Madras Forest Department was established on 19 December 1856 under the charge of Cleghorn, who was designated Conservator of Forests. In November 1861, on the Governor General's orders, Cleghorn proceeded to Punjab (which had been acquired a decade previously) to examine the forests of Western Himalayas and to institute a systematic plan of conservancy and management. He spent three years exploring the countries adjacent to our northwest frontier, including part of Kashmir and the Trans-Indus territory.

Dietrich Brandis, up to 1862

Brandis was born in Bonn and successively educated at Copenhagen, Bonn, and Göttingen Universities. He returned to Bonn to obtain his doctorate in 1848 where the next year he was appointed a privatdozent. In 1854, he married Rachel Marshman (1804–1862), 20 years his senior. She was the daughter of famed Serampore Missionary Dr Joshua Marshman (1768–1837) and was earlier married to J.O. Voigt (1795–1843), well known for his botanical work. Voigt, a Danish doctor, came to Serampore in 1827 and became a disciple of Carey. On Carey's death, Voigt took care of his garden and when he held charge of the Calcutta Garden for a short time, he combined the catalogues of the two gardens and published *Hortus Suburbanus Calcuttensis* in 1842.

Rachel's sister, Hannah, was married to Major General Sir Henry Havelock (1795–1857) who had served with distinction in the First Anglo-Burmese War during 1824–1826. Her brother John Clark Marshman (1794–1877) was highly regarded in Calcutta circles. Brandis' marriage opened Indian doors for him. Rachel impressed upon her brother the desirability of bringing her and Brandis to British India. Marshman in turn took the help of Havelock.

The two brought Brandis to the notice of the Governor General who found an opening for him.

British annexed Pegu in 1852 and appointed John McClelland (1805–1883) as the Superintendent of Forest. He resigned in 1855, and the appointment was now given to Brandis. Referring to Brandis, it has been claimed that the British Government "turned to Germany for expertise in forestry."[159] This is not correct. Although Brandis was well qualified for the job, his name reached the Governor General through informal channels. In 1858, the forests of Tenasserim and Martaban were added to Brandis' charge making him responsible for forests of whole of Burma. In 1861, the Indian Government succumbed to pressure from commercial interests and ordered the opening of forests of Pegu province to private exploitation. Brandis had raised strong objections, but they were ignored. But, Brandis was vindicated by London. London strongly objected to this surrender to commercial interests. Dispatch of 24 March 1862 from the Secretary of State for India reversed the government policy. Brandis remained in charge of Burma forests till December 1862 when he was transferred to India.

Brandis and Cleghorn

In January 1864, Brandis and Cleghorn were appointed Joint Commissioners of Forests to reorganize the Forest Department. Three months later, Brandis was appointed Inspector General of Forests from which position he retired in 1883. The pair worked together on the Indian Forest Act, which came into effect on 1 May 1865 and was subsequently modified. During 1864–1865 and then 1866–1867, when Brandis was on leave in Europe, Cleghorn acted as Inspector General.

The Indian Forest Service was formally notified in 1869, but in 1867 itself Brandis employed two Germans, Dr William Schlich (1840–1925) and Berthold Ribbentrop (1843–1915) both of whom had a long distinguished career. Later in 1866, seven candidates were selected for forest service. Out of these, two were trained at Hanover in Germany while the other five were sent to Nancy in France. The Nancy five included 20-year-old Framjee Rustomjee Dasai, son of a Bombay merchant, who thus became the first Indian forest officer. He entered the service in 1869, rose to be a Conservator, and retired in 1901. At the end of 1875, the professional education was entirely transferred to Nancy. In 1879, the Central Forest School was opened at Dehradun for the training of forest officials. The first batch of trainees left the School in **1881**, three with Ranger's Certificate and two with Sub-Assistant Conservator's Certificate. Subsequently, the school trained candidates sent by native states as well. The school was upgraded to a Forest Research Institute in 1906.

Schlich succeeded his mentor Dietrich Brandis as Inspector General of Forests in 1883, but two years later, in 1885, moved to England to take up the pioneering post of Professor of Forestry at the Royal Indian Engineering College at Cooper's Hill, the first formal forestry course in England. Scientific forestry thus arrived in England from Germany via India. In 1905, upon the closure of the college at Cooper's Hill, he moved to Oxford, to found Oxford's forestry programme. He retired on 1 January 1920. Ribbentrop succeeded Schlich as Inspector General and remained in office from 1885 till his retirement in or after 1900. Rudyard Kipling modelled his head forester Müller in the Mowgli story "In the Rukh" after Ribbentrop.[160]

After retirement, Brandis contributed towards the training of English and American foresters. He shifted to the London area and from 1888 to 1896 every year he took forestry students on tours of German and Swiss forests. In 1905, his protégé Gifford Pinchot (1865–1946) became the first head of the US Forest Service. In appreciation of Brandis' work "for the cause of forestry in the United States," President Theodore Roosevelt sent him his inscribed photograph in 1905.[161] In 1906, for his final resting place, Brandis returned to Bonn which he had left 52 years previously. He "never let his students forget a great truth" "that in the long run Forestry cannot succeed unless the people who live in and near the forest are for it and not against it."[162] Regrettably, in India, colonial constraints prevented Brandis from giving practical shape to his sound philosophy.

Cinchona and Its Domestication

The malaria-curing properties of the bark of what came to be called the cinchona tree were first noticed by the Jesuits in Central America. They learnt about the tree in Peru in the 1620s or 1630s. According to an oft-told story, in 1638, the Countess of Chinchon, the wife of the Spanish Viceroy of Peru, was cured of her fever by the intake of the powder of cinchona sent by the Governor of the Province of Loja. According to a 1662 England account, "On her return to Europe, she carried with her a quantity of the healing bark, which was sold in Seville for a hundred reals a pound, and went by the name the Countess's powder."[163] The story is now declared to be a legend, and the Countess never returned to Spain. But there must be some basis for the later nomenclature (perhaps the Count himself was cured of his fever thanks to the bark). The bark was regularly used in Jesuit colleges in Europe from 1650 with the Pope's approval. An early and enthusiastic popular dispenser of the remedy was the Rome-based Spanish Cardinal de Lugo (1583–1660), who probably obtained the Peruvian bark from Jesuit sources in the initial stages. He purchased large amounts of it at his own expense, and "gave it gratis to the fevered poor, on condition only, that they did not sell it and that they presented a physician's statement about the illness." Such was the medicine's association with the Jesuits that it came to be known as the Jesuit's or the Cardinal's bark/ powder.[164] It is said that Oliver Cromwell (1599–1658) preferred to die of fever than try the "popish remedy." The story may be apocryphal, but the message is clear. The bark was considered to be a Catholic remedy and accordingly shunned, at least in the initial stages, by the Protestants. The bark was popularized in England by Robert Talbor (1642–1681), who was a pharmacist and not a physician, and therefore open to "observation and experiment." The bark entered the London Pharmacopoeia in 1677 as *Cortex peruanus*.[165]

Cosmic science provided a convenient subterfuge for gathering botanical intelligence. In 1735, the French Government sent an expedition to South America ostensibly for the measurement of an arc of the meridian in the Spanish territory of Quito in what later was named Ecuador. The expedition, led by Charles Marie de la Condamine (1701–1774), was secretly instructed to find the fever tree.[166] In 1738, Condamime published the first clear and detailed illustration of the tree. On the bases of this publication and the specimens provided by Condamime, Linnaeus described the tree in 1742, labelling the genus Cinchona. It should have been called Chinchona, but the misspelt name has stuck. The alternative would have been to name it after Lugo. Probably, Linnaeus preferred to name it after a Catholic countess rather than a Catholic cardinal.

A number of attempts were made to identify the active ingredient of the various types of fever barks. Finally, in 1820, in a major breakthrough, two Frenchmen, Pierre Joseph Pelletier (1788–1842) the Director of the School of Pharmacy in Paris, and his colleague, Joseph Caventou (1795–1877), succeeded in extracting the alkaloid of quinine from cinchona bark. About the same time, attempts at synthesizing quinine were also initiated. Lab quinine did not come about but the exercise produced an unexpected bonus. In 1856, an 18-year-old chemistry student William Henry Perkin (1838–1907) while assisting his professor in the synthesizing experiment made the private discovery of the first aniline dye, mauveine or aniline purple, thus laying the foundation of the synthetic chemical dye industry. Quinine would at last be synthesized in 1944 to meet Second World War requirements, by Robert Burns Woodward (1917–1979) and William von Eggers Doering (1917–2011) at Harvard.

In 1834, a French army doctor, Francois Clement Maillot (1804–1894), deviating from the current medical practice, cured his patients of malaria by giving them high doses of quinine and good nutrition. In 1881, glowing tributes were paid to him: "It is thanks to Maillot that Algeria has become a French land; it is he who closed and sealed forever this tomb of Christians."[167]

Next, in 1854, thanks to quinine, the English ship, the *Pleid*, sensationally returned after 112 days of voyage in Africa, with all European members alive.[168] At this time, all the world's cinchona bark came from the forests of Peru, Bolivia, Ecuador, and Colombia. The message was clear. If Europe was to retain and expand its colonial empire, dependence on the Andes for cinchona should cease.

France

France sent England-born, France-educated physician and botanist Hugh Algernon Weddell (1819–1877) to South America who spent two years (1845–1847) in the forests of Bolivia studying cinchona trees. He identified no less than 15 distinct species and brought calisaya seeds to France which germinated. The French Government tried to grow cinchona in Algeria but the experiment failed due to a combination of factors such as the inexperience of officials, lack of proper adoptive habitat, etc.[169] In a good gesture, Weddel's advice and his *Cinchona calisaya* were made available to all in Europe. Attempts were made to grow cinchona in European colonies, using Weddel's seeds and saplings. On the failure of the exercise, the Dutch and the English sent official expeditions to South America.

The Netherlands

In 1851, the Netherlands obtained a Weddel calisaya tree from Paris, nursed it in Leyden, and successfully planted a cutting in the mountainous region of Java where it flourished and multiplied. In December 1852, the Dutch Minister for the Colonies, C.F. Pahud, sponsored Justus Karl Hasskarl's (1811–1894) trip to South America. He left Europe for Peru under a pseudonym from where he sent some seeds and plants to the Netherlands which were raised there and then brought to Java. He himself returned to Java in December 1854 with his baggage of 80 surviving plants, *C. calisaya* and *C. pahudiana*.[170] Notwithstanding the great effort, the *pahudiana* plants would turn out to be quite useless.

In 1859, England sent its own expedition to South America to collect cinchona seeds and plants for cultivation in India. The expedition was led by Clements Robert Markham (1830–1916), then a junior clerk at the India Office who was accompanied by John Weir, a gardener at the Royal Botanic Gardens, Kew. Markham came to the South Peru district of Caravaya and found that the yellow bark calisaya grew there as a shrub rather than a tree. European "commercial men" there told him that the shrub bark was of no value and that good calisaya bark came from big trees in Bolivia.[171] Still, he collected 529 yellow bark shrubs. In March 1860, Markham wrote from Peru to E.D. Bourdillon, Secretary, Public Department, India Office, in an idiom typical of the times: "The Bolivians are the most ignorant, barbarous, and jealous of all the South American republics, and they have an intense hatred and suspicion of foreigners."[172] The abuses were hurled at Bolivians because they were protecting their property!

Grey barks were collected from Northern Peru by G.J. Pritchett, "an agent engaged by Mr Markham." The third branch of the expedition was led by a

European already familiar with the cinchona land of Ecuador. Dr Richard Spruce (1817–1893), an English schoolmaster turned botanist and botanical explorer, spent 15 years (1849–1864) exploring the Amazon from the Andes down to its mouth. Towards the end of 1859, Spruce was entrusted with the task of collecting red bark seeds and plants and a gardener Robert Mackenzie Cross was sent from England to assist him. Both collected about 100,000 seeds and went on to raise some plants themselves. The seeds and the saplings were then dutifully sent to Kew.[173]

India

Markham personally escorted his yellow barks to India. They were planted at Ootacamund in the Nilgiri Hills under the superintendence of William Graham McIvor (1825–1876), already the superintendent of the Horticultural Garden there. Cultivation began on 12 October 1860, but within two months all the plants were dead.[174] In April 1861, Cross personally brought to Ootacamund his collection of red bark plants fit for cultivation. Arrangement for the investigation of the alkaloidal yield of cultivated plants was made in 1866 when John Broughton was appointed as a chemist in Ootacamund. This centre however turned out to be short-lived.

The other cinchona centre came up at Calcutta Botanic Garden, under Thomas Anderson, with Darjeeling as the field station. Calcutta focused on grey and red barks, the former of which failed to take root. Indian plantations were mostly the red bark which had low quinine content. At the end of 1864, Java had a little more than 10 million plants. Out of these, as many as 96.5% were the worthless pahudiana.[175] Things changed in 1865 when the old Peruvian bark was crossed with the newly acquired Bolivian bark.

Dutch and English expeditions have been much discussed. They are important as case studies of 19th-century colonial adventures. The initiative, planning, and subversion of the laws and regulations of cinchona-producing countries all greatly added to the colonial aura. The scientific value of these expeditions was however limited. As far as world production is concerned, it was made possible not by the much-publicized adventures of colonialists but through the initiative of an unscrupulous and patriotic Englishman. In the Euro-centric world of the 19th century, how the natives were exploited and sacrificed in furtherance of the colonial cause was described in detail and with relish. As times changed, these accounts became brief and sanitized. For example, a 1979 account blandly says that the seeds of high-yielding species were "smuggled out of Bolivia by the Aymara servant of a British trader, who sold one pound of seed to the Dutch government in 1865."[176] The story however deserves to be told in some detail and in the framework of its own time.

Ledger and Manuel Incra Mamani

Charles Ledger (1818–1905) came to Peru in 1836, at the age of 18 to join a merchant house that was trading in that country's two staples: cinchona bark and alpaca wool. After two years, he was sent to run a branch in the southern port of Tacna, where he set up his own business.[177] Ledger had the good fortune to have in his employ a knowledgeable and loyal man, Manuel Incra Mamani, who joined his service in 1843. Ledger may have been short on scruples from today's standards and a failure as an entrepreneur, but his patriotism cannot be doubted. We know about his activities from a letter he wrote to his brother George in 1880, which was published in a magazine called *The Field* on 5 February 1881 and reprinted in the *American Journal of Pharmacy*, a month later.[178] The letter does not read as part of a correspondence between two brothers but as a write-up meant for publication. This of course is not to doubt the veracity of the basic points.

Ledger read in the newspaper about Markham's visit and his plans to visit Bolivia. Mamani told Ledger that the inhabitants of the cinchona district of the Yungas "most implicitly" believed that if their cinchona was successfully propagated in other countries by plants or seeds, their own plants would perish. Mamani ominously told Ledger that if Markham really obtained the "rojo" plants and seeds, he would not "leave the Yungas in good health." Ledger decided to convey this intelligence to Markham, whom he did not know personally. Towards this end, he dispatched a messenger on foot to the British consul situated 600 miles away warning Markham against venturing into Bolivia.[179] The letter arrived too late to be placed in Markham's hands who in any case had already decided to skip Bolivia. Ledger's account is corroborated by Markham who recorded that while he was in Peru, Ledger "made some attempt to open up communication with me which unfortunately was not successful."[180]

Europe had to wait for 20 years and Ledger's personal initiative before it could lay its hands on the right seeds. Wishing to see his "own dear country" "free from being dependent on Peru or Bolivia for supply of life-giving quinine," Ledger decided "to do all in my power to obtain the very best cinchona seed produced in Bolivia" through Mamani and deception. "Manuel was never aware of my requiring seed and leaves for propagating purposes; he was always told that they were wanted to make a special remedy for a special illness." Ledger was honest enough to admit to himself and to his brother that if Mamani had been told the truth, he would have refused, even though "he was very much attached to me." At the end of May 1865, Mamani arrived with the precious cargo. By July 1865, Ledger had sent the seeds to his brother George in London.

Ledger's greed killed Mamani. In 1872–1873, he was sent again "to get another supply of the same class of seed for me," but this time "poor Manuel" "lost his life." Undeterred, Ledger now entrusted the task to "another old

Indian friend, poor Poli" who also died while bringing seed and flowers in 1877.[181] Ledger had already done his patriotic duty by depositing the Bolivian cinchona seeds in England. If Mamani and Poli had come back alive, what would have Ledger done with the new consignments? Maybe, he had various European botanic gardens in mind as potential buyers unmindful of the risk to his native associates.

Ledger's brother, George, tried to sell the 1865 consignment to the Kew Garden. But Sir William Hooker had just died, his son Joseph was away ill, and the curator was not interested. Through the London-based cinchona expert, John Eliot Howard (1807–1883), George Ledger sold a pound weight of the seeds to the Dutch consul general in London, for use in Java. A down payment of 100 francs was made, and a further payment was promised if the seeds germinated. After a year it was reported that about 20,000 had germinated. Ledger was now paid the further sum of 500 francs. As it turned out, the volcanic soil in the Preanger district of Java was very good for the new species, which in 1876, was named C. *calisaya ledgeriana* by Howard (there was obviously no question of naming it after Mamani.) Java successfully combined these plants with the red bark species to produce a sturdier version.

Contrary to popular perception, these seeds did reach India. As against the purchase of only one pound weight by the Dutch, the remaining 13 pounds were purchased by James William Bayley Money (1818–1890), a barrister and cinchona cultivator in the Nilgiris. He however exchanged them for a quantity of the red bark seed, which had by then begun to be freely produced on the Nilgiri plantation. About 60,000 seedlings were raised by McIver, but "It would appear that most of these died out." Some seeds were sown in the Sikkim Himalayas including Darjeeling where they did well.[182] In the three decades, from 1893 to 1913, prices dropped drastically by more than 90%. Java because of economy of scale and through cartelization was able to withstand the price drop, but India and Ceylon were driven out of competition. In Ceylon, plantation area dropped from 26,000 hectares in 1883 to a mere 300 in 1910. Similarly, in India, many trees were uprooted.[183] The end result was that Java came to control more than 90% of the world quinine market.

Ronald Ross

Quinine was an empirical solution to the malaria problem, but there were studies of the cause as well. The Almora-born India–based British physician, Ronald Ross (1857–1932), showed that the germ of malaria is carried by Anopheles mosquitoes and received the 1902 Nobel medicine prize. Not un-expectedly, he could carry out his research only intermittently during his spare time when he was not on duty as a regimental doctor and entirely at his own expense, which included payment of an anna (one-sixteenth of a rupee) per mosquito to the patient (Husein Khan) who permitted Ross's 10 mosquitoes to have a good feast on his blood.[184] During Ross' visit to the USA in 1904, he was invited to visit Panama, which he did for a week in October 1904 (the canal had a medical adviser, John W. Ross of the US Navy; the two Rosses have at times been confused.)

Panama Canal

The American historian David Gaub McCullough (1933–2022) addressing an audience in a college in 2005 declared:

> I think often about why the French failed at Panama and why we succeeded. One of the reasons we succeeded is that we were gifted, we were attuned to adaptation, to doing what works, whereas they were trained to do everything in a certain way. We have a gift for improvisation.[185]

Such self-congratulation is uncalled for. The USA succeeded not because of superior skills but because of advancements in science. The French failed because in their time the cause of malaria and yellow fever, both caused by mosquitoes but of different kinds, was not understood. The canal could not have been dug before a Nobel laureate Ronald Ross came on the scientific scene. In Panama under the Americans, mosquitoes were prevented from breeding and the environment became healthy and labour-friendly.

While the Panama Canal was constructed after eliminating the mosquitoes, the European conquest of Inner Africa was accomplished not by removing malaria but by feeding abundant quinine to the invading soldiers. The discovery of quinine is a major scientific accomplishment. Africans however would have been happier without it. Because of quinine, they lost their independence but still had malaria.

Zoology

Zoology was a late starter in British India because animals had no commercial value. Academic studies could not take place early because of the known aversion of Sir William Jones, the founder of the Asiatic Society. In his tenth anniversary discourse in 1793, he famously expressed himself in poetic language:

> Could the figure, instincts, and qualities of birds, beasts, insects, reptiles, and fish be ascertained either on the plan of BUFFON, or on that of LINNÆUS, without giving pain to the objects of our examination, few studies would afford us more solid instruction or more exquisite delight; but I never could learn by what right, nor conceive with what feelings,

a naturalist can occasion the misery of an innocent bird and leave its young, perhaps, to perish in a cold nest, because it has gay plumage and has never been accurately delineated, or deprive even a butterfly of its natural enjoyments, because it has the misfortune to be rare or beautiful.

In 1796, two years after Jones' death, the Society announced their intention of establishing a natural history museum and invited donations. It was however only in 1814 that contributions of animals, plants, minerals, etc., were solicited and arrangements made for their reception. In 1837, Dr J.T. Pearson of the Bengal Medical Service was appointed to look after the museum. Two years later, in 1839, the Court of Directors sanctioned a grant for the museum. In 1841 Edward Blyth (1810–1873) was brought from England as the curator. He remained in office till 1863 when he returned to England due to ill health. In spite of the drudgery of his routine work and unpleasant disputes with his employers, Blyth built up the museum and emerged as an authority on Indian and Burmese birds. In 1888, he was described as the Father of Indian Ornithology. He became an acclaimed expert on Indian fauna and domesticated animals and was Charles Darwin's informant on these for 15 years.

Like many others, Blyth turned towards India because of poverty (he had to seek £100 in advance from the Asiatic Society to enable him to make the journey to Calcutta.) Unlike others, however, he remained poor. His salary was low to begin with and remained stagnant throughout. From 1844, he indulged in the ethically dubious but then normal two-way trade of live animals. He even tried to strike a deal with Darwin and John Gould. They declined, but significantly, there was no sense of outrage. Blyth arranged to supply to England animals which were in demand there for private and public zoos. Similarly, he imported live animals into India; "Natives of enormous wealth are the purchasers, who care not what they give for what they particularly fancy." A particularly fancied import item for the zenana was a pair of marmosets, monkeys imported from the Americas.[186] Thanks to Blyth's official exertions, the Museum built an impressive collection. John Anderson took over as the curator in 1865. Next year, he became the superintendent of the Indian Museum which was founded using the Asiatic Society Museum collection as its nucleus.

Botanical Survey of India

In 1891, the Botanical Survey of India was constituted, but by this time the best in colonial field science was already over. Further, in 1916, the anthropological and zoological sections of the museum were made into the Zoological Survey of India, a step of administrative significance rather than scientific.

Role of Indians

Indians employed as assistants in colonial natural history were in general not considered worthy of notice. In a handful of cases, their names are recorded, but no other details are available. Regrettably, but unsurprisingly, none of the assistants has left behind any account or family papers.

Probably the most trivial duty assigned to an Indian was at Botanic Garden Calcutta. To prevent the ants from eating the specimens and the paper on which they were glued, the feet of the cabinet were kept immersed in troughs of water. Wallich hired a person to keep the troughs filled with water "until the shadows of evening came on and relieved him from his tedious and monotonous task."[187]

Far more exciting was the task assigned by Alexander Pedler to his assistant "Balm [Babu?] Poolin Behary Saor," who was thanked for his help in extracting poison from live cobras – "a work not always pleasant to the feelings, and always more or less dangerous in its nature."[188]

Collection of plants from the field, preparation of specimens and drawing their sketches were important parts of a European naturalist's project. These tasks were entrusted to the Indians. To retain ownership of drawings and specimens, the colonial naturalists who otherwise drew a salary from the government for official duties preferred to pay their staff from their own pocket rather than bill the Company, as was done by Buchanan and Roxburgh to their disadvantage.[189]

The most creative use of the locals was in painting natural history specimens. Different parts of India had their distinct painting traditions. Emperor Jahangir, for instance, commissioned paintings on natural history. In general, painting in North India flourished under Royal patronage, while in South India temple paintings were an important phenomenon. Indians who first took to sketching the flora under the watchful European eye came from families with painting traditions. Europeans gave traditional painters European paper, introduced them to European concepts, and asked them to use watercolours. The resultant hybrid style is known as the Company School of Painting. It is now of interest not only to students of natural history but also to art history.

Mary Impey

One of the earliest colonial natural history enthusiasts in India was Mary Impey, whose husband Sir Elijah Impey was the first Chief Justice of the Supreme Court, Calcutta, from 1773 till his recall in 1783. Mary Impey established a menagerie of Indian and Southeast Asian birds and animals in their extensive grounds. In 1777, she commissioned artists (including Shaikh Zain ud-din, Ram Das, and Bhawani Das) to paint her exotic flora and fauna. These skilful and accurate paintings numbered 362 and became part of a collection known as the Impey Album.

Lutchman Singh (Lakshman Singh or Lachhman Singh) employed in the Calcutta garden was a painter notable for his versatility.[190] He painted a portrait of George Potter in the "Murshidabad style" in 1828, when Wallich was away to Europe. His services were borrowed by Royle in Saharanpur where he made three zoological drawings. Interestingly, Lachhman Singh "decamped for a spell to work as a Court painter in one of the Punjab hill states."[191]

Dapuri Drawings

During 1847–1850, Gibson commissioned drawings of about 170, both indigenous and imported plants grown, at the Dapuri and Hewra Gardens. The artist is unnamed but presumably was an Indian with Portuguese roots. Many drawings were said to be "not botanically correct" but informative enough "to give a picture of the plants."[192]

Rungiah and Govindoo

Two Telugu artists served a succession of Madras naturalists: Rungiah and his pupil Govindoo. Only their personal names are known; family names are not recorded. Rungiah belonged to the Raju community; Govindoo was probably related to him. There is indirect evidence to suggest that their forefathers had worked for the Rajas of Tanjore. It has been speculated that the early South Indian flora painters transferred from textile or mica painting to European natural history.[193] Rungiah might have served Wight's predecessors as well. He was taught the use of a microscope by William Griffith. Wight utilized the services of Rungiah from his arrival in 1826 till 1845 and of Govindoo from 1845 till Wight's retirement in 1853. Wight commissioned 3000 botanical drawings from Indian artists including Govindoo whose name he immortalized by introducing the generic name *Govindooia*. Post-Wight, Govindoo transferred to Hugh Cleghorn (1820–1895) as well as his successor Richard Henry Beddone (1830–1911). The collection of illustrations commissioned by Hugh Cleghorn during his 25 years as an East India Company surgeon and pioneering forester now forms an important part of collections at the Botanic Garden in Edinburgh.

Except for mere names in some cases, we know nothing of the peripheral natives in the colonial scheme of natives.

Notes

1 Pascoe, 1901, 1, 471–472.
2 Jürgens, 2004, 46.
3 Blunt, 2001, 211.
4 Jensen, 2014, 337.

5 Jürgens, 2004, 63–64.
6 Jensen, 2014, 340.
7 Sterll, 2008, 117.
8 http://www.kew.org/floraIndica
9 Royle, 1840, 49.
10 Love, 1913, 3, 178.
11 Royle, 1840, 50.
12 Smith, 1911.
13 Love, 1913, 3, 178.
14 http://apps.kew.org/floraindica/htm/biography_koenig.htm
15 Dance, 1967, 8.
16 Fenger, 1863, 297–298.
17 Desmond, 1992, 39; Arnold, 2000, 46.
18 Fenger, 1863, 316.
19 Foulker, 1861, 3, note.
20 Burkill, 1965, 15.
21 How, 1878, 369–370.
22 How, 1878, 369–370.
23 Wight & Walker-Arnott, 1834, xi.
24 Fenger, 1863, 289.
25 Wight & Walker-Arnott, 1834, xii.
26 Fenger, 1863, 291.
27 *Analytical Review*, 1796, 23, 219.
28 Fenger, 1863, 302–303.
29 Foulker, 1861, 5.
30 Foulker, 1861, 7–8.
31 How, 1878, 373.
32 Foulker, 1861, 2.
33 Gentleman's Magazine, 1837, 8 (Jul.-Dec.), 431–432; Stansfield, 1957, 29.
34 Wight & Walker-Arnott, 1834, vii.
35 Fenger, 1863, 302.
36 Boylston, 2012.
37 Love, 1913, 3, 332.
38 Scots Magazine, 1811, 73, 906.
39 Hawgood, 1994, 1303.
40 Macie was the illegitimate child of an influential person, who later became the
   First Duke of Northumberland. His mother was a wealthy widow whose late
   husband's name Macie took. In 1801, he adopted his father's name as his own and
   became James Smithson. He inherited considerable wealth from his mother's side
   which he bequeathed to found Smithsonian Institution in Washington, DC, USA.
   His illegitimacy weighed heavily on him. Although he had never been to USA, he
   believed that social background did not matter there. https://www.smithsonianmag.
   com/history/how-james-smithsons-money-build-smithsonian-114828409/
41 Raman et al., 2014.
42 Robinson, 2003, 4.
43 Love, 1913, 333–334.
44 Robinson, 2003, 172–173.
45 Love, 1913, 409–410.
46 Robinson, 2003, 38.
47 Love, 1913, 410.
48 Phillimore, 1950, 2, 405.
49 Phillimore, 1950, 2, 113.
50 Phillimore, 1950, 2, 113.

51 Phillimore, 1950, 2, 406; Noltie, 2007, 1, 31.
52 Stransfield, 1957, 26.
53 Noltie, 2007, 1, 32.
54 I thank Alexandra Milne, the Archivist, for information.
55 *Madras Quarterly Journal of Medical Science*, 1865, 8, 137; *Asiatic Journal and Monthly Register*, 1822, 13, 97.
56 *Asiatic Journal and Monthly Register*, 1826, 22, 625.
57 *London Literary Gazette and Journal of Belles Lettres for 1826*, 111.
58 https://plants.jstor.org/stable/history/10.5555/al.ap.visual.kmdc1707.
59 https://discovery.nationalarchives.gov.uk/details/r/1326d3a6-5a70-4167-a9ec-f5f5f39f6331.
60 Cleghorn, 1873, 4.
61 Noltie, 2006, 15.
62 Cleghorn, 1873, 3–4.
63 Noltie, 2006.
64 *Bulletin of Miscellaneous Information (Royal Garden Kew)*, 1913, 7, 256.
65 Noltie, 2007, 1, 14.
66 *Bulletin of Miscellaneous Information (Royal Garden Kew)*, 1913, 7, 262.
67 *Edinburgh Literary Journal*, 1831 (Jan.-Jun.), 308.
68 Kochhar, 2022.
69 Cleghorn, 1873, 9.
70 Desmond, 1992, 118.
71 Hooker & Thomson, 1855, 50.
72 Biswas, 1950, 4.
73 Biswas, 1950, 8.
74 Carey, 1814, ii.
75 Carey, 1814, ii.
76 Crawford, 1914, 2, 143; Sterll, 2008, 117.
77 Robinson, 2003, 82.
78 Crawford, 1914, 2, 144.
79 Jacquemont, 1834, 90.
80 Hyde, 1962, 48.
81 Hyde, 1962, 50.
82 Hyde, 1962, 51–52.
83 Hyde 1962, 55.
84 *Calcutta Review*, 1845, 3, 164, note.
85 Burkill, 1965, 33.
86 Murchison, 1868, xxv.
87 *Quarterly Journal of Science*, 1868, 5, 482.
88 Murchison, 1868, xxvii.
89 Murchison, 1868, xxviii.
90 Murchison, 1868, xlv.
91 Murchison, 1868, xxx.
92 Murchison 1868, xxvi.
93 Hawgood, 1994, 83.
94 Lieutenant Colonel James Tod (1782–1835), who joined Company service as a cadet in 1799, was Heatly's sister's son.
95 Homfray, 1842, 734.
96 Heatly, 1842, 825.
97 Heatly, 1842, 825.
98 Heatly, 1842, 835.
99 Ghosh, 1997, 142.
100 *Calcutta Review*, 1845, 4 (Jul.-Dec.), 478.

101 Blechynden, 1905, 174.
102 *Calcutta Review*, 1845, 4 (Jul.-Dec.), 479.
103 Ghosh, 1997, 146.
104 Blanford, 1865, 156.
105 Ghosh, 1997, 146.
106 Blanford, 1865, 156.
107 Blanford, 1865, 156.
108 *Calcutta Review*, 1845, 4 (Jul.-Dec.), 480.
109 Kling, 1976, 94–95 & 99.
110 New Monthly Magazine, 1816, 6, 526.
111 Phillimore, 1954, 3, 367.
112 He was created Marquess of Hastings in 1817. It is however better to refer to him as Moira than Hastings which might cause confusion with Warren Hastings.
113 Phillimore, 1954, 3, 367.
114 Phillimore, 1954, 3, 367. Bengal Directory and Annual Register for 1838, p. 427 lists him as "Minerological Surveyor" and a resident of Almora, not knowing that he was dead by then.
115 Phillimore, 1954, 3, 499.
116 Quarterly Oriental Magazine, 1824, 1, cxi; Phillimore, 1954, 3, 509.
117 Blanford, 1865, 5.
118 It may be noted in passing that de la Beche inherited the slave-worked sugar plantation of Halse Hall in Clarendon in Jamaica. He was opposed to the abolition of slavery and wanted the condition of the slaves to be improved slowly.
119 Fox, 1947, 889.
120 Sharpe & McCartney 1998, 142, letters 2135 & 2136.
121 Kumar, 1995, 45.
122 Sharpe & McCartney, 1998, 142, letter 2136.
123 Hooker, 1854, 10.
124 Sharpe & McCartney, 1998, 82, letter 1116.
125 Sharpe & McCartney, 1998, 83, letter 1122.
126 Blanford, 1865, 17.
127 Fox, 1947, 889.
128 Wood, 1913, 105–106.
129 Charlton, 1841, 68, note. Otherwise dependable, Ukers, 1935, 145 is wrong in saying that Charlton and Jenkins were both given medals at the same time, on 3 January 1841.
130 Johnson, 1843, 67.
131 Ukers, 1935, 135.
132 Johnson, 1843, 67
133 *Asiatic Journal and Monthly Miscellany*, 1841, 36, 263, 261–262.
134 http://www.internationalministries.org/download/38072-timeline-baptist-mission-in-northeast-india-doc.
135 Robinson, 1841, 137; Charlton, 1841, 27.
136 Mann, 1918, 8.
137 Tea Parliamentary Papers, 1839, 40.
138 Tea Parliamentary Papers, 1839, 65.
139 Tea Parliamentary Papers, 1839, 71 & 84.
140 Charlton, 1841, 40.
141 Charlton, 1841, 40.
142 Ukers, 1935, 140.
143 Mann, 1918, 5.
144 Ukers, 1935, 144.
145 Ukers, 1935, 145.

146 Tea Parliamentary Papers, 1839, 77–79.
147 Gait, 1906, 351.
148 Desmond, 1992, 238.
149 Transactions of the Agricultural and Horticultural Society of India, 1841, 8, 283.
150 Ukers, 1935, 149.
151 *Calcutta Review*, 1864, 40, 295.
152 Gait, 1906, 351.
153 *Journal of the Society of Arts*, 1861, 9, 140
154 Robinson, 1841, 136.
155 Charlton, 1841, 32–33.
156 *Hooker's Journal of Botany*, 1852, 4, 316.
157 *Journal of the Agricultural and Historical Society of India*, 1843, 2, Part 2, 286.
158 http://www.bl.uk/manuscripts/FullDisplay.aspx?ref=IOR/P/351/8_10_Nov_1852_nos_8521-24.
159 Saldanha, 1996, 197.
160 Pinchot, 1947, 67.
161 Pinchot, 1947, 18.
162 Pinchot, 1947, 17.
163 *Saturday Review*, 1862, Dec. 15, 717.
164 Lee, 2002, 189.
165 Bruce-Chwatt, 1988, 1486.
166 Lee, 2002, 191.
167 Headrick, 1981, 7.
168 Headrick, 1981, 67 & 69.
169 Cinchona Parliamentary Papers, 1863, 39.
170 Van Gorkom, 1883, 182 & 184. The name Pahudiana was given to the species in honour of the Dutch minister, by an Englishman, John Howard.
171 Cinchona Parliamentary Papers, 1863, 39.
172 Cinchona Parliamentary Papers, 1863, 40.
173 Brockway, 1979, 456 wrongly places Cross in Bolivia and makes him independent of Spruce.
174 Williams, 1962, 436.
175 *Calcutta Review*, 1866, 42, 394.
176 Brockway, 1979, 57.
177 Esch, 2007, 197; Allen, 1989, 388.
178 Ledger, 1881.
179 Ledger, 1881, 10.
180 Holland, 1932, 1.
181 Ledger, 1881, 10–11.
182 King, 1870.
183 Headrick, 1988, 235.
184 Dodd, 1956, 40.
185 http://teacherweb.com/KS/StMarysColgan/KyleWolf/READ----Knowing-History-and-Knowing-Who-We-Are.pdf.
186 Brandon-Jones, 1997, 147.
187 Murray, 1834, 967.
188 *Proceedings of the Royal Society of London*, 1878, 27, 29.
189 Noltie, 2007, 2, 15.
190 Arnold, 2000, 49.
191 Noltie, 2007, 2, 35.
192 Lucy Watson; https://www.nhbs.com/the-dapuri-drawings-book.
193 Noltie, 2007, 1, 15.

7

HORSES, CATTLE AND AGRICULTURE

The British in India owned horses for personal use, but the realization that cavalry should be part of their army dawned on the top leadership of the East India Company only after military encounters with the Mahrattas, Haidar Ali and Tipu Sultan of Mysore.[1] Horses were bred in the interior and brought to the annual fairs held at a number of places throughout the country, where they were sold by the thousands.[2] A saddle horse for riding was called a mount, and its replacement was remount. Indian Army's Remount and Veterinary Corps reckons its beginning in 1779 when an army stud department is said to have been established in Bengal. The official history[3] of the corps however does not seem to make any mention of the department or the date.

As an obvious first step, the British in India made use of the extant texts, be they in English or Persian. As early as 1765, Charles Thompson published in England a book *Rules for Bad Horsemen*. It became very popular and underwent many revised editions. An edition, "lately printed in London," was "revised and corrected" and published in Calcutta in 1788. The book must have been in demand because a revised edition was brought out in 1799. The Mughal royalty and nobility had been very fond of horses.

In Shah Jahan's reign, the Uzbek-origin Abdullah Khan Feroze Jung, a high-ranking nobleman and a scholar, translated Shalihotra's encyclopaedic work into Persian under the title *Tarjamah-e-Saloter-e-Asban* [Translation of Shalihotra on ashva or horses]. For the sake of completeness, Feroze Jung even incorporated material from an old Persian work *Farasnama-e-Farsi* from Mahmud Ghaznavi's time. Joseph Earles' translation of Feroze Jung was published in 1788 from Calcutta under the title *Saloter*, with the name of the Sanskrit author, now used to mean horse care and horse carer.

DOI: 10.4324/9781003466406-7

The treatise described "different colours and marks of horses" as well as "all the disorders they are subject to."[4] A reprint was brought out in 1799. In 1794, John Pelling Pigott, "Lieutenant of Cavalry," published from Calcutta *A Treatise on the Horses of India.*[5]

It has been said that Lieutenant William Fraser appropriated a Persian book on horsemanship at the 1799 storming of Tipu Sultan's capital, Seringapatam, carried out its translation and published it from Calcutta in 1802.[6] The claim as it stands does not seem to be true. Libraries around the world, including the British Library, do not have it in their catalogues. This Fraser (d. 1809), also spelt Frazer, should not be confused with his better-known namesake, William Fraser (1784–1835), a British India civil servant who was the Commissioner of the Delhi Territory, was assassinated, and is known for Fraser Album.

Fraser joined the 16th Madras Native Infantry in 1781 and successively rose to become a Lieutenant in 1783, Captain in 1803, and finally Major in 1805. After the penultimate Mysore War, during 1790–1792, Fraser wrote a long letter to the Governor General on 14 September 1793 pointing out that there was a serious shortage of suitable cavalry horses and that "almost no animals of the right kind were bred in the Company's territories." What made the situation worrisome was that even that supply of horses was "liable to be cut off at a moment's notice by the Marathas across whose territories most of them had to come."[7] The remedy lay in the Company's creating its own stud in its North Indian territories which at the time were restricted to Bengal, Bihar and the Zamindari of Benares. His proposal was accepted and it was decided to set up a stud with Fraser as its superintendent. To oversee its working, a Board of Superintendence, with a paid secretary, was established in October 1794. It was hoped that the stud would "establish a good steed for the Company" and at the same time "encourage and excite the natives to breed horses of a proper size."[8] As it turned out, the hopes were belied.

In 1796, acting on Fraser's recommendation, the Government acquired a vast 1350-acre estate located on the bend of the river Burhi Dandak [Dunduck] near a village called Pusa in Tirhut in North Bihar (now in Samastipur district). It soon became clear that the choice of the site was wrong. "The damp and lowlying Pusa neighbourhood" was not suitable for horse breeding operations.[9] Neither the Superintendent nor the Board overseeing his work knew anything about horses. Fraser in addition turned out to be a poor manager. Eventually, the experiment was declared to be a costly failure and the stud closed down in 1874.

The stud consisted of three branches: Home, Nisfee and Zamindari. In the Home branch, stallions, mares and their produce belonged to the Government. In the Nisfee system also, both mare and stallion belonged to the Government, but the mares after being covered by the stallions were boarded with farmers on the promise of an equal share in the produce. In the Zamindari [Zumeendaree] branch, Pusa provided stallions for servicing the mares belonging to the farm-ers.[10] By 1802, over 1300 people were working at the studs. The staff included a person hired at four rupees a month and three others at one rupee each for striking the hour to "encourage" regularity among the servants in their hours of attendance.[11]

Fraser's services were terminated in 1808.[12] His successor was William Moorcroft (baptized 1767, d. 1825) who took charge in December 1808. He was an illegitimate son of a daughter of a wealthy landowner who brought him up. He was apprenticed as a surgeon but was persuaded to become a vet. The twin medical training would stand him in good stead in his explorations. He went to France in 1789 to study at the veterinary college in Lyons, becom-ing on return England's first qualified vet.

In 1791, Veterinary College, London (renamed Royal Veterinary College in 1875) was established, according to a plan prepared by the visiting Frenchman, Charles Vial de St Bel (1753–1793) (commonly referred to as Saint Bel), who was appointed professor. The post however fell vacant in 1793 on his untimely death. Moorcroft taught there but only for six weeks when he set up a private equine practice at Oxford Street in London which proved very lucrative and included the royal family among its clientele. He however lost a fortune at-tempting to make horseshoes by machine. His association with India began in England itself. To systemize the supply of stallions to Pusa for breeding pur-poses, the East India Company established a stud farm in Padnell near Romford in Essex in 1802. Moorcroft was chosen to be the Company's equine shipping agent and appointed Superintendent of the Essex Company stud in 1803.[13] Next, he was persuaded to transfer to India to take up the Superintendence of the Pusa Stud at a fabulous annual salary of £3000 as compensation for London practice. He brought about an all-round improvement in the estab-lishment. He introduced oats cultivation in India, at Pusa. However, oats never became popular as horse feed, and gram continued to be the preferred horse diet. His leadership of the stud effectively came to an end in 1819 although he continued in service till his death in 1825.

Great Game

It was Moorcroft's firm belief that the horse ideal for breeding purposes in India was not the Arab but Turkmen. He decided to make an effort to pro-cure them from the source. He was permitted by the government to under-take the journey but was not granted "any accredited authority, or political designation." The government often felt that he was exceeding his brief and castigated him for his transgressions. History, however, remembers him as an explorer, an astute commentator on geopolitics of the time, and an early player in the so-called Great Game, the contest between Russia and Britain for power and influence in Central Asia.

Moorcroft's May–November 1812 visit to Kumaon and Western Tibet in the context of geography has already been noticed (p. 37). Moorcroft found a flock of Kashmir goats, a source of fine wool; he collected both the goats and some plants with which to return to his base. The plants were the first to be sampled from the area, but his employers were not convinced he had achieved much on this trip. The goats were sent to Scotland where they died. In 1812, Moorcroft sent Mir Izzet Ullah on a preparatory tour to those countries which Moorcroft planned to visit at a favourable time. Izzet Ullah made a round trip to Bokhara. He reached it by the north-of-Himalayas route and returned via Afghanistan. He entered Tibet through Kashmir. From Tibet, he reached Yarkand on the southern rim of the Taklamakan Desert in the Tarim Basin. From here he travelled to Samarkand and thence to Bokhara. For his return journey, he touched Balkh and Khulm. From Khulm, he went to Bamian and then to Kabul, from where he returned to the plains of Hindustan. Izzet Ullah's account was translated from Persian to English for publication in a Calcutta journal. It must have been considered of sufficient value to be reprinted in 1843 in London. Donning a superior and patronizing air for the benefit of home audience, Wilson wrote: "[it] contains information regarding parts of Turkestan and Central Asia, which is not derivable from any better source, as the countries have not been visited in modern times by European travellers."[14] The value of work by native explorers like Izzet Ullah lay precisely in the circumstance that they alone could have carried it out; a European traveller ran the risk of losing his life on such a journey.

Moorcroft's second expedition began in 1819 and abruptly ended six years later with his death (suspected murder). He travelled to Leh but did not get the requisite permissions to proceed. He spent almost three years, 1819–1822, exploring Ladakh and Kashmir. In 1823, he made an attempt to reach Turkestan through Hindu Kush but without success. As a last resort, he decided to take the easiest and the most obvious path. He decided to enter Afghanistan through Punjab, becoming in 1824 the first Englishman to describe the Khyber Pass. Despite being recalled to India, he reached his destination, Bokhara (in present-day Uzbekistan) in February 1825. He found few horses to buy. He was seen not as a horse trader but as a spy. Shortly after beginning his return journey, he died at Balkh, Afghanistan, on 27 August 1825.

He botanized in Ladakh and Punjab. Among a bundle of 23 plant specimens he sent to Nathaniel Wallich in Calcutta Botanic Garden were several species new to science, such as *Gentiana moorcroftiana* Wall. and *Salvia moorcroftiana* Wall. ex Benth.

Hissar, Haryana

Moorcroft had formed the view that "Huriyana" was "favourable to the health of the Horse" as well as horse breeding. He however was unable to provide the government with "something specific on the subject" because he had not yet visited the area.[15] This was in 1814. The choice of Hissar for horses must therefore have been made after this date. Hissar was already in the picture in the context of other animals. So far, the practice had been to transport gram for horses by bullock carts. In 1803, when the Mahrattas attacked Oude [Oudh, Avadh, Eastern Uttar Pradesh], it was decided to send gram on camels. The experiment proved a success and gradually became commonplace. At first, camels and gram were procured through contract. Then an agency for gram was created with Lieutenant James Lumsdaine (d. 1816) as agent. In 1809, the Commissariat Department was created and Lumsdaine was promoted. He was now one of the two assistant commissary generals.

Lumsdaine's centre of activity was Hissar (now in Haryana). First, a camel stud was opened and then a bullock farm. Both were under the Commissariat. Probably, in 1815, the home stud was opened in Hissar on Moorcroft's initiative. It was part of the Pusa establishment though placed under Lumsdaine's charge. It was closed down in 1842 and restarted at Kurnaul [Karnal] in 1865. The Indian Army website mentions a Remount Depot at Babugarh (Hapur) since 1811. Hapur in 1820 and Saharanpur [Saharunpore] became home to a stud in 1843.[16]

In about 1815, a professionally qualified vet, J.T. Hodgson (retired 1834) arrived at Hissar presumably as in-charge of horses sent from England for the studs. His date of birth is not known nor even his full name. On 17 March 1821, he was appointed as veterinary surgeon to the Governor General's Bodyguard at Calcutta and placed in charge of the Veterinary Establishment at Ballygunge, the Bodyguard's cantonment. Established in 1773, the Bodyguard was not merely a ceremonial outfit but a cavalry regiment "capable of rendering Useful Service in the Field." Hodgson was shown as a sub-assistant veterinary surgeon in 1823. He resigned in 1824 and came to London. He was readmitted to service and joined as a veterinary surgeon on 29 May 1826. Notwithstanding the pioneering nature of his employment, his exit from it was rather unceremonial. During 1832–1834, he was posted as a veterinary surgeon at the Hapur Stud. Here, in 1833 along with some others, he entered into a bitter feud with the Stud Superintendent Captain McKenzie on the latter's personal misuse of official resources in connivance with native staff. Corruption in studs was a common phenomenon. In 1829, Lieutenant Charles Manning of the 30th Regiment Native Infantry who held the post of a sub-assistant at the Hissar Stud was dismissed from service for having "embezzled, or fraudulently misapplied" public money in the purchase of colts for the stud.[17]

The enquiry commission that examined the complaints along with the Military Board dismissed Hodgson's "complaints as the ravings of a lunatic." The commission however recommended leniency,[18] and he was presumably permitted to retire which he did in 1834.[19] His later whereabouts are not known, but he continued to publish in British veterinary journals.

Hodgson was the first army veterinary surgeon in India (Moorcroft was a civilian). He was asked to superintend the tuition and instruction of eight veterinary students to be drawn from among the assistant apothecaries and selected under instructions from the Commander in Chief. Apothecaries were half-castes or Eurasians, designated Anglo-Indians in 1911. After training, they were to be placed in the next higher pay scale of Apothecaries under the designation of sub-assistant veterinary surgeons. The selection of Hodgson's pupils was made on 12 May 1821. However, a year later, first on 1 April and then on 18 May 1822, Hodgson stated his reasons why the proposed plan was not likely to be of advantage to the service and suggested one of his own. It envisaged the appointment of a professor to be stationed at the London Veterinary College and entrusted with the job of teaching appointees to the Indian service.[20] Nothing however came out of it, and after the failure to draft half-castes into subordinate veterinary service, the government had no option but to bring vet surgeons from England. In 1827, a total of 12 of them were sent out to India, followed by another 13 in 1828. Replacements were sent when casualties occurred. In 1832, there were in all 31 vet officers in the Indian Army.

The Pusa Stud was closed in 1874. In its 80-year-long history, Moorcroft's 11-year stewardship was the only bright spot.

Major General Sir Frederick Smith in his history of the Army Veterinary Corps was unsparing in his criticism: after Moorcroft, the Pusa breeding establishments "returned to the control of their original incompetent superintendents, inexperienced infantry and cavalry officers." Horses bred at Pusa were "the laughing-stock of the Army and the despair of the East India Company." "From first to last the Studs cost millions; the mismanagement was staggering and unbelievable."[21]

The efforts at Pusa had been confined to breeding of remounts required for British cavalry and artillery and that too only in the Bengal Presidency; nothing had been done towards the breeding of horses for general use or for teaching native breeders how to breed effectively and on correct principles; nothing had been done to encourage mule breeding or to train native salutaris in veterinary work."[22] The outbreak of cattle plague (known as Rinderpest in German) epidemic in Britain during 1865–1867 compelled Britain to pay attention to the cattle problem in India in a wider, non-Army, context.

The man chosen for the reorganization of the Indian Veterinary Organization was Veterinary Colonel John Herbert Brockencote Hallen (1829–1901). Educated at Edinburgh, he spent his entire working life in India. He joined service in the Bombay Army in 1850 and became the Principal Veterinary Surgeon in 1862. That year he established the Army Veterinary School at Poona. This was the first such institution in India. He was appointed Superintendent of the Stud Department of the Bombay Presidency in 1863. In 1866, he was permitted to go back home to take over as the principal of the

Royal (Dick) Veterinary College in Edinburgh but was recalled a year later.[23] He participated in the Abyssinian campaign in 1867–1868 as the Principal Veterinary Surgeon of the Force, and, with ten veterinary surgeons, had veterinary charge of upwards of 50,000 animals of cavalry, artillery, and transport corps of the force.

Hallen was appointed the president of the Indian Cattle Plague Commission, which was entrusted with the task of enquiring into the subject of cattle diseases prevalent in India. The commission was notified on 27 November 1869, began work on 21 December 1869 and submitted its 1,000-page report (which additionally included many maps) a year later on 31 January 1871. Two Indians were associated with the commission. Baboo Hem Chunder Kerr, Deputy Magistrate and Collector, figured in the original notification itself whereas Jan Mahomed Ali, Deputy Collector, was added two months later, on 19 February 1870. The presence of a Hindu and a Muslim in the commission gave it a semblance of representativeness. What their exact contribution was is not quite known.

Hallen was appointed as Inspecting Veterinary Surgeon of the Bombay Army in March 1871, and additionally of Bengal Army in July 1872. In addition, from 16 December 1872 until 31 March 1876, he worked for the Special Stud Commission which recommended the closure of the Pusa Stud. Furthermore, he was asked to undertake the organization of a veterinary college in Calcutta, under the Department of Agriculture, Revenue, and Commerce, and was appointed the principal of the proposed college. His other multifarious duties delayed work at the veterinary college.

In 1876, Hallen was appointed to the important post of Superintendent of Horse Breeding. He initiated the import of donkey stallions from France, Italy, Cyprus, and Arabia for mule breeding. In Native States, such as Rajputana and Kathiawar, chiefs were aided in procuring good stallions and encouraged to breed horses of "superior stamp."[24] In September 1889, the superintendence of horse breeding was transferred from the Military Department and placed under the Department for Agriculture. Finally, Hallen retired in 1894 at the age of 65, after 44 years of service.

We have already noticed how the pre-existing Amrit Mahal cattle breeding establishment in Mysore was taken over by the Madras government in 1813 for research on pack animals for the army.

Veterinary Education: Army and Civil

The Army Veterinary School (1862) at Poona was a result of Hallen's personal initiative. After 15 years, there began the institutionalization of vet education at the all-India level. India's first vet school was opened at Babugarh (Hapur district in the United Provinces) in 1877. It however did not last long. The Lahore Veterinary School was opened in 1882, with Colonel George Kettlewell as

Principal. The Babugarh school was now closed and its 35 students transferred to Lahore.[25] It was established in order to train veterinary assistants (known as salutris after the Sanskrit Shalihotra) for the Horse Breeding Department and the Indian Cavalry Regiments. The regiments sent their enlisted soldiers (sowars, savaars) to the school for training. The trained soldiers enjoyed "considerable professional independence in equine surgery."[26] The course consisted of two years of training. Instructions were given in Urdu and the requisite textbooks were compiled in it. The school staff included the European Principal, an army veterinary officer, and Indian teachers. In the course of time, the school extended its activities to include civilian students who got employment under local bodies in connection with horse breeding and cattle disease. In 1900, the course of study was increased to three years in Urdu, and the name of the institution was changed to the Punjab Veterinary College. In 1905, a veterinary school that had been opened in Ajmere [Ajmer] in 1894 was closed and its Indian staff was absorbed in Lahore.

It became clear that if epizootic diseases were to be dealt with, "a higher course of instruction, necessitating a longer period of study" would need to be introduced. An attempt was made to start a four years' course in Urdu for civilian students to be carried on simultaneously with a three-year course for military students. It was commenced but did not materialize, owing to various reasons, one of which was the incidence of the First World War. Finally, in 1919, a four-year course was introduced, not in Urdu but in English.[27]

The Bai Sakarbai Dinshaw Petit Hospital for Animals was opened in Bombay in 1874. A veterinary college came up in 1886 in its compound with Professor J. H. Steel as its first Principal. In January 1894, a veterinary school was opened in Calcutta, and raised to the status of a college in 1898 with Colonel F. Raymond as its principal.

Madras was the only place where veterinary science and agriculture were seen in a composite manner. Tipu Sultan's Mysore was home to a cattle breeding establishment, Amrit Mahal, which was a continuation from still older times. It was taken over by the Madras Government in 1813. A School of Agriculture was opened at Saidapet in 1876, which started veterinary instruction two years later, in 1878. A separate veterinary college was opened at Madras in 1903, even after that agricultural school continued to instruct its students in animal husbandry and dairying.[28] The brief notice of early attempts is indicative of the initiatives, dead ends, accommodations, and progress. In 1947, at the time of Independence, there were only nine veterinary colleges in India.[29]

Veterinary Research

The beginning of veterinary research in India was spurred by Pasteur's "dramatic demonstration" in 1881 "of the practical value of anthrax immunization."[30]

A committee recommended in 1885 the establishment of a veterinary research lab. In 1888, two persons were deputed to Paris with a view to studying "Pasteur's system": J. Cooper, a veterinary surgeon in Berar and N.N. Banerji [also spelt as Banerjee in records] who was at the time a Government of India scholar in England at the Royal Agricultural College, Cirencester. They returned with "the anthrax vaccine seed." Banerji, now an agricultural officer to the Bengal Government, was asked to work on the anthrax vaccine. In 1888–1889, he pointed out that anthrax was not common in Bengal and the indiscriminate use of vaccination would spread the virus. He advised that "unless it is established beyond doubt that the anthrax of Europe prevails and that too to a large extent, in India, extreme caution should be exercised in introducing the virus."[31] His advice did not go unheeded.

Since in certain seasons of the year experiments could not be conducted in Calcutta, it was decided to send the equipment to Poona where the Imperial Bacteriological Laboratory started functioning in 1890 in a five-acre site adjoining the College of Science donated by Dinshaw Petit. England-educated Dr Alfred Lingard was appointed the Imperial Bacteriologist who joined the lab sometime during July–November 1890.

In preparation for the new lab, at a discussion meeting presided over by the Governor of Bombay, it was recommended

(1) That, as far as possible, through the agency of veterinary surgeons throughout the country, a preliminary survey of existing diseases should be made, there being reason to suspect that cattle diseases in India differ, even under the same name, from those in Europe, sometimes in degree and sometimes in character.

(2) That when sufficient information may have been collected as to the comparative prevalence of various kinds of disease, an attempt should be made in the laboratory at Poona to discover the peculiar character of the disease germ and the vaccine required to counteract it.[32]

Lingard's duties were defined thus:

To investigate diseases of domesticated animals in all Provinces in India and to ascertain, as far as possible, by biological research both in Laboratory and, when necessary, at the place of outbreak, the means of preventing and curing such diseases.[33]

Lingard felt that the lab needed to be located in a colder climate. Accordingly, it was shifted to Muktesar [Mukteshwar] in Kumaon hills in 1893. Research into rinderpest was initiated on the basis of advice given by the famous German bacteriologist, Robert Koch, who visited the lab in 1897 at the request of the Government of India.[34] In 1899, the lab issued for field use the first anti-rinderpest serum to be prepared in India. Between 1901 and 1906, anti-sera against haemorrhagic septicaemia, anthrax, and tetanus, a vaccine against black quarter, and a product known as mallein, employed in the diagnosis of glanders in horses, were added to the list of products.[35] The name of the lab was changed to a more impressive Imperial Veterinary Research Institute in 1925. After independence, Imperial made way for Indian.

Izatnagar

Mukteshwar has had a plains station attached to it since 1901 at Kurgaina. It was used for work during the winter months but proved unsuitable owing to lack of space. The Izatnagar site, about four miles north of Bareilly City, was acquired in 1913 but because of the First World War, it could not be brought into use until 1922. The Kurgaina site was then sold by auction. Izatnagar also was used only during the winter months for the first year or two but has been open throughout the year since October 1924. To begin with, it was known as the Branch Institute of Veterinary Research, its head being known as the officer in charge. In the course of time, it underwent many changes in name in keeping with its expansion.[36] In a role reversal, Izatnagar became the centre of activity with Mukteshwar as a branch.

In 1935, it was estimated that India had 215 million cattle. This number was one-third of the world cattle population and more than the combined strength of the USA and Soviet Union. Veterinary colleges and labs opened under the auspices of the colonial government were very small in number and therefore with small impact. The British Indian emphasis remained on horses and cattle that were the state property and in the service of the Army.

Agriculture

Agriculture was a low-priority area for colonial India. The British interest in Indian agriculture primarily focused on industrial cash crops. After the 1874 closure of the stud, the Bengal Government operated a model farm at Pusa to see among other things whether a "race of rice" known as Garpa which grew in Dacca could be grown.[37] The government however soon felt that tobacco was more important than rice. The farm lasted barely a year, 1875–1876. In 1877, the land in Pusa was given on a 20-year lease to Messrs Begg, Dunlop and Co. for growing, curing, and manufacturing tobacco "after the American methods."[38] The lessee would have liked to continue the lease but for purposes other than tobacco. This however was not acceptable that in 1897 on the completion of the lease, the land was reverted to the Bengal Government.[39]

Even when agriculture proper was paid attention to, the methodology adopted was Euro-centric and therefore counter-productive. Madras created a

Department of Agriculture in 1863 and made the mistake of turning to the West for aid. The Department's first act was to order from England a steam plough, some harrows and cultivators, seed-drills and horse-hoes, threshing-machines and winnowers, chaff-cutters and water-lifts. "To find employment for this elaborate consignment," a farm was started in 1864 at Saidapet and entrusted, as a "model farm," to a "committee of amateur enthusiasts." The committee was dissolved in 1871 and the farm was passed to official control.[40]

An agricultural school was established at Saidapet in 1868. The agricultural branch was opened at the College of Science, in 1879. A forest school was opened at Dehradun in 1876. These institutions blossomed in the first decade of the 20th century when other colleges also came up.

An Imperial agricultural department was established in 1871 "chiefly in relation to the supply of cotton from India." The department was however declared to be a failure and closed in 1878. Food agriculture received attention when famine loomed large. The Famine Commissioners in 1880 strongly recommended the creation of agricultural departments in all provinces. These departments would inform the government of the "approach of famines," suggest measures for their prevention in future, and take charge of operations in case of an actual famine.[41] Accordingly, a central agriculture department was set up afresh in 1881. On the Government of India's initiative, John Augustus Voelcker (1854–1937), a consulting chemist to the Royal Agricultural Society, arrived in India towards the end of 1889 and left by early 1891. In 1893, he published his *Report on the improvement of Indian agriculture*. His assessment was a radical assessment. He

> did not share the view so commonly held that Indian agriculture was primitive and backward. He believed that in many parts of India there was little or nothing that could be improved, while, where agriculture was manifestly inferior it was more generally the result of the absence of facilities which exist in the better districts than of inherently bad systems of cultivation.

"He recommended therefore the systematic prosecution of agricultural enquiry and the spread of general and agricultural education and laid down, in considerable detail, the lines on which agricultural improvement was possible."[42]

Voelcker's protégé became India's first European agriculture scientist. John Walter Leather (1860–1934) arrived in 1887 as an agricultural chemist to the Government of India for a five-year term, that is till 1892. His responsibility was research. An assistant chemist was also appointed along with him and entrusted with the twin task of teaching at Poona, Dehradun, and Saidapet and "the disposal of chemical questions connected with forests and agriculture."[43]

The new Viceroy, Lord Curzon, read Voelcker's Report and decided to act upon it. In 1901, James William Mollison (1858–1927), at the time Deputy

Director of Agriculture in Bombay, was appointed the Inspector General of Agriculture, with the responsibility of acting as an adviser on agricultural matters both to the Imperial and Provincial Governments. The Imperial scientific staff were augmented with the appointment of a cryptogamic botanist (or mycologist) in 1901 and an entomologist in 1903. The scientists now needed laboratories and farms to make discoveries and test them in the field.

The money for the proposed agricultural research facility came from America through Curzon's in-law connection. Millionaire and philanthropist, Henry Phipps, was a family friend of Lady Curzon, herself a daughter of an American millionaire. Phipps used to visit India and stay as a guest of Curzon's. Phipps made "a generous donation of £20,000, to which £10,000 was subsequently added" to Lord Curzon who "decided to devote the greater portion of it to the equipment of the new research institute."[44] On 26 December 1903, the Government of India took over the Pusa estate from the Bengal Government and opened the Agricultural Research Institute in 1905. It began with five departments, Agriculture, Cattle Breeding, Chemistry, Economic Botany and Mycology to which Bacteriology was added in 1907. The institute was dignified with the name Imperial Agricultural Research Institute, the acronym of which has remained in use ever since. In 1929, the Indian Council of Agricultural Research (ICAR) was established as a registered society in pursuance of the report of the Royal Commission on Agriculture.

Using the 1934 earthquake that damaged Pusa buildings as a pretext, IARI was shifted to Delhi in 1836 where the campus was named after Pusa for old time's sake. A small unit called the botanical sub-station was left over at Pusa and eventually (1975) became the IARI Regional Station. Pusa is also home to Dr Rajendra Prasad Central Agricultural University.

Notes

1 Bryant, 1995.
2 Bhalla, 1988, 3.
3 Bhalla, 1988.
4 Earles, 1788.
5 Pigott, 1794.
6 https://electricscotland.com/history/nation/fraser.htm.
7 Alder, 1979, 10.
8 Alder, 1979, 12.
9 Alder, 1979, 24.
10 Moorcroft, 1862, 3.
11 Alder, 1979, 15.
12 He died the next year when the ship which was taking him to England sank.
13 https://blogs.bl.uk/untoldlives/2020/03/the-east-india-companys-stud-farm-in-essex.html.
14 Ullah, 1843, 283–284.
15 Moorcroft, 1862, 50–51.
16 Bhat & Yadav, 2018, 98.

17 *Asiatic Journal and Monthly Miscellany*, 1829, 29, 724–725.
18 Mishra, 2012, 1134.
19 Hodson, 1910, 300.
20 The Veterinarian, 1837, 10, 149–150.
21 Smith, 1927, 97–98.
22 Williams, 1904, 643.
23 Macdonald et al., 2005, 55.
24 Williams, 1904, 643.
25 Samad, 2014, 501.
26 Walker, 1927, 336.
27 Walker, 1927, 336.
28 Madras Veterinary College Golden Jubilee Souvenir, 17 January 1955, pp. 9–10.
29 Samad, 2014, 501.
30 IVRI, 1940, 2.
31 *Calcutta Review*, 1890, 90 (Jan.), 208 & 417.
32 IVRI, 1940, 9.
33 Holmes, 1913, 1.
34 IVRI, 1940, 4.
35 IVRI, 1940, 4–5.
36 IVRI, 1940, 47.
37 Imperial Gazetteer of India, 1881, 7, 463. London: Trübner.
38 Statistical Tables for British India, 1886, p. xi. Calcutta: Government Printing.
39 https://www.rpcau.ac.in/about-pusa/ wrongly credits the lease to a different company calling it Beg [sic] Sutherland and wrongly states that it abandoned the estate. https://ctri.icar.gov.in/for_origin.php mixes up the government farm with the leased farm and gets the dates wrong, claiming that Virginia tobacco was grown during 1875 to 1903. These errors should be considered serious because they occur in official websites which are routinely consulted and cited without cross-checking.
40 MacKenna, 1915.
41 Voelcker, 1893, 2.
42 MacKenna, 1915, 4.
43 MacKenna, 1915, 4–5 does not mention Leather by name nor identify his junior.
44 MacKenna, 1915, 17.

8
EDUCATION UNDER COLONIAL AUSPICES

The role assigned to Indians by the colonialists steadily increased and improved. The 1813 Charter asked the government to spend every year not less than 1,00,000 rupees (£10,000) on education. The systematic disbursement of educational funds began with the formation of the General Committee of Public Instruction (GCPI) in 1823[1] (it was renamed the Council of Education in 1842). The Hindoo[2] College (the school section to begin with), Calcutta, opened on 20 January 1817 as a private institution but started receiving aid from the government in 1824 which placed its representatives on the management. Following it, the Agra College was established in 1823 and the Delhi College in 1825. In Bombay, the Elphinstone College came into existence in 1835. The Delhi College was ransacked in 1857 and finally closed in 1876, with the transfer of students and assets to Lahore.

Early efforts, in what was still the Mughal Delhi, to transplant English science education into Urdu became counter-productive. An uncommon mathematician of early days flourished not in Calcutta, but in the still Mughal Delhi.

Master Ramchandra

Master Ramchandra (1821–1880) was born in Panipat but moved to Delhi after his father's death. He passed out from the English Department of Delhi College in 1844 and was appointed in the College itself as a teacher of European Science in the Oriental Department (Madrasa section) through the medium of vernacular. He built a strong reputation as an Urdu journalist, translator, prose writer and modern mathematician. In 1850, he published,

DOI: 10.4324/9781003466406-8

from Calcutta at his own expense, a mathematical text, *A Treatise on Problems of Maxima and Minima Solved by Algebra*. The book was published. Much to the author's disappointment it received a negative review from the influential journal, Calcutta Review. The journal found no merit in the work, both as regards its object and its execution. His method was said to be applicable to only a small portion of the problems that continually occur. The mode of execution was declared to be, "in general, clumsy and school-boy-like." "As it is, we state with much pleasure our conviction, that the mind, which formed this conception, is capable of far better things than are achieved in the work before us."[3]

Ramchandra travelled to Calcutta where he was introduced to John Elliot Drinkwater Bethune (1801–1851), the Legislative Member of the Supreme Council of India. He obtained 36 copies of the work, paid him Rs 200 for them as honorarium and sent them to individuals in England. One of them was the famous British mathematician, Augustus De Morgan, who persuaded the Court of Directors to reprint it for circulation in Europe and India. An edition was brought out in 1859 under the superintendence of De Morgan who wrote a preface for it. The preface is important for giving biographical details of Master Ramchandra, obtained directly from him.[4]

De Morgan's praise of the work is not unstinted, but patronizing and orientalist.

"The Hindu" "fed himself and his pupils upon the chaff of obsolete civilization, out of which Europeans had thrashed the grain for their own use. But the mind thus degenerated is still a mind; and the means of restoring it to activity differ greatly from those by which a barbarous race is to be gifted with its first steps of progress."

If the matter was being put before "a scientific society," a short paper, with a few examples, would have sufficed. But "Europeans must remember that his purpose is to teach Hindus." The work has, De Morgan argued, "merit of a peculiar kind, the encouragement of which ... was likely to promote native effort towards the restoration of the native mind in India."[5]

The Company presented a khillut (dress of honour) of five pieces to him and also gave a cash reward of Rs 2000. "Encouraged by such appreciation," Ramachandra published in 1861 his second work, *A New Method of the Differential Calculus*. His impact on modern science and education in India remained non-existent. Much to the horror of the native communities, Ramachandra converted to Christianity in 1852.

Since he was by far the most advanced in English studies, it was inevitable that his name should be held up for a warning, as to what results might happen if the English language were allowed to be taught to the young.[6]

Half-hearted attempts were made to introduce science education in Bengal under colonial and missionary auspices but without any lasting effect.

Chemistry in Calcutta

As soon as the Hindu College, Calcutta, came under government control, it was decided to appoint a professor of experimental philosophy and "to separate Chemistry from the rest, and appropriate a practical course in that science alone." In 1824, the appointment was given as an additional charge to the foreman of the Calcutta mint, David Ross. The experiment was a failure partly because the teacher's own knowledge did not go beyond soda. One of his students, Krishnamohan Bandhyopadhyay (afterwards famous as Reverend K.M. Banerjea), contributed to the papers a sarcastic article entitled "Soda and his Pupils."[7] In any case, it is not clear what use Indian students would have been put to if they had learnt chemistry. In 1828, the college acquired the services of Robert Tytler, an "eccentric but talented" mathematics teacher.[8] It was the mathematical talent at the Hindoo College that the Trigonometrical Survey tapped.

In July 1823, the British India Society in London presented a large collection of scientific instruments along with a "considerable number of books on scientific subjects" for use at the [Government] Sanskrit College Calcutta, which came into existence in 1824. The instruments included a telescope, terrestrial and celestial globes, and lab and workshop apparatus. The books included Ure's *Chemical Dictionary* and Mackenzie's *1,000 Chemical Experiments*. The government was even ready to appoint a lecturer or a professor, but expecting the pandits enrolled at the College for Sanskrit to show enthusiasm for European scientific gadgetry and literature was an exercise in naïveté. If the books and the apparatus had been preserved, even if not used, they would have been priceless museum pieces.

Chemistry in Bengali

The [Baptist] Missionaries based at the Danish enclave Serampore near Calcutta very ambitiously decided to try "every practicable means" "to allure the natives to the love of natural science." Reverend John Mack, who specially trained in chemistry at Edinburgh University for a session as preparation for his Indian assignment, arrived in September 1821 and set up a well-equipped science lab at Serampore College which was primarily meant for Christian youth but admitted others as well. In December 1823, Mack began by giving a series of lecture demonstrations in English at Calcutta and followed this by a regular and repeated course in Bengali and English for students at Serampore. Based on his lecture notes, he published, in 1834, a 337-page bilingual book *Principles of Chemistry*, Volume 1/*Kimiya Bidyara Sara* with English and

Bengali texts on facing pages. In the Appendix, it gives an account of the steam engine. This was the first modern science book ever published in India. It is also the first science textbook in an Indian language. While the Serampore Missionary work on Sanskrit, Bengali, and printing won appreciation, their efforts in science neither made any impact in their time nor were recalled later. Since the missionaries packaged Christianity and Western science together, people rejected the package.

The introduction of science education into the college system would have to wait till the 1870s. Till then, some science was taught only in Western medical colleges.

Medical Education

Native Medical Institution

As the Company territory expanded, the army had to be distributed widely for its protection. A great number of the native battalions were broken down into two and sometimes more sub-divisions. Because of the limited number of European surgeons, it was not possible to allot one to each of these numerous detachments. The same problem was faced, even to a greater degree, at the civil stations. To remedy the situation, the Medical Board proposed that there should be established at the Presidency, a regular school for the education of native doctors. Accordingly in June 1822, orders were issued by the government for the formation of the school, designated the Native Medical Institution, for imparting instruction through the medium of Hindustani. The Court of Directors "expressed a preference for the simpler plan adopted at Fort St. George, of educating half castes for medical service, by admitting them as dressers in the hospitals." Ever disdainful of natives, it felt that "the knowledge proposed to be imparted was not merely novel, but of a nature possibly too abstruse and refined for the rude and unprepared minds of the pupils."[9] Calcutta however stood its ground.

The students were paid a stipend, enlisted as soldiers, and appointed to the Army or Civil Department as vacancies arose. With a view to maintaining the respectability of native doctors, it was ordered in 1832 that they "are not to be submitted to the degradation of punishment by flogging, to which, as enlisted men, they were then liable."[10]

In its lifetime, the school saw three superintendents. The first, James Jameson, took over in 1822 but died the next year. His main qualification was that he was the Secretary of the Medical Board and essentially appointed himself. He was succeeded by a very capable man, Peter Breton, who even declined promotion to remain at the helm of the school. On his death in 1830, the post went to John Tytler (1787–1837) who held office till its abolition in 1835.

Breton

Breton brought out "various essays or short treatises" to be used by his students as well as others. They were all in Hindustani and printed "in both the Persian and Naguree characters." Two of these may be noticed by way of illustration: Translation of *London Pharmacopoeia*, in two volumes, and "Substance of a [class-room] Lecture on the Cholera Morbus." During the prevalence of cholera in Calcutta in 1825, the school students acquitted themselves exceedingly well by distributing medicines and affording assistance "to the wretched and numerous victims of the disease."

Although the European system of medicine was taught at the school, Breton was alive to the importance of the native system which contained useful remedies. "In teaching the students Anatomy and Medicine according to the European system," Breton stated,

> it is not intended that they should be wholly excluded from the advantages derivable from the native Practice. Many native Remedies are probably superior to those of Europe, and possibly only require to be made known to English Professional men to be rendered extensively beneficial.

A Muslim oculist, "Sautcouree," was an expert in the removal of cataracts by couching. Obviously, he was not acquainted with the structure of the eye, but he could perform the delicate operation dexterously and with a 90% success rate.[11] Breton saw him carry out the surgery, both in his residence and at the General Hospital and examined the eyes of the patients after the operation. Sautcoree performed such an operation on Mr J.B. Birch, Justice of the Peace, and restored his eyesight. Breton engaged Sautcouree to teach his pupils the method. Five of the students practised the art, during the training period, upon the eyes of sheep and goats, while, one of them, Pursun Singh, performed the operation successfully on the cataract in the left eyes of two old men in Breton's house and restored their sight. Breton wrote a small tract entitled "On the Native Mode of Couching" (1826). The well-respected British medical journal *Lancet* duly reported on it, but lest its readership be overly impressed made it a point to add that the "degree of success" "could scarcely be anticipated from the rudeness of the implements and the ignorance of the operators, who are utterly unacquainted with the anatomy of the eye."[12] Modern accounts are more balanced. In 1817, Helenus Scott (1760–1821)[13] of the Bombay Medical Service had described surgery for the removal of cataracts, but Breton's "is one of the most detailed accounts of Eastern practices by a knowledgeable eyewitness just prior to the development of modern medicine."[14]

An experiment was begun in 1826, engrafting Western medicine in translation onto traditional medical learning. Accordingly, medical classes were begun in Calcutta Madrasa and the Sanskrit College. Breton taught at the Calcutta Madrasa. To facilitate his work, he was authorized to purchase a skeleton and collect medical books. The introduction of Western medicine in the Sanskrit College was more systematic. While in Madrasa, executive action hardly impressed the community, in the case of the Sanskrit College Hindu leadership, for example, Ram Comul Sen, worked hand in hand with British officers. John Tytler who was posted in Calcutta towards the end of 1827 as Presidency Surgeon was appointed to teach Mathematics and Anatomy to the medical class at the Sanskrit College. On appointment as the NMI Superintendent, he relinquished the charge of medical class, but retained the mathematical class because "a competent successor was not to be found."[15] The Sanskrit College at the time admitted only Brahmin and Baidya students. The latter could opt out of Logic (Nyaya) or Law (Dharma Shastra) and instead attend medical lectures in Sanskrit and English. To make their education complete, a small hospital was attached to the medical class, in 1832.[16]

Calcutta Medical College

In 1835, medical classes at Madrasa and Sanskrit College were closed, NMI was abolished, and the Calcutta Medical College was established. The abolition of classes had a finality about it. No attempt would ever be made for the translation of modern texts into Arabic or Sanskrit for the benefit of traditional students. But, NMI's abolition was a matter of expediency. Tytler with his zeal for Oriental translation had fallen foul of the newly assertive Anglicist establishment. The abolition of NMI was a means of getting rid of him. It was revived four years later as part of the Calcutta Medical College. Many similar schools would be set up in different places in North India.

NMI "has been much lauded as a colonial establishment teaching both indigenous and western medicine side-by-side, with state support. Historians have written of the 'halcyon days' which, it is claimed, displayed a short-lived British tolerance of indigenous medical systems."[17] Available facts do not support such an assessment. NMI was wholly devoted to disseminating modern medicine through the vernacular. Traditional healthcare had no place in it. The introduction of medical classes in Oriental Colleges four years after the establishment of NMI was an independent development. NMI Superintendent, Breton, no doubt, held classes in Madrasa, but the classes continued even after his death in 1830. Tytler taught at the Sanskrit College but that was before he succeeded Breton. He in fact discontinued teaching on taking charge in NMI. The confusion regarding NMI and medical classes seems to have arisen because both NMI and medical classes were closed at the same time.

When the British set up government in Bengal in the 1770s under Warren Hastings, they by choice maintained continuation with the preceding Mughal administration. With a view to enlisting support from within India, they projected themselves as patrons of ancient learning. By the 1830s, the situation had changed. The British control of India was total. The Industrial Revolution had been completed. England was now an industrial power, full of notions of racial and cultural superiority. For reasons of economy, British India needed Indians in subordinate roles. The government needed Indians to learn English and vernaculars, and not Arabic or Sanskrit. Although no extant Oriental Colleges were closed following Macaulay's Minute and Bentinck's Resolution, support for Orientalism was minimized. The transitional phase that began with Warren Hastings had to end. It ended with Bentinck.

Teaching modern medicine to traditional Hindu physician castes in the Sanskrit College served an important purpose; it smoothened the way towards the acceptance of Western medicine as part of the educational mainstream.

Human Dissection

In the Native Medical Institution, dissection had been performed on the bodies of sheep, and students had been taken to witness post-mortems. However, modern medical education would be incomplete without human dissection. Would the students agree to it? What would be the public reaction? An Indian junior faculty member, Madhusudan [Muddosoodun, etc.] Gupta (1800–1856), took on the task of anchoring modernity onto medical tradition.

Gupta was a Baidya by caste. As soon as Ayurvedic classes started at the Sanskrit College, in 1827, he enrolled as a student and acquitted himself so well that he was given a faculty position in 1830. He translated Hooper's *Anatomists' Vade-mecum* into Sanskrit for which he received a honorarium of 1,000 rupees. On the winding up of the Ayurvedic department, he was hired for the Medical College which he joined on 17 March 1835 as a demonstrator in the Departments of Medicine and Anatomy, headed by Henry Hurry Goodeve (1807–1874). Madhusudan himself carried out human dissection on 10 January 1836 under European supervision. Months later, on 28 October 1836, he led four students to the dissection room. Subsequently, in a public disputation organized on orders from the Lieutenant Governor, Madhusudan quoted from scriptures to convince the doubting Pandits that human dissection was consistent with past practices. The British needed a learned Hindu to act as an intermediary; left to themselves, they could not have persuaded Hindu students to effect a break with the past. It was said that "a gun was fired from the ramparts of Fort William in honour of the dissection" by Madhusudan.[18] The story is now declared to be apocryphal, but it does signify the importance assigned to the event by the government and the society alike.

Training in London

In 1845, the College deputed Goodeve to take with him four students for completion of their education at University College, London. Two of them were sponsored by Dwarka Nath Tagore. The other two were financed by public subscription and government grants. Three of them Dwarka Nath Bose, Bhola Nath Bose, and Gopal Chunder Seal passed the examination for MRCS (Member of the Royal College of Surgeons) in 1846 and returned to India. Seal however died by drowning soon thereafter. The other two joined the uncovenanted Medical Service. The fourth one is historically important because he became the first Indian to be admitted to the Covenanted Medical Service.

Soorjo Coomar Chuckerbutty

Soorjo Coomar Chuckerbutty [Surjo Kumar Chakraborty] (1827?–1874) was born in a village called Kanaksar in the Dacca district. Orphaned at the age of six, he was obliged to make his own way in the world. He studied initially at the village pathshala (school), where he learnt Bengali and elementary Sanskrit and Persian. At 13, he moved to Comilla, 60 miles distant to enrol at the English School. He along with several other students stayed at the house of a well-to-do gentleman, Shri Golok Nath Sen, who was an official at the district court there. As was usual at the time, Chuckerbutty and other students had to cook their food in turns. He arranged to serve as a cook in the schoolmaster's household in exchange for lessons in English. For Brahmins, it was an easy matter to get employment as a cook. Subsequently, he came to Calcutta and became a student of the Hare School. In 1844, he was admitted to the Medical College and sent to England the next year. He could take his MRCS only in 1848 when he reached the admissible age. He passed the first examination for M.B. in the first division in 1847 and the second and final examination in the second division in 1849. The same year, he passed the M.D. examination in the first division standing second in order of merit. During the years of his study at University College, he was awarded the gold medal for comparative anatomy and many certificates of merit. Chuckerbutty had discarded the "sacred thread," the symbol of his Brahmanic caste, on his admission to the Medical College. In 1848, he became a Christian, adding Goodeve to his name.[19] Goodeve informed the Medical College, and The Lancet[20] placed on public record, that the conversion was purely voluntary. D.N. Bose was already a Christian when he left for England. On return, he was admitted to the uncovenanted medical service in 1850. His "ambition had always been to become a member of the Covenanted Service of the East India Company, and thus remove from his race, the stigma of a proscription which denied them a career of honourable ambition in their own land." When the Covenanted Medical Service was opened to all, in

1854, he resigned his position and came to England to appear at the first open competitive examination held on 8–11 January 1855. He was placed second in merit in a list of 22 candidates who passed.

He was appointed assistant surgeon (1855) and successively became surgeon (1867) and surgeon major (1873) in the Bengal Army. He held charge of various hospitals and dispensaries in Calcutta. In between, in 1857, 1860 and 1864, he was temporarily appointed to the *Materia Medica* chair at the medical college. He obtained it permanently in 1866 and held it till death in 1874. As one of the earliest Indians to contribute to Western medicine, he published in medical journals such as *The Lancet*, the *British Medical Journal* and *The Indian Medical Gazette*.

D.N. Bose was already a Christian when he left for England.[21] Such was the cultural climate of Bengal by then that Chuckerbutty's conversion seemed to have caused no ripple. In general, when upper castes converted, their social status remained that of pre-conversion. A glaring example of this phenomenon was Reverend K.M. Banerjea.

Bhola Nath Bose

The case of Bhola Nath Bose demonstrates that the Empire's interest in the education of Bengal boys could be excessive. Lord Auckland and his friends "used every now and then to visit the Barrackpore School," which Auckland himself had set up. A student, Bhola Nath Bose (1825–82), "soon attracted His Lordship's notice by his intelligence and progress in studies." In 1840, Auckland transferred Bhola Nath to the Calcutta Medical College with a stipend of Rs 10 a month, which he paid from his own private purse. On the eve of his return to India from England, Auckland, already in England since 1842 and as the First Lord of Admiralty, sent him a bank draft so that Dr Bose could take with him "some token of remembrance." The money sent by Auckland must have been substantial because Bhola Nath decided to buy a gold watch with it. Auckland and others tried to "obtain for Dr Bose admission into the Covenanted Medical Service of India," but the Court of Directors refused. Soon after his return to India in 1848, Dr Bose was appointed superintendent of Sukea's Lane Dispensary in Calcutta, attached to the Calcutta Medical College Hospital. The dispensary "in fact was established solely to employ him in town." The acerbic journalist Sambhu Chandra Mookerjee (1839–1894) referred to Bhola Nath and others as "the poor, pet native boys" of Lord Auckland and Charles Hay Cameron (1795–1880), President of the Council of Education. Bhola Nath left his whole property for charitable purposes; from his bequest, Bhola Nath Bose dispensaries were set up in Barrackpore and Mandalai.[22]

The Medical College instituted the Military Class in Hindustani in 1839 and the Bengali class in 1851. In 1864, the Bengali class was divided into two sections: The Native Apothecary section, which trained students for government employment, and the Vernacular Licentiate section that gave instructions in medicine and surgery in order to enable the students to practice among the less affluent sections of Indians. When the Calcutta University came into existence in 1857, regulation of the college proper was transferred to it, while the Urdu and Bengali classes remained in the Principal's domain.

The Madras Medical School, founded in 1835, "was, at first, on a level with the Calcutta Native Medical institution."[23] Medical Schools were opened at Agra (1853) and Lahore (1860). When the Campbell Medical School, Sealdah, Calcutta, was established (1873), Bengali classes were transferred to it. Similarly, the military class was accommodated in the Temple Medical School, Bankipore, Patna (1874). The Calcutta Medical College now became an educational institution regulated by the Calcutta University. The ten-member University Medical Faculty which included two Indians, Khan Bahadur Munshi Tamiz Khan and Rai Bahadur Kanailal De [also spelt Dey], unanimously passed a resolution on 15 May 1878 that having a homeopath on the faculty will "deteriorate the value of the University Medical degrees" and cause "serious loss" to "all present and future Medical Graduates," and will be "to the manifest discredit of the University in public estimation."

Like NMI before it, the military class at the Calcutta Medical College was predominantly attended by Muslims most of whom came from North India. In 1856–1857, in the Hindustani class, there were 118 students; out of these 87% were Muslims and only 13% were Hindus. Among the Muslims, 53% were natives of North-West Province and Assam and 39% were of Bengal. In the English class of 119, one student was from Ceylon and just one Muslim. Of the remaining, 24% were Kayastha, 17% Brahmin, and 10% Baidya. The Bengali class was populated by 88 pupils out of whom just one was Muslim. Among the Hindus, 43% were Brahmins, 21% Baidya, and 20% Kayastha.[24] Muslim presence in the English and Bengali classes was thus negligible. One would have thought that the traditional physicians, the Baidyas, would respond to English classes with great enthusiasm, but that was not the case. They however overtook Kayasthas in the Bengali class. Perhaps, they wished to combine their traditional knowledge with medical school instruction. "Medical College in the vernacular departments [Hindustani and Urdu] is far more largely dependant on the lower section of the middle class than the upper."[25]

The Calcutta University was very keen to protect the worldwide reputation of its Medical College. Its medical faculty refused to accept Dr Mahendralal Sircar as a member, saying, in 1878, that "they are unable to associate themselves as a Faculty of Medicine with a member who professes and practices Homeopathy." Having a homeopath on the faculty will "deteriorate the value of the University Medical degrees" and cause "serious loss" to "all present and future Medical Graduates," and will be "to the manifest discredit of the University in public estimation."[26]

The next full-fledged medical college after Calcutta was the Grant Medical College, Bombay, which formally opened in 1845 with 12 students.[27] In the initial years, the admitted students were not sufficiently well versed in English to be able to follow the lectures. It was therefore decided to begin medical classes in Gujarati and Marathi. Several books from English were translated, with prominent citizens of Bombay endowing scholarships for translational work. The classes became popular and should have been continued from a long-term perspective. But, as soon as a sufficient number of matriculated students became available for admission, the experiment was abandoned.[28]

As the number of hospitals conducted by the government began to increase, there was a demand for a large number of "hospital assistants," who "need not be so highly educated as the degree course of the Bombay University." Accordingly, medical schools were opened in Poona and Ahmedabad where boys and girls were admitted. Two separate schools were opened in Hyderabad, Sind, where boys and girls sat separately.[29]

Women Doctors

Miss Allen D' Abreu and Miss Abala Das after passing in 1881 their First Arts Exam and Entrance Exam, respectively, applied to the Council of Calcutta Medical College but were denied admission on the grounds that they had not passed the B.A. Exam. This led to a strong opposition to female students not being accepted into the college. Abala Das went to Madras in 1882 on a Bengal Government scholarship to study medicine but had to give up because of ill health.

River Thompson, the Lieutenant Governor looked into the matter and put it to an end by passing an order on 29 June 1883 to allow women's admission into the Calcutta Medical College after finishing their FA. Kadambini Ganguly, a Bengal Brahmo, became the first woman student at the Calcutta Medical College. She however did not receive MB. In 1884, the government offered scholarships of Rs 20 per month to all female students. Bidhu Mukhi Bose and Virginia Mary Mitter received these scholarships and became the first Indian women to graduate during 1888–1889.

Engineering Education

The technological content of the Empire increased with time; two notable early examples being steam to decrease travel time between England and India and telegraph for better communication within the country. The British however had no interest in promoting higher education in technical subjects to promote industrial development.

The introduction of steam in 1829 brought Bombay into prominence and necessitated the upgrade of native skills.

> The prompt repair of the engines of the numerous steamers arriving in Bombay posed a problem. Few of the European engineers and drivers could withstand the climate, and those who were enabled to do so proved so troublesome that a remedy for the inconvenience appeared of paramount importance.[30]

(i)

The remedy was Ardaseer Cursetjee Wadia (1808–1877), a scion of the Wadia shipbuilding family and then an assistant builder at the dock. He had a natural flair for engineering. He even assisted Arthur Bedford Orlebar, a professor of natural philosophy at the Elphinstone College, "in instructing the natives, especially in mechanical and chemical science."[31] (Interestingly here we have Cursetjee referring to his fellow countrymen as natives.) He was officially sponsored to visit England. Duly trained and networked, he was appointed Chief Engineer and Inspector of Machinery at the Company's factory and foundry in Bombay in 1840. It was noted in the press that a "body of English workmen" would be under his charge. In 1841, he became the first Indian to be elected a Fellow of the Royal Society of London. Of course, the Society was then more a gentleman's club than the learned body it became later. The Fellowship however does not seem to have made any impact in India. Bombay was too practical to make sense of an honour bestowed in London while it was too early for Calcutta to be interested.[32] Steam arrived in Bombay for colonial reasons, but became a vehicle for the industrialization of Bombay. Cowasji Nanabhoy Davar (1814–1873) floated Bombay's first steam-based cotton mill in 1854, thus laying the foundation of Bombay's cotton textile industry. It came up on Indian initiative and with Indian capital. The initiative was resented by the English textile industry but welcomed by manufacturers of textile machinery who were happy to see their market expand. The requisite manpower was trained on the job or in England. In 1863, Ardaseer's 14-year-old grandson, Nowrosjee Nusserwanjee (1849–1899), along with his younger brother, was dispatched to Liverpool for schooling and factory training. He set up the Bombay Dyeing and Manufacturing Company in 1879 and then the Century Mills which subsequently changed hands.[33] Cursetjee however remained non-typical.

Telegraph

Telegraph was introduced into India as a result of government-backed pioneering efforts by Dr William O'Shaughnessy (1809–1889) who was a professor in the Calcutta Medical College as well as the in-charge of the Calcutta Mint. He introduced the therapeutic use of *Cannabis sativa* to Western medicine. He was assisted by a subordinate of his, Seeb Chunder Nandy (1822–1903), who had joined the refinery department of the Mint in 1846. The first telegraph line in India was opened in 1851, when Nandy transmitted the first signal from Diamond Harbour to Alipore Station, Calcutta 27 miles away, where it was received by O'Shaughnessy in the presence of the Governor General, Lord Dalhousie. By the end of 1856, India had 4250 miles of electric telegraph and 46 receiving offices. In 1857, O'Shaughnessy was in England, and his European substitute, Lieutenant Patrick Stewart, was away from Calcutta. As a result, Nandy was in charge. Acting proactively, in order to "secure the communication between Calcutta and Bombay, he laid down a portion of the alternate line from Mirzapur to Seoni via Jubblepore."[34]

On 10 May 1857, armed rebellion broke out in Meerut. The rebel soldiers cut the telegraph lines between Meerut and Delhi and marched to Delhi. The next day, two 18-year-old signallers conveyed the news to Umballa before running away for their own security. Umballa (Ambala) promptly transmitted the news to Lahore, Rawalpindi, and Peshawar. Acting swiftly, the British officers disarmed native soldiers and thus prevented the spread of rebellion. As Sir Robert Montgomerie put it simply and effectively, "Electric telegraph saved India [for the British that is]." If the rebellion had broken out before the telegraph was introduced, it might well have succeeded.

Nandy was promoted to Assistant Superintendent in the Telegraph department, in 1866, and awarded the title *Rai Bahadur* in 1883. He retired the next year on special pension and was made an Honorary Magistrate. On his death, Calcutta post offices were closed for a day, and the Municipal Corporation named a street, Sibu Nandy Lane, after him.[35] In 1953, India issued postage stamps to commemorate, with a delay of two years, the centennial of the installation of the telegraph. India honoured not only those who laid down their life in the 1857 rebellion but also those who helped the British suppress it.

The two signallers who sent the Umballa telegram, William Beresford Brendish (1839–1907) and J.W. Pilkington, were Eurasians. If they had been Hindu or Muslim, they might have chosen not to send the telegram. It is not known where the signallers were trained. Lawrence Asylums [now Schools] at Sanawar and Lovedale, meant for Eurasians, offered a training programme in telegraphy. There was however no provision anywhere for the training of Indians in general.

Engineering Colleges

For reasons of economy, administration, and good governance, roads were laid and repaired, buildings constructed, and canals renovated and dug. To meet the technical manpower requirements, a number of institutions, which became engineering colleges, were opened: Roorkee (1847), Poona (1854), Calcutta (1856), Madras (1858) and Mughalpura, Lahore (1924).

Roorkee

While the mathematical needs of the Trigonometrical Survey could be met at the existing level of educational facilities, the engineering requirements of canals called for a new initiative. This is how the Roorkee College came up in 1847. In 1854, it was named Thomason College of Civil Engineering in honour of James Thomason,[36] who served as the Lieutenant Governor of the North West Provinces (Western Uttar Pradesh of today) from 1843 to 1853. The western and eastern Yamuna canals were re-opened in 1825 and 1830, respectively. An entirely new and ambitious project, the Ganga Canal, was next planned. Although the excavation work commenced in April 1842, work in the right earnest began only in October 1847 under the superintendence of Proby Cautley and the canal was sufficiently complete to admit water in April 1854, when it was formally inaugurated with great fanfare. In the meantime, the 1849 annexation of Punjab brought the splendid Indus River system under British control. In 1855, public works which so far had been the responsibility of the Military Board were placed in the charge of a newly created civilian Department of Public Works.

In May 1843, by an official notification, the control of educational institutions in North-West Provinces was transferred from the Governor General to the Lieutenant Governor in Agra. However, the follow-up order allotting educational funds came only a year later on 20 March 1844. Thus empowered, Thomason decided on a small pilot project "to raise a body of native Civil Engineers" who could assist "in the operations of surveying and laying out water-courses, as well as in the preparation of maps and plans, and formation of Estimates." In true Orientalist fashion, it was noted that "All these are operations for which the native mind is well adapted." The European officer would be able to "throw off" the routine work upon trained "native subordinates" and focus on "the more important duties of direction and general supervision." Going beyond the nitty gritty, Thomason pointed out to the Military Board:

> Young men of education have now high prizes held out to them in the Judicial and Revenue Services, as well as in the Medical profession, and in the Educational Department. There is large field for their profitable employment as Engineers, but it is useless to expect that they will turn their attention to the subject, unless they meet with suitable encouragement.

Canal-centred engineering education began informally, in 1845. The Saharanpur-based superintendent of the eastern Yamuna canal, Lieutenant Richard Baird Smith (1818–1861), was hand-picked by the Lieutenant Governor to run the training programme which would be a meeting ground for two distinct streams. It was decided that "young men of very high mathematical attainments" from the Delhi and Agra Colleges be brought in for practical training. Masters were appointed in these colleges for instruction in architectural drawing and survey-ing.[37] There were also, at the time, young men, known as Lallahs, in semi-employment of the canal establishments, who received a small salary, partly from the government and partly from the zamindars, "whose water-courses they make or keep in repair." It was hoped that some of them would benefit from formal training. No details are available of the Lallahs who came under Baird Smith's care, but we know about two students who were selected, on a substantial stipend, for one-year training beginning January 1845: Munnoo Lall from the Agra College and Pitumber Shah from the Delhi College. Another (un-named) youth from the Benares College was placed under the charge of the executive engineer at Ghazeepoor [Ghazipur].[38] The training programme was followed by the creation, in October 1845, of the grade of sub-assistant execu-tive (also referred to as civil) engineer at a monthly salary of Rs 100. The number was first fixed at four, but a year later was increased to 20. The num-ber was small, but this was only the beginning. One of the posts went to Munnoo Lall, who later became Head Native Master at Roorkee. Petumber Shah's performance was slow; he was asked to train for another six months.[39]

While the twin Yamuna canals were renovations, the Ganga canal was an entirely new project. "The science that was necessary to construct a work of this magnitude, would also be constantly kept in exercise for its maintenance, improvement, and extension." Roorkee suggested itself as the ideal location for ensuring a "constant supply of well trained, experienced Civil Engineers." Located near the Solani aqueduct, it had large workshops, as well as a library and a model room. "Above all a number of scientific and experienced Engineer Officers are constantly assembled on the spot, or occasionally resorting thith-er."[40] The Roorkee College, spread over 365 acres, was "designed to give theoretical and practical instruction in Civil Engineering to Europeans and Natives, with a view to their employment on the public works of the coun-try." The college maintained three departments, the first and the last being for Indians and the middle one for Europeans. The first department was meant for training leading to appointment as sub-assistant civil engineer. It would take properly prepared students, under the age of 22, who were either study-ing in colleges or were recommended by superintending engineers and execu-tive officers of canals, roads, or public works.

Unlike in medicine where the British doctors arrived in India after training, engineers were trained in India. The second department admitted European non-commissioned officers and soldiers for absorption in PWD as overseers. Later, a Native Class was also added. The establishment of the Royal Indian Engineering College, Cooper's Hill, England in 1871 (closed in 1906) de-pressed European admissions to Roorkee, after 1876. As against 55 such admissions in 1876, only 20 were made in 1878. This had a positive conse-quence for Indians; more of them appeared as candidates for entry.[41] Some of the native students were given stipends and free accommodation.

The third department also admitted Indians, but for lower appointments, in surveying, levelling and plan drawing.[42] The candidate should have "a fair acquaintance with Arithmetic in Native form, and an ability to read and write Oordoo in the Persian characters." A total of 16 students would get a stipend of six rupees, but others could join at their own expense. The Roorkee College began on 1 January 1848 with the admission into the Third Department "by the transfer of a few young Indians, who were being instructed by Major W. E. Baker of the Bengal Engineers, then Director of the Ganges Canal."[43]

The annexation of Punjab added 78,000 square miles of territory to British India. Its requirements necessitated the enlargement of the college facilities. A notable new feature was the improvement and superintendence of the village schools around Roorkee to use them as feeders for the third Department of the College.[44]

In 1896, the administration of the college was transferred from the Public Works Department to the Education Department, "emphasizing the fact that the College was not only intended as a nursery for PWD, but also to supply the need for Technical education of the Provinces [note the plural] in general."[45] While the civil engineering side remained as before, the technical and scientific sides were greatly strengthened.

Shiv Narayan Agnihotri

British Punjab offered various opportunities to the alumni of the Roorkee College. A student of the drawing class gained fame in an entirely different context. Shiv Narayan Agnihotri (1850–1929) joined the class in 1866, became a drawing master in the Government High School, Lahore, in 1873, and went on to found Dev Samaj, in 1887. There were others who made their name in line with their training.

Rai Bahadur Kanhaya Lal

An early and notable product of the Roorkee College was Rai Bahadur Kanhaya Lal (1830–1888). He was born in Jalesar in the Etah district (Uttar Pradesh) and sent to the local madrasa where he learnt Urdu and Persian. In 1843, he joined the Government College at Agra, where he highly distinguished himself. On the advice of his professors, he joined at Roorkee. In December 1851, prizes for Mathematics, Engineering and Surveying were awarded to him, with the certificate of qualification for admission to the Public Works Department as sub-assistant civil engineer. After employment for a short time on the Eastern Jamna Canal, he was transferred, in 1852, to Punjab, at that time a new British possession, where works of many kinds were being carried on. The executive engineers of the Indian Public Works Department were ranged in four grades, rising from the fourth grade to the first. Kanhaya Lal steadily rose in the hierarchy and retired as an executive engineer of the first grade.[46] Kanhaya Lal donated a substantial amount of Rs 1,322 to the Punjab University College.[47]

Sir Ganga Ram

Ganga Ram's (1851–1927) father, Daulat Ram, and his wife migrated from Muzaffarnagar (Uttar Pradesh) to Punjab, where in Mangtanwala in Nankana Sahib district he took up a job as sub-assistant inspector. Ganga Ram was born here, but soon the family shifted to Amritsar where Daulat Ram took a low-paid employment as a Persian copyist in the district court. Ganga Ram was a bright student, but for some reason, he failed to clear the matriculation examination at the Calcutta University on his first attempt. His second attempt, through the Government High School, Amritsar, was successful, and he joined the Government College, Lahore in 1869.[48] He passed the First Arts examination of Punjab University, Lahore, in October 1871. He now entered the Thomason Engineering College, Roorkee, with a scholarship of Rs 50 per month. He appeared in his final examination in 1873, which he passed, won a gold medal, and was appointed an assistant engineer. He was posted to Lahore to serve his apprenticeship under Kanhaya Lal, the then-executive engineer of Lahore. Impressed by his all-round work, the Government of India sent him to Bradford for two years for specialized training in waterworks and drainage.[49] On return, he was deputed to prepare a water supply and drainage scheme for Peshawar. Later, he introduced similar schemes in Ambala, Karnal and Gujranwala.

In 1885, he was posted to Lahore as assistant engineer. He now supervised "two monumental pieces of Lahore architecture," namely the new High Court Buildings and the Cathedral. He was selected by the Chief Engineer, Sir Aeneas Perkins, as a special engineer for the designing and construction of the Aitchison Chiefs' College at Lahore. "To him goes the credit of designing and constructing the magnificent buildings of the Lahore Museum, the Mayo School of Arts, the General Post Office, the Albert Victor Wing of the Lahore Mayo Hospital, and the Government College Chemical Laboratory." His "influence went much deeper than the spectacular outside buildings which every one can see, and affected a much larger number of people than a cursory glance might estimate."

Ganga Ram's work in Punjab and Delhi was widely appreciated. He was the best engineer the Buildings and Roads Department possessed but he was not promoted to the grade of superintending engineer because he was an Indian. The British let Indians rise in their own hierarchy and bestowed titles and awards which would enhance their status among fellow natives, but would not permit them to enter the White man's domain.

Feeling insulted, he took retirement in 1903 even though his superannuation was still a few years away. As a reward for his services, the government granted him "twenty squares of land in the Chenab Colonies." He obtained more land on lease and brought engineering into agriculture. He introduced lift irrigation, made his money from land and spent substantial amounts on philanthropy.

Aswan Dam, Egypt

The Engineering College Roorkee served the cause of British colonialism elsewhere as well. Perhaps, internationally the most well-known name from among Roorkee old students is the Indian-born Sir William Willcocks (1852–1932). His father was an engineer in the Ganga Canal works. Willcocks passed from Roorkee in 1872 and served in the irrigation department of the United Provinces for 11 years. In 1883, following the British occupation of Egypt, he was transferred to Cairo to join the Egyptian Public Works Department. He proposed and built the first Aswan Dam, the scale of which had never been attempted previously. He later undertook other major irrigation projects in South Africa and the Arab regions of the dying Ottoman Empire.

Bombay

Engineering education made its appearance in Bombay in two disjointed initiatives. In 1824, the rule-of-thumb training was given through the vernacular to produce a class of assistant surveyors and builders. An Engineer Institution was established in Bombay "to train European and native youths for the subordinate functions of the engineer and survey departments." It was placed under the superintendence of Madras-born Captain George Ritso Jervis (1794–1851) of the Bombay Engineers who at the time was Secretary of the Bombay Native Education Society.[50] A great votary of education through the vernacular, he took upon himself "the irksome and difficult task of translating into the Mahratta and Guzerattee dialects, for the use of the pupils, some of the standard books of instruction in the European languages on arithmetic and geometry." The institution opened with 36 native and 14 half-caste students. In 1826, the institution had 86 students on its rolls: 15 in English class, 51 in Marathi and 20 in Gujarati. The "further history of this pioneer experiment" is not known.

Next, instruction was given through the medium of English to produce "scientific Civil engineers, fully grounded in the theory of their art."[51] In 1844, an engineering class was introduced in the Elphinstone Institution. The experiment however was declared a failure and the class was closed in 1847. Of the ten students examined, none was found suitable for the higher grade of assistant engineer. Thread was picked up again in 1854 with the establishment of Engineering Class and Mechanical School in Poona. Ten years later, in 1864, the institution was converted into a full-fledged Civil Engineering

College. In 1866, it was affiliated to the Bombay University which awarded the first degree of Licentiate of Civil Engineering in 1869.[52] In both medical and engineering education, Parsee philanthropy was a significant factor.

Calcutta

Engineering education was slow to develop in Calcutta. In 1843–1844, a Professorship in Civil Engineering was created at the Hindu College. The Civil Engineering College was started in 1856 and affiliated to the Calcutta University on its establishment in 1857. The first degree examination in Bachelors of Civil Engineering was held in 1864 in which only two students graduated. In 1865, the college merged with the Presidency College, Calcutta and from 1865 to 1869 the college functioned as the Civil Engineering Department of the Presidency College. The College treats 1856 as its year of establishment.

Madras

The history of the Madras College is the dullest. The Civil Engineering School was set up in 1858 and upgraded as the College of Civil Engineering, Guindy in 1859 under the Madras University. The name was generalized to the College of Engineering in 1861 with the inclusion of the mechanical engineering course.

Lahore

Given the proximity of Lahore to Afghanistan, special attention was paid to the establishment of a rail network. Lahore was the node of numerous railroad companies in Punjab. All of them were amalgamated in 1905 to form the North West Railway. By 1904 itself, a large well-equipped railway workshop was functional at Moghalpura [Mughalpura] in Lahore and mechanical artisans were trained there. The Indian Industrial Commission chaired by Sir Thomas Holland submitted a detailed report in 1918 after two years of deliberations. One of its important recommendations was adequate academic training for the apprentices. The scheme for an engineering college thus got initiated in 1919 primarily for railway workshop apprentices. The foundation stone of the Moghalpura Technical Institute was laid in 1921 by Sir Edward Douglas Maclagan (1864–1952), the Lieutenant Governor of Punjab. Maclagan was elevated as the first Governor of Punjab before his retirement in 1924. The Moghalpura Technical College which commenced admitting students in October 1923 was named Maclagan College of Engineering in 1924. It admitted 50 students in electrical and mechanical engineering in two types of classes, A and B. Course A was to provide theoretical and practical training for a career as an engineer. In 1932, Class A students became eligible for the BSc engineering degree at the University of Punjab. Course B trained its pupils for employment as technicians and associate engineers. From 1935 till 1950, the college conducted an 18-month Course C to produce artisans and skilled tradesmen.[53] A three-year civil engineering course was introduced in 1939.

Many doctors became wealthy through private practice. An untypical example is Badan Chandra Chaudhuri (1810–1907) who passed out from the Calcutta Medical College in 1841 and took appointment as a sub-assistant surgeon in the Imambara Hospital in Hughli. He retired in 1857 and set up a lucrative private practice. He multiplied his money manifold through wide and judicious investments in "zamindari, etc." When he died at the ripe old age of 97, his fortune was estimated to be 20 lakhs.[54]

Thanks to higher education at various levels, persons who had no pedigree or family wealth, attained eminence, became well-off and politically aware and took up community leadership positions. Engineering and medical education had a profound all-round impact. Students who succeeded because of professional education considered it their duty to support educational and intellectually-oriented initiatives in the country. In general, doctors became important members of the society and commanded respect in official and European circles. Since they were dealing with the human body, which recognizes no hierarchy or class distinction, they could speak with moral authority. Doctors and lawyers (who could quote English law to the British) came to play an important role in public life and nationalist movements.

Gilchrist Scholarships

In 1869, it became possible for the first time for meritorious Indian young men to go to Britain on scholarship to obtain an academic degree or prepare for the Indian Civil Service (ICS) examination. The Gilchrist Educational Trust prepared a scheme in consultation with the Secretary of State for India, according to which two Indian scholars drawn from all the three Presidencies were to be selected on the basis of an entrance examination, which was "analogous in character and difficulty" to the matriculation examination of the London University and which included papers on Latin as well as English language and English history. Open to native and Eurasian students, the scholarship enabled the winners to spend four to five years at London or Edinburgh University for graduation. The requirement of graduation was waived in case of such candidates as they gave "evidence that they are efficiently preparing themselves for the Civil Services examination." The trust paid £100 per annum to the scholar, while the government paid for the passage.

The trust was set up in accordance with the will of John Borthwick Gilchrist (1759–1841) who left a major part of his estate "for the Benefit, Advancement, and Propagation of Education and Learning in every part of the World" at the "absolute and uncontrolled discretion" of the trustees. Because of the prolonged litigation, which reached the House of Lords, the trust could come into existence only in 1865. Most scholars opted for law, literature, medicine, engineering or ICS. Candidates who availed of the scholarship for a degree in science were all drawn from Calcutta. They were three in number. Aghornath Chattopadhyaya (1850–1915), better remembered as Sarojini Naidu's father, won the scholarship in 1871. He has the distinction of being India's first doctorate in science (Chemistry) but regrettably he failed to live up to the promise. He availed of the scholarship at Edinburgh where in 1875 he was selected for the Hope Prize Scholarship. Next year, in May 1876, he won the two-year Baxter Physical Science Scholarship, which required its holder to take "the Degree of Doctor of Science in the first year of his tenure of it."[55] On return to India, Aghor Nath moved to Hyderabad where he rose to be the principal of Nizam College. Notwithstanding his brilliance as a student, he became a firm believer in alchemy. India's first geologist (Pramatha Nath Bose) and first modern chemist (P.C. Ray) were Gilchrist scholars. India's first modern physicist (Jagadish Chandra Bose) was also trained in England, but went on family money.

John Gilchrist: Brief Biography

It could hardly have been foreseen that shipment of rum from Calcutta to Australia would eventually benefit Indian science. Edinburgh-born John Gilchrist, who added the middle name Borthwick in 1806 by royal license, was trained at George Heriot's Hospital and served in the Royal Navy as a surgeon's mate for some time. He landed in Bombay in 1782 at his own expense and was admitted to the Bengal Medical Service in April 1783. However, his career as a doctor lasted barely two years. He became interested in Hindustani, the spoken language of North India, and set out to transform it into a classroom language. He published an English–Hindoostanee dictionary in two parts in 1787 and 1790, and Hindoostanee grammar in 1796. Over the years he wrote many books, some of which being "abridgement or amplification of others." In December 1798, he was appointed to give daily lessons to junior civil servants in Urdu and Persian.[56] When in 1800, Fort William's College, Calcutta, was opened for the instruction of young civil servants, Gilchrist was appointed as a Professor of Hindustani. He returned to Britain in 1804, but formally retired from the Company service only in 1809. On 30 October 1804, Gilchrist received an LLD from the Edinburgh University for his linguistic work.

In 1816, he moved to London to give private lessons in oriental languages to candidates for the Indian service.[57] Those days, service in the East India Company held great attraction for "sons of Gentlemen." A prerequisite for such an employment was knowledge of the eastern languages. All persons appointed as assistant surgeons were required by the Company to attend a course of his lectures on Hindustani and produce a certificate from him to that effect. The arrangement lasted six years, from 1819 to 1825. His conduct as instructor was considered unethical and brought him into disrepute. He misused his classroom authority to promote the sale of his heavily priced books. In 1828, he was appointed professor of Hindustani at London University to teach the language for free. He however fell ill and never took the post.

Two of his financial dealings ended up placing the trust on firm footing. In 1807, along with a partner, he established a bank in Edinburgh. However, the venture failed and the partnership was dissolved in 1815. During this period, he acquired 100 shares of the Commercial Bank of Scotland, which would subsequently through mergers become part of the Royal Bank of Scotland. These shares eventually fetched the trust a welcome amount of £38,000.[58]

Even more profitable for the trust was Gilchrist's dealings with Australia while still in Calcutta no details of which are known. A fellow Scottish surgeon, William Balmain (1762–1803), began his career as a surgeon's mate in the Royal Navy in 1780. Six years later, in 1786, he sailed with the first fleet that came to settle the new colony of New South Wales. On 26 April 1800, the Governor gave him gratis a land grant of 550 acres near Sydney. "William Balmain departed Sydney Town for England on 26 August 1800, never to return.[57] Twenty days before, he had transferred title to his 550 acres to former surgeon Gilchrist whom he probably met at Edinburgh during training in 1779–80".[59]

Earlier in the year, on 11 January 1800, Balmain received a shipment of 9000 gallons of rum from Calcutta (worth £9000 in Australian market). It is surmised that the Calcutta deal was financed by Gilchrist who was compensated by the transfer of Balmain estate. A part of the estate was sold by auction in 1836 in Gilchrist's own lifetime for £4000.[23] The remainder was sold for the substantial sum of £66,000 by the trust, which now had the financial strength to embark on its educational programme.

The scheme for India was gradually withdrawn towards the end of the 19th century. The details about the beneficiaries of the scheme while it lasted are not available in one place. Not all scholars did equally well. The Gilchrist connection has been noticed in passing in the biographies of some of the recipients. The information given is however not always reliable. At times, the dates given are wrong. Also, unsubstantiated claims have been made about a person having topped the examination or being the first one to earn such and such distinction. There is a need for a reliable, systematic and contextual study of the Indian Gilchrist scholars with reference to India, on the basis of the trust archives at the University College London and other sources. Table 8.1 gives an incomplete list of early scholars, mostly based on documents accessible on the internet, including the official lists of students of the London and Edinburgh Universities.

TABLE 8.1 Early Gilchrist Scholars 1869–1882

Year	Name	College in India	University/College in Britain	Remarks
1869	Anundoram Borooah (1850–1889)	Presidency College, Calcutta	London	ICS, 1872. Sanskrit scholar
1869	H.L. Simmons	St Xavier's College, Calcutta	–	Could not avail because of health
1870	Alfred John Read	La Martiniere School, Calcutta	London, BA, 1878	Joined the bar at Rangoon
1870	Prasanna Kumar Ray (1849–1932)	Dacca College	London, BSc, 1874 London & Edinburgh, DSc, 1876	First Indian Principal, Presidency College, Calcutta
1871	Srinath Datta	Presidency College, Calcutta	London	
1871	Aghornath Chattopadhyay (1850–1915)	Presidency College, Calcutta	Edinburgh BSc. (Phys) 1875; DSc. (Chem) 1876	Principal, Nizam College, Hyderabad. Father of Sarojini Naidu.
1872	Nunda Kumar Ray	Presidency College, Calcutta	London	
1872	Balai Narayan Das [Barua] =Bolinarayan Borrah (1852–1927)	Presidency College, Calcutta	Royal Indian Engineering College, Coopers Hill, 1877.	Joined PWD 1878. Married P.N. Bose's wife's sister. Kaisar-i-Hind, May 1900
1873	?			
1874	Pramatha Nath Bose	St Xavier's College, Calcutta	London, BSc. 1877	Officer in Geological Survey of India; Geologist Mayurbhanj; Advised J.N. Tata on iron ore.
1875	Upendra Krishna Dutt (1857–1938)		London, medicine	Practitioner, Father of the Marxist Rajani Palme Dutt.
1876	Matilal Gupta	Presidency College, Calcutta	London, LLB, 1882	Inner Temple. Brother of Bihari Lala Gupta ICS

(Continued)

TABLE 8.1 (Continued)

Year	Name	College in India	University/College in Britain	Remarks
1876	?			
1878	Phani Bhusan Mukerji		London, BSc, 1882	Professor, Hooghly College, Inspector of Schools, Presidency Division, Bengal
1879	Joseph Rosamond Adie (d. 1915)	La Martiniere College, Lucknow	London, MB, and MRCS, 1884	Indian Medical Service, Lieutenant Colonel
1879	Parvati Nath Dutta (d. 1944)	Medical College, Calcutta	London, B.Sc. 1885	Joined the Geological Survey of India in 1888.
1880	Basanta Kumar Basu	Medical College, Calcutta	London	Did not complete graduation
1880	Charles E. Samuel	St Xavier's College, Calcutta		
1881	Mancherji Pestanji Kharegat (1864–1943)	St Xavier's College, Bombay	Balliol College, Oxford	ICS 1884
1882	Prafulla Chandra Ray (1861–1944)	Metropolitan College, Calcutta	Edinburgh, B.Sc. (Phys), 1886; D. Sc. (Chem.),1887	Professor of chemistry at Presidency College, Calcutta, and Calcutta University
1882	Kaikhushroo Nusserwanji Bahadurji (1860–1898)	St Xavier's College, Bombay	London	MD, Professor, Grant Medical College Bombay

Notes

1 It was replaced by Council of Education in 1842.
2 At the time, the letter u was used to denote short a (thus Umballa for Ambala); no distinction was made between short and long u. The spelling Hindoo occurs in the rules of the College. At some later stage, spellings were changed to the more modern form.
3 Reproduced at https://mathshistory.st-andrews.ac.uk/Extras/Calcutta_Review_1850/.
4 De Morgan, 1859.
5 https://mathshistory.st-andrews.ac.uk/Extras/De_Morgan_1859_Preface/.
6 Andrews, 1929, 36–37.
7 Ray, 1918, 175–176.
8 Pres. Coll. 100, 1956, 3.
9 Fisher's Memoir, 1833, 270.
10 Crawford, 1914, 2, 119.
11 *Lancet*, 1826, 10, 690.
12 *Lancet*, 1826, 10, 690.
13 Scott's daughter Augusta's son David Scott Mitchell (1836–1907) was the benefactor of the Mitchell Library in Sydney.
14 Leffler et al., 2020.
15 *Asiatic Journal*, 1837, 23, 12.
16 Ray, 1990, 150–151.
17 Khaleeli, 2001, 77.
18 Deb, 1905, 88, footnote.
19 Kumar, 1997, 167 is wrong in saying that Chuckerbutty converted before leaving for England.
20 *Lancet*, 1848, 14 October.
21 Deb, 1905, 88, footnote.
22 Kochhar, 2021, 87.
23 Crawford, 1914, 2, 447.
24 General Report on Public Instruction in the Lower Provinces of the Bengal Presidency, 1856–1857, pp. 198–199.
25 General Report on Public Instruction in the Lower Provinces of the Bengal Presidency, 1870-1871, p. 73.
26 Kochhar, 2008b.
27 Richey, 1922, 336.
28 *Bombay Education Review*, 1956, 312.
29 *Bombay Education Review*, 1956, 312.
30 Cursetjee, 1840, ii.
31 Cursetjee, 1840, iii.
32 Kochhar, 1993b.
33 Kochhar, 2008b.
34 Shridharani, 1953, 21.
35 Shridharani, 1956, 160.
36 He was the son of Reverend Thomas Thomason.
37 General Report on Public Instruction in the North Western Province for 1843–1844, App. D, p. vi.
38 General Report on Public Instruction in the North Western Province for 1843–1844, p. 3.
39 General Report on Public Instruction in the North Western Province for 1843–1844, p. 3.
40 Account of Roorkee College, 1851, p. 5 (Agra: Secundra Orphan Press).
41 Thomason Civil Engineering College Calendar for 1929, p. 27.

42 A student of the drawing class gained fame in an entirely different context. Shiv Narayan Agnihotri (1850–1929) joined the class in 1866, became a drawing master in Government School Lahore and went on to found Dev Samaj, in 1887.

43 Thomason Civil Engineering College Roorkee Calendar for 1929, p. 20.

44 Thomason Civil Engineering College Roorkee Calendar for 1914, p. 18. Pp. 15–32 give the history of the College up to 1914.

45 Thomason Civil Engineering College Roorkee Calendar for 1914, p. 18.

46 Minutes of the Proceedings of the Institution of Civil Engineers, 1888, 94, 313–317.

47 Bruce, 1933, 54.

48 Bedi, 1940, 22.

49 No further details are available.

50 Minutes of the Proceedings of the Institution of Civil Engineers 1852, 1, 106–109.

51 Ritchey, 1922, 35.

52 Bom. Edu, 1958, 340.

53 Naz, 2004.

54 Crawford, 1914, 2, 77 & 441.

55 Edinburgh University Calendar for 1878–1879, pp. 149, 342.

56 Crawford, 1914, 2, 170.

57 James, 1979, 236.

58 *Journal of the National Indian Association*, 1881, 427.

59 Reynolds, 2014, 12.

9

CULTIVATION OF SCIENCE IN 19TH-CENTURY BENGAL

Culturally, Calcutta and Bombay developed along different lines. Bombay, for long an isolated British possession, focused on commerce. Calcutta, the imperial capital, on the other hand, came with its vast hinterland where Cornwallis' Permanent Settlement of land revenue created a class of absentee landlords with small to large holdings. Government interest and investment in the education of Bengal's upper castes was sustained and very high. Calcutta remained largely untouched by engineering and technology and was drawn to science through the colonial education system.

The 1860s and 1870s were conflicting times for Bengal. The Hindu leadership was still in the hands of the landed class which was coming under increasing pressure to yield place to the new self-made middle class. The first ever Indian initiative for a middle-class organization was in the name of science. Because of science, it could seek and obtain goodwill and support from the government as well as the landed class. In December 1869, Dr Mahendra Lal Sircar launched a campaign for the establishment of the Indian Association for the Cultivation of Science which came up on 29 July 1876. Three days earlier, the same set of people who were associated with the Science Association set up a political organization, the Indian Association, which became the precursor of the Indian National Congress.

While the Science Association was in the subscription stage, Calcutta University introduced science into its system. Chemistry stood apart from other scientific disciplines; it was a part of the British Indian governance. The Ghazipur opium factory had a post of opium chemist. Various government departments of industry hired industrial chemists while the Calcutta Municipal Corporation maintained a chemical laboratory. Unlike other industrial products, it was not very viable to import sulphuric, nitric and hydrochloric acids.

DOI: 10.4324/9781003466406-9

Being hazardous, these chemicals could only be brought in as deck cargo, which entailed heavy freight making their landed cost prohibitively high. A Scottish immigrant Dr David Waldie (1813–1889) who arrived in Calcutta in 1853 set up chemical works for manufacturing mineral acids in large quantities. Limited amounts were produced by three or four small units through "primitive and wasteful methods."[1]

Chemistry had to wait another 50 years for a second chance. In the meantime, from 1863 till 1875, Henry Francis Blanford (1834–1893) of the Geological Survey of India served as a broad-spectrum professor of natural science at Presidency College Calcutta where he taught the outlines of a number of subjects ranging from physical geography to physics.[2] In 1872, Calcutta University permitted First Arts (FA) students to opt for chemistry in place of psychology. Also, BA was split into two streams: the traditional A course (literature) and the new B (science) course. Two years later, chemistry (along with physical geography) was made a compulsory subject for the B course while two papers in physical science were made optional.[3] Science gained immediate popularity. In 1874, among the 96 regular FA candidates in Presidency College, as many as 83 opted for chemistry. Similarly, in the BA examination, 60 out of 84 opted for science in the third year and 48 out of 84 in the fourth year.[4]

While the Science Association was being campaigned for, the government undertook a number of science-related steps. Two science professors were appointed. It was left to the far-sighted and therefore unpopular. Lieutenant Governor Sir George Campbell (tenure 1871–1874) asked for specialist professors in chemistry and botany (Ray, 1918, p. 21). [Sir] Alexander Pedlar (1849–1918) joined in 1874 at the young age of 25 and later rose to become the Vice-Chancellor of Calcutta University. For his own research done in India, including on cobra poison, he was elected a Fellow of the Royal Society in 1892. He can truly be called the founder of chemistry education in India. Similarly, [Sir] George Watt came as a professor of botany at Hughli College and later moved to Krishnagar.

"Under instruction from the Government," Pedlar "came with a considerable supply of chemical apparatus" and started practical classes in 1875.[5] Presidency College Calcutta was the best-funded college in the whole of the country and the only one in Calcutta, apart from St Xavier's, which offered science. Other private colleges did not have the resources to do so. Their students were however permitted to attend classes in Presidency College on payment of a small fee. The popularity of science can be gauged from the number of these out-students. The number was four in 1871 and zero in both 1872 and 1873. But with the arrival of new equipment, the number rose rapidly. It was 14 in 1874; 21 in 1875; 45 in 1876; and as high as 63 in 1882. However as the science facilities were increased in non-government colleges, there was a sharp fall in the number of out-students so that by 1884, "this class of students disappeared altogether."[6]

Pedler recommended the appointment of an additional member of the faculty. The addition, in 1889, of P.C. Ray turned out to be historically significant. The Presidency College chemistry laboratory refurbished in 1893 helped P.C. Ray attain international fame as an experimental chemist and also found a flourishing school (see below). India would go on to establish a successful chemical industry which in turn has led to a pharmaceutical industry now known the world over for its ability to produce generic drugs at low cost. Although facilities existed for other science subjects, they did not receive the same attention as chemistry because chemistry was a compulsory subject while the others were not. Notwithstanding the science facilities in the Presidency and St Xavier's Colleges, the general lack of laboratory facilities made science education under university auspices mostly a theoretical exercise. Dr Chuni Lal Bose (1861–1930), who studied medicine at Calcutta Medical College, recalled while addressing the Science Association on 29 September 1920 that "in my student days it was possible for a B.A. student to pass his university examination in chemistry without entering a laboratory or touching a test tube." (Sen 1988: 11)

On arrival in India, Pedler's attention was markedly directed to the problem of snakebite which caused as many as 15,000 deaths per year. He carried out a chemical analysis of the cobra poison with a view to finding effective antidotes. On the basis of this work and other research, he was elected a Fellow of the Royal Society in 1892. Pedler was also an analyst for the municipality. Among his duties in this capacity was to send a daily report on the analysis of municipality water and gas supplies. He also had a private practice testing wines for big import firms. Ruchi Ram Sahni (1863–1948), the first Indian officer in the India Meteorology Department, spent three months in Calcutta, January–March 1885, as a trainee. Still nominally an MA student at Government College Lahore, he was permitted as a guest student in Presidency College Calcutta. It was the first time he was seeing a chemistry laboratory. Ruchi Ram describes the wine testing hierarchy. For the analysis of each bottle, Pedler was paid a substantial sum of Rs 32. He kept the money and passed on the bottle to his official assistant who in turn passed on a small quantity of wine to Ruchi Ram and happily enjoyed the rest. Ruchi Ram at the lowest rung of the ladder was also happy because he got valuable laboratory experience, be it on water, wine or gas.[7]

Mahendra Lal Sircar: Life Sketch

The major source of biographical information on Sircar is a fellow homeopath, Sarat Chandra Ghose, who first published an obituary of Sircar in 1904 in *The Hindustan Review and Kayastha Samachar*. This was expanded into a book in 1909, the second edition of which appeared in 1935.[8] This is a valuable source which has not been fully tapped by self-conscious historians because of its homeopathic orientation. Sircar was born on 2 November 1833 into a poor family in a small village named Paikpara some 30 km west of Howrah. He described himself "as a man of the people sprung from the actual tillers of the soil."[9] Later, his son thought it fit to remind the readers of his father's obituary that the family was "certainly not from what are called the lower orders of Society".[10] When he was five years old, his mother brought him and his younger six-month-old brother to her own brothers' house in Nebutola in Calcutta. A few days after his arrival in Calcutta, the death of his father occurred at Paikpara. The family went back for the last rites but soon returned to Calcutta for good. If Sircar's mother had to shift with her sons to her brothers' place even when her husband was alive, the family must have been extremely poor.[10] The mother also died four years later, due to cholera, leaving the orphaned boy in the care of his maternal uncles who themselves were not well off. A brilliant student, young Sircar received support from a number of people whom he always remembered with a sense of gratitude. He was sent to a traditional *pathshala* for learning Bengali and to a tutor for English. At the age of seven, he was admitted to David Hare's School where he received free education.

Sircar finished school in 1849 with a junior scholarship to go to Hindoo College where he won a senior scholarship. Sircar did not think much of Hindoo College where "the principal object of education was to teach the pupils how to read and write the English language."[11] His "fierce passion for science" made him shift to the Medical College, "the only place in those days where the students were given practical lessons in some of the more important sciences."[11]

Sircar joined the Medical College in early 1854 and passed the Licentiate in Medicine and Surgery examination in 1860. In the meantime, Calcutta University was set up in 1857. In 1862, Sircar successfully wrote to the university saying that his senior scholarship certificate be recognized as a BA diploma to enable him to sit for the MD examination.[12] He obtained his MD in 1863 in first class. As a private practitioner, Sircar was able to translate his academic brilliance into professional, financial and social success. When in 1863 the Bengal chapter of the British Medical Association was opened through the efforts of Dr Goodeve Chuckerbutty, Sircar became an active member.[13] After serving as its secretary for three years, he became a vice-president in 1867. However, much to the shock of his colleagues and former teachers, he took to homeopathy. He announced his conversion in February 1867 from the August platform of the Medical Association itself for which sin he was unceremoniously thrown out.[14]

After an initial setback, Sircar was soon able to establish a very successful and high-priced practice. In September 1874, he increased his fee for a single prescription in Calcutta from Rs 10 to Rs 16. Subsequently, it was further raised to a whopping Rs 32.[15] In 1875, he was charging as much as Rs 500 per day for an outstation visit.[16] He was consulted by many eminent, rich and influential personages of his time including the greatly revered mystic Ramakrishna Paramhans.[17] Sircar's medical contacts would stand him in good stead in his later fund-raising drive.

His social connectivity can be gauged from the fact that one January 1882 morning he called on the Calcutta University Vice-Chancellor with the audacious request that his son Amrita Lal be given some grace marks to enable him to pass the intermediate examination. It is a separate matter that the vice-chancellor refused to oblige.[18] His social rise began in 1883 when the popular liberal Viceroy, Lord Ripon, made him a Companion of the Indian Empire. He served as the sheriff of Calcutta (1887) and honorary presidency magistrate (1887–1902). He was a nominated member of the Bengal Legislative Council from 1887 to 1893. He remained an elected commissioner of the Calcutta Corporation for several years and made his mark on the Municipal Board, especially in the department of sanitation. For many years he was a trustee of the Indian Museum as a representative of the Asiatic Society.[19] In 1899 he was invited to give evidence before the Indian Plague Commission.[20]

He had a long association with the Calcutta University, which lasted till 1897. He was appointed a Fellow of the University in the Faculty of Arts for life with effect from 1871.[21] For ten successive years, he was a member of the Syndicate and frequently acted as its president in the absence of the Vice-Chancellor. He was also for four successive years, 1893–1897, president of the Faculty of Arts (Buckland, 1906: II: 1065). The University in 1898 bestowed on him the honorary degree of doctor not in science, but law, for "his labours in the cause of science" and for his service to the university. His efforts to become a member of the Medical Faculty failed.

He however did serve as an examiner for Medical College examinations. In spite of his own commitment to and public defence of homeopathy, it was not taught at the Science Association although Hahnemann's anniversary was celebrated.

Science Association: Manifesto

Within a year of his conversion to homeopathy, Sircar founded in January 1868 a journal called the *Calcutta Journal of Medicine* with the object of popularizing his new creed. It was billed as "a monthly record of medical and auxiliary sciences." In the issue brought out on 8 December 1869 (though nominally dated August 1869), Sircar published an essay entitled "On the desirability of a national institution for the cultivation of the Sciences by the natives of India." The essay was published separately as a pamphlet. This is a historically important document. It sought to use Indo-Europeanism to Indians' own advantage.[22]

Sircar begins by citing an article "On the teaching of natural science in schools" published in the July 1869 issue of the (British) *Quarterly Journal of Science.* He then makes an unnecessary digression charging the whole of Europe with being uncivilized by definition because

> Until men should learn to respect each other's honest convictions, and until they should be free from all prejudice, in other words, be fearless of the consequences of the discoveries in the fields of knowledge, they cannot be said to have become civilized men.[22]

This diatribe seems to be directed against critics of homeopathy.

Sircar then comes to his main thesis where he makes the first Indian use of the race theory. Where did he get his input from? Sircar became a life member of the British Association for the Advancement of Science in 1864. If he had at hand its earlier proceedings, he would have been familiar with Max Muller's paper, entitled "On the relation of the Bengali to the Arian and aboriginal languages of India," which was read at the 1847 meeting. Max Muller argued that Indians are "one great branch of the Caucasian race, differing from other branches of the same race merely by its darker complexion." He stated that

> it is curious to see how the [English] descendents of the same [Arian] race, to which the first conquerors and masters of India belonged, return ...to accomplish the glorious work of civilization, which had been left unfinished by their Aryan brethren.[23]

The phrase Aryan brethren, Max Muller's own coinage, profoundly influenced the thinking of Indian leadership throughout the 19th century. The charismatic Brahmo Samaj leader, Keshub Chunder Sen (1838–1884) declared at a public meeting in Calcutta in 1877: "Gentlemen, in the advent of British nation in India we see a reunion of parted cousins, the descendents of two different families of the ancient Aryan race."[24] In the far-off Durban in South Africa, Mohandas Gandhi addressed an open letter (before 19 December 1894) to the members of the Legislature Council and Legislative Assembly, protesting against the ill-treatment of the Indians, and circulated it among the Europeans in Natal. In it, Gandhi pointed out "that both the English and the Indians sprang from a common stock, called the Indo-Aryan".[25] [Indo-Aryan is wrong. It should have been Aryan]. In fact, Mohandas Gandhi becomes Mahatma Gandhi only when he jettisons this historiography.

Sircar argued that "the once glorious Hindu nation" has been "downtrodden for centuries by foreign yoke and a most de-energizing religion." The Hindu mind, thanks to this religion that has been swaying it for centuries without number, and thanks no less to its other surroundings, has lost "much or its original Aryan vigor" and energy. Fortunately, help was at hand for the all-important tasks of regeneration. The British increasingly recognized that they had "a duty to perform towards us," that is their "brethren, now fallen and degraded." It must be acknowledged with gratitude that England, despite all shortcomings inseparable from a foreign rule, is doing her duty right royally. She has become aware that her true glory "should consist not in simply holding under subjection the people of India, but in elevating them in the scale of nations, in taking them by hand and reconciling them to their long alienated brethren, her own children" [that is, the English people themselves]. "Let us thank Heaven then, that though nominally under a foreign power... we have fuller opportunities of developing the ends of our being, of fulfilling our destiny."

The Western scientific methodology could reside harmoniously with "tradition" in the Sircar household. There is an interesting entry dated 11 December 1890 in the diary of Sircar's son Dr Amrita Lal Sircar, himself an LMS

Father's *alwan* [a kind of shawl] and a pair of golden spectacles have been stolen. Nothing could be made out as to the party who did the action, and therefore Kamiruddin of Danga Digha has been brought down to find out the man by nalachalaa [some sort of divination to catch the thief]. He will do it tomorrow.[26]

Nalachalaa was indeed done on 12 December 1890 (Friday), "but the final decision could not be arrived at. So the man will again come on Monday and then he says he will come to a definite decision." It is not known how the story ended.[26]

Sircar was clear that

The best method...the only method... by which the Hindu mind can be developed to its full proportions is... by the cultivation of the Physical Sciences. The great defects, inherent and acquired, ... of the Hindu mind... of the present day can only be remedied by the training which results from the investigation of natural phenomena.[22]

The envisaged institution "shall be for the instruction of the masses, where lectures on scientific subjects will be systematically delivered, and not only illustrative experiments performed by the lecturers, but the audience should be invited and taught to perform them themselves."[22] "And we wish that this Institution be entirely under native management and control" so that "we may begin to learn the value of self-reliance without any serious risk."[22]

Where would money come from for the proposed science institution? Sircar hoped that the Rajahs and noblemen

will be willing...to spend a fraction of their wealth for such a glorious purpose as the amelioration, nay regeneration, of their own country, when their ancestors could spend so liberally on such ignoble and ridiculous occasions as the marriages and burials of dogs and cats.

Sircar also hoped that aid would be forthcoming "especially from the English community," to which "it will be gratifying to see that we have at last learnt to beg for such noble purposes, which we must gratefully set to the credit of their own example."[22] Finally, to reassure the administration and fellow loyalists, he hoped that the foundation stone of "the Temple of Positive Science" [quotes in the original] would be laid by the Prince of Wales during his forthcoming visit.

Later in 1872, no doubt bowing to the public opinion, he tried to tone down his criticism of the traditional society and declared:

> It is hardly necessary for me to formally declare that I have never meant the cultivation of the physical sciences to be a panacea for all ills incident in human nature, and certainly I never meant that the Association in question was the only remedy I could propose for the evils that teem to my unfortunate country.[27]

In subsequent campaign writings, he tended to use the term Indian rather than Hindu. However, in 1891 he recalled: "It is to help in reluming the light of knowledge in the breasts of my countrymen in order to restore their old Aryan vigour of intellect, that this Association has been established (p. 362)."[22]

Far more significant is the response of Sircar's contemporary, the well-known Bengali author, Bankim Chandra Chatterjee (1838–1894), who wrote an article in 1872 in his popular magazine *Bangadarshan* advocating the cause of the Science Association.[28] He also gave a donation of Rs 500 on 14 January 1876.[29] Bankim seems to have drawn on the Sircar thesis while bringing his influential novel *Anandamath* to a close. As we shall see in the next section, a December 1875 report prepared by the provisional committee called "the restoration and elevation of the people of India" as "the mission of England."[30] More specifically, Sircar in the sketch of the scheme for the proposed Science Association declared in the closing paragraph that he had "a right to expect aid from all countries and peoples, especially from those which are enjoying the advantages and privileges of the cultivation of science."[31] Going overboard in December 1875, Sircar wrote on the eve of the visit of Prince of Wales to India:

> I hope that the Prince in whose veins runs the best blood of the most intellectual nations of Europe, will lend a helping hand in laying the foundation of an institution which will be a pledge as it were of England's good wishes to India, and serve as a lasting monument to remind India's children of the debt immense of India's gratitude they owe for their intellectual moral revivification to England's noble sons.[32]

In *Anandamath*, after the sanyasis have crushed the Muslim rebellion and wish to take on the English, a Healer (*Chikitsak*) appears on the scene.

This Healer could have been Dr Mahendra Lal Sircar himself even though transported a century back. The Healer explains that knowledge is of two kinds: outward and inward. "For a long time now the outward knowledge has been lost in this land, and so the true Eternal Code has also been lost."[33] It is noteworthy that in the first edition of *Anandamath*, Bankim used *Arya dharma* in place of the Eternal Code (*sanatana dharma*). The Healer continues:

> The outward knowledge no longer exists in this land...The English are very knowledgeable in the outward knowledge, and they are very good at instructing people. Therefore we'll make them king. And when by this teaching our people are well instructed about external things...the true Code shall shine forth by itself again.[33]

This point about Sircar possibly having been the model for Bankim's *Chikitsak* does not seem to have been made before.

Campaign

Sircar wanted his institution to be like the Royal Institution and the British Association for the Advancement of Science. The Royal Institution came about in response to the dual revolutions: the industrial and the French.[34] It was established in 1799 by "improving landlords," who decided to improve the level of food production by scientific means in order to mitigate the problems of the poorer classes.[34] However, since the number of such landlords was too small to sustain the institution, its base was soon expanded to include the professional classes. The British Association, founded in 1831, "was able to combine the cultivators of science into a body politic, an intellectual union which was able not only to offer advice to the government but also to secure attention to that advice."[35] Both were irrelevant for India as in Sircar's time neither had improving landlords nor men of science. Nor was there any counterpart in India of the strains caused in Europe by the Industrial and the French revolutions.

Sircar's Science Association project was not driven by any historical necessity. It did not fulfil any felt need. No wonder then that the type of funding and support Sircar had envisaged was not forthcoming. If Sircar was able to establish his institution and sustain it for three decades without any regular source of income or grant, it was due to his tenacity. It of course helped that he was a successful physician and in the good books of the government.

We can distinguish between three phases in the campaign for an early sustenance of the Science Association. (i) The first phase, extending from 1870 through 1874, during which Sircar tried to generate enthusiasm for the project on his own strength. (ii) The second phase, from 10 March 1875 when the Lieutenant Governor, Sir Richard Temple, showed interest in the project till the Association's inauguration by Temple on 29 July 1876. During this period, Sircar had to guard against subversion by Temple, raise funds and also gain legitimacy from the community through widespread support. This is the most fascinating part of the campaign often sanitized by the assertion that Temple supported the project. (iii) The third phase ran from the establishment of the association till Sircar's death in 1904. During it, Sircar sustained himself through large donations from wealthy people even if the support he received remained below his expectations.

The scheme when announced was well received by the press. A brief three-paragraph prospectus was published in the *Hindoo Patriot* on 3 January 1870, the influential mouthpiece of the British Indian Association. Through it "[A]ll well-wishers of Progress and of India" were "solicited to contribute their quota in furtherance of the project."[36] (p. 46) The first donor was the eminent zamindar from Uttarpara, Joykissen Mookerjee, who paid a rather small sum of Rs 1000. Iswarchandra Vidyasagar also contributed the same amount. Donations from the landed class were not substantially higher than those from the professional class.[36] The first year of soliciting (1870) brought in 17 subscribers/donors. The number fell sharply after that: to seven in 1871, five in 1872, only two in 1873 (including Sircar himself who gave Rs 1000), and zero in 1874. The only saving grace was an unexplained contribution of 5000 rupees in 1870 from the Maharaja of the far-off Patiala. In 1874, the Maharaja of Kashmir's "Chief Justice and General Manager" Nilambar Mukherjee told Sircar that the Maharaja was willing to "patronize the Science Association" by paying the substantial sum of 300,000 rupees provided the institution was set up in Benaras, the ancient seat of learning, but Sircar was not ready to move away from his home ground.[37] It is not known what Sircar's link to Patiala was. Did he render unrecorded medical service to the Maharaja? Or, did a high official in Patiala have a Bengal connection like in Kashmir? In 1884, Sircar offered to go to Kashmir to treat the Maharaja for his hereditary diabetes, provided the Maharaja made a contribution to the Science Association. The matter however remained undecided.[38]

Father Eugene Lafont

Sircar found a valuable ally in the Belgian Jesuit priest, Father Eugene Lafont (1837–1908), the science professor at St Xavier's College Calcutta. He was the first European to discuss modern science with Indians. No doubt, there were British men of science in India but they kept their distance from the natives. For 17 long years, from 1876 till 1893, he uninterruptedly lectured at the Association and was "one of its perpetual Vice-Presidents".

Lafont was born in Mons, South Belgium, and admitted into the Society of Jesus in December 1854. He was first educated at St Barbara's College,

Ghent, and then at (1863–1865), Jesuit College, Namur (now a university). In the meantime, the Belgian Province of the Society of Jesus opened the Bengal Mission in Calcutta which in turn established St Xavier's College in Calcutta on 16 January 1860. Lafont arrived in Calcutta in December 1865 to teach at St Xavier's College, with which he remained associated till his death. In 1869, Lafont was ordained and made a vicar and then the priest at St Thomas Parish. He held the charge for more than 20 years. He owes his place in history to science rather than faith. He was the Rector of the college from 1871 to 1878 and then again from 1901 to 1904. He visited Europe twice, during 1878–1879 for health reasons and in 1900 to see the Paris exhibition. Both times, he brought back the latest scientific equipment.

Lafont began by teaching school pupils, but in 1867 when BA classes were opened he was transferred to the college section where he taught natural philosophy and also mental and moral philosophy. Lafont converted a small part of the terrace of the college building into a laboratory and furnished it with barometers and thermometers. Noting a sharp fall in the barometer reading of atmospheric pressure on the morning of 1 November 1867, he predicted the impending arrival of a severe cyclone, which dutifully made its presence felt the same evening. The prediction helped limit the damage and enhanced his prestige in the government circles as well as the native society. It also facilitated the establishment in the college of a valued meteorological laboratory.[39]

He did not know English when he arrived, but by 1870 he had gained fluency in it. He was not an "original thinker or original worker", but he was an excellent teacher and science communicator who "did yeoman service for science in Bengal."[40] St Xavier's College was a prestigious institution. Its students were drawn from "the domiciled European and Eurasian population of Calcutta and Lower Bengal," and in this way, he "secured great influence among these classes." The College was "also popular with native Indian gentlemen, and by his influence with Rajas and other men of note, Lafont was able to obtain several endowments for the purchase of scientific apparatus." The College possessed "an excellent supply of most costly lecture apparatus, especially of the kind necessary for popular science demonstration, in which way that college is better equipped than any in India."[40]

Like Sircar, Lafont was well honoured in his own lifetime. He was made a Companion of the Indian Empire in 1880 and also Officer de l'Academie de France (1886). His own King of Belgium made him a Knight of the Order of Leopold (1898). In 1877, Calcutta University appointed him a Fellow of the Senate for life, which in turn elected him to the Syndicate a number of times.[41] Calcutta University awarded him an honorary doctorate in science in 1908, the year such a degree was introduced.[42] Recall that Sircar was given a doctorate in law, not science.

The 1874 Transit of Venus brought in an Italian team led by Pietro Tacchini (1838–1905) of Palermo Observatory, which set up an observing station in

Muddapur with full support and participation from Lafont. The temporary event produced a permanent result. Tacchini persuaded Lafont to establish a spectroscopic observatory in his college for which he himself drew the plan. Temple who held office from April 1874 till January 1877 (when he was transferred to Bombay as Governor) visited Lafont on 5 February 1875 accompanied by Mr Mountstuart Elphinstone Grant-Duff. "By the end of the month, the Government of Bengal sanctioned a grant of Rs 5000 towards the erection of the observatory, on condition that a like sum be gathered by private subscription before the end of March."[43] Lafont's appeal for public funds was enthusiastically received. "A special performance was given at the Opera's theatre of Calcutta for the proposed Observatory."[44] A total of Rs 21,000 was soon collected, the construction of the building began, and high-class equipment was ordered from Europe.[45] The first ever attempt to introduce basic modern scientific research outside the government failed to take off.

It is likely that during Temple's visit to St Xavier's, Lafont put in a word for Sircar.[46] Sircar met Temple briefly on 10 March 1875 on the latter's invitation. After the meeting, Sircar claimed that Temple had supported his scheme. In the absence of any official record of the meeting or reference to it in Temple's published memoirs, it is not possible to say what exactly transpired at the meeting. We learn from Sircar's diary that he rather sheepishly "put on trousers and *chapkan [jacket]* and a *pagri [turban]*" for the occasion. "It appeared from the conversation we had with the Lt Governor that I could appear with my ordinary dress, even with my slippers."[47] It is curious that Sircar did not record in his diary anything more substantial than this trivia about the momentous meeting.

Sircar's name does not figure at all in Temple's reminiscences. If Temple's official reports and actions, subsequent writings as also the official archives since made available are any guide, it is very likely that Sircar was putting a spin on the outcome of the meeting for local consumption. Temple could not possibly have asked Sircar to start the institution as Sircar had envisioned. Temple supported the proposal only to the extent that he did not reject it outright. The relationship between the colonial government and the native leadership had already become quite complex. The government was wary of opposing a cause that seemed to command native support. Native support in turn was forthcoming if the government seemed to be positively inclined.

The news that the Lieutenant Governor had invited Sircar for a private audience enhanced Sircar's prestige among the native gentlemen, who saw themselves as distinct from ordinary natives and changed the Association's fortunes.

The Native Gentlemen

The first meeting of the subscribers came about five long years after the prospectus was issued but within four weeks of the Sircar–Temple meeting.

From 1870 up to the meeting, Sircar had been able to enlist only 32 subscribers (including himself) who paid an average of slightly less than Rs 1700. Now a month's labour brought in as many as 35 donors even though their contribution per person was only Rs 400.[48] By 1876 end, Sircar had collected about 100,000 rupees from 171 subscribers. Later subscribers were more numerous but low-paying. This division suited Sircar fine because a large number of low-paying subscribers spelt widespread support for Sircar and bestowed legitimacy on the project. Once the project got going, Sircar targeted big donors. The number of subscribers would drop down to 100 in 1901.[49]

First Subscribers' Meeting

At the first subscribers' meeting, held on 4 April 1875, Sircar described his recent meeting with Temple thus:

> At this stage, an impetus comes from an unexpected quarter. His Honor, the Lieutenant-Governor, animated with an ardent love of the sciences, full of zeal for the introduction of science teaching into our educational institutions, accidentally hears of my project, and becoming acquainted with its scope and objects, so far as I could in a short conversation render them intelligible, asks me to start the Institution, and His Honor goes so far as to hint that some aid might be granted from Government.

Curiously, as Sircar continued he himself did not sound very confident of the government support. He insisted rather defensively that while government aid would be most welcome, the institution would be "solely native and purely national." "And, I believe,... that His Honor, far from being desisted from granting us the contemplated aid, will come forward as generously with it, as His Honor has done with reference to the spectro-telescopic observatory of Father Lafont."[50]

Four days after the meeting, that is on 8 April 1875, Sircar sent a letter to Temple. The letter itself does not seem to be on record but we learn about its contents from the reply it elicited from Temple. The reply dated 3 May 1875 and sent by the private secretary quotes Sircar as

> explaining that the meeting intended to be held on behalf of the Scientific Society had been postponed, and that it is proposed to hold a meeting at some future time, or whenever His Honor might be in Calcutta, and expressing your [Sircar's] hope that he will accord a general support to the Society's operations.[51]

Temple's detailed response to Sircar's letter is historically important because it was the first time he was engaging himself with the native leadership on the important question of education. It would be instructive to place Temple's response in a larger context.

Quasi-disloyal Discontent

Those were the days when the British were getting increasingly worried about the discontent among educated Indians, especially in Bengal, and were keen to modify the extant education policy. The colonial authorities indeed had many occasions to recall the blunt assessment of Lord Ellenborough, who was the Viceroy from 1842 till 1844, that English education was "the surest means of putting an end to British rule in India."[52] His prescription in 1858 as the Secretary of State for India was:

> Education and civilization may descend from the higher to the inferior classes, and so communicated may impart new vigour to the community, but they will never ascend from the lower classes to those above them; they can only, if imparted, solely to the lower classes, tend to general convulsion, of which foreigners would be the first victims. If we desire to diffuse education, let us endeavour to give it to the higher classes first.[53]

Ellenborough would have approved of the 1870 founding of Mayo College, Ajmer, where "the sons of Chiefs, Princes and leading Thakurs" would be educated and taught British values.

Lord Mayo, who was Viceroy from 1868 till 1872, wrote to a retired judge friend of his back home in England:

> In Bengal we are educating in English a few hundred Bábus at great expense to the State. Many of them ... have no other object in learning than to qualify for Government employ. In the meanwhile we have done nothing towards extending knowledge to the million. The Bábus will never do it. The more education you give them, the more they will try to keep it to themselves, ... If you wait till the bad English, which the four hundred Bábus learn in Calcutta, filters down into the 40 millions of Bengal, you will be ultimately a Silurian rock instead of a retired judge. Let the Bábus learn English by all **means**. But let us also try to do something towards teaching the three R's to 'Rural Bengal'.[54]

Through a resolution dated 9 September 1869, the Government of India "expressed disapproval of the expenditure of large public funds on higher education to the detriment of the vernacular education." The beneficiaries of English education were not ready to accept this lying down. At a big public meeting held on 2 July 1870 in Calcutta under the auspices of the British Indian Association, a resolution was moved by Joykissen Mookerjee and seconded by Sircar. Joykissen asserted that "the country's advancement in every direction was due to English education," and that "the Indian army-men would not have joined the Mutiny of 1857 had they enjoyed the benefits of English education." He warned that "nothing should be done to starve the English institutions for the sake of feeding vernacular schools."[55] Unmindful of the public sentiment, Sir George Campbell, Lieutenant Governor during 1871–1874, "pursued with energy the policy of encouraging primary education, [and] discouraging the expansion of English education so eagerly sought by the bhadralok."[56] He paid for his initiative with his job.

The Bengal middle class's hostility to the move to encourage primary education can be gauged from the comments made in London in 1871 by Surendranath Banerjee who had then just joined the Indian Civil Service and would emerge as an important national leader. While participating in a discussion on a paper on "Popular education in India" read by an India-returned former civil servant, William Tayler, Banerjee loftily agreed that "We all recognize the great importance of mass education. We all know it would be impossible to civilize India without it."[57] But he warned that "it is unwise on the part of Government to withdraw the aid it gives to high English education for the purpose of mass education." Banerjee declared that "I, for one, would stand up for English education" as against the vernacular, adding that "We have had enough of the stories of the wars between gods and goblins in the Ramayana and other works. At the present moment we ought to give them an education which will make them ...better men."[57] (p. 26-27) Banerjee's use of the term civilizing India in the context of mass education is significant. By this time, the Indian baboos had started speaking the language of the colonialists while the more sensitive British India officials were taking a more progressive line partly out of conviction and partly with the object of putting the middle class in its place.

By now, the English-knowing middle class was sufficiently large, self-assured and articulate to protect and advance its class interests. If Campbell rooted for grass-root level education, Temple sought a solution in technical education. But Temple had no intention of going the Campbell way. Instead of forcing his solution down the native throats he tried to carry them along. If he eventually failed, it was not for want of trying. In the "Lieutenant-Governor's Resolution" appended to the annual report of the Director of Public Instruction, Temple persistently put forward his thesis. Para 19 of the 1873–1874 report asserts:

The Lieutenant-Governor would impress upon all concerned that one main object of scientific and technical education is to enable the rising generation in Bengal to earn their own living in practical pursuits, such as mechanics, engineering, surveying, mensuration, the higher branches of agriculture, the special culture of valuable products and the like...

Continuing in the same vein in the next year's report (1874–1875), Temple talks of "engrafting upon our education system (which is mainly of a general and literary character) of the study of practical sciences," on the ground that "If the educated youth are to find employment, there really is no alternative but that a portion of them should resort to those employments…for which practical sciences afford the indispensable qualification." Significantly, the report records that the Lieutenant Governor "has encouraged the wealthier and more enlightened classes of the natives to bestir themselves on this behalf." These unquestionable views were for record. Clues to the philosophy behind them come from a letter Temple wrote on 18 February 1875 to the Viceroy, Lord Northbrook, referring to the "quasi-disloyal dissatisfaction" displayed in the Bengali press

> No doubt the alumni of our schools and colleges do become as a class discontented. But this arises from our higher education being too much in the direction of law, public administration, and prose literature, where they may possibly imagine… that they may approach to competition with us. But we shall do more and more to direct their thought towards practical science, where they must inevitably feel their utter inferiority to us.[58]

Temple felt constrained in Bengal because Calcutta University was under the direct control of the Viceroy. He did try unsuccessfully in 1877 to set up a university for Bengal distinct from the "all India" Calcutta University.[59] But when he went to Bombay as Governor (1877–1879), he also became the Chancellor of Bombay University. His initiatives there are worth noting because they provide a glimpse into his thinking.

Bombay University

At Bombay, Temple could implement some of his ideas. He introduced drawing as an optional subject in secondary schools. To him goes also the credit for the introduction of agricultural education in 1879 in the Bombay Presidency.[60] He also introduced the BSc degree in Bombay. He later recalled:

> By this time [1879] a project long in my contemplation was matured. This was the conferring of Degrees in Physical Science. I thought at Bombay, as in Calcutta, that the superior instruction had been too exclusively literary, and had not been sufficiently directed to the Physical Science which might lead to practical results. At Calcutta I had been powerless to remedy this, but at Bombay I was Chancellor, and had power to nominate the Fellows of the Governing Body. As vacancies occurred, I had accordingly nominated men of science as well as persons of literary distinction. Thus the science element was by degrees raised to its due proportion. I remember

that at the decisive meeting the requisite motion was made in my presence by Dr (afterwards Sir Guyon) Hunter. Thus was passed a scheme of Science Degrees, more adequate than anything which had as yet been attempted in India.[61]

The decisive Senate meeting Temple refers to was held on 12 April 1879. It was unprecedented in the history of Bombay University that a business meeting of the Senate (other than convocation, etc.) was chaired by the Chancellor himself. The course for the proposed degree comprised English, mixed mathematics, physical geography and one of the following: physics, zoology, botany, and geology. Since there was yet no Faculty of Science the BSc degree was instituted in the Faculty of Arts. Science students came from Engineering College at Poona which offered geology, chemistry, botany, forestry and agriculture and from Grant Medical College in Bombay which established a chair in biology.[62] Bombay University thus became the first university in the country to award BSc in 1882. However, the prominent nationalist leader Sir Pherozeshah Mehta criticized Temple for his attempts to run the university as a government department.[63] Allahabad University followed with a science course in 1897, Punjab University, Lahore, in 1902, and the Calcutta in 1907. It is a separate matter that the course did not become very popular. In 1901–1902, only 13 candidates took it: six in Bombay, three in Allahabad, two each in Calcutta and Punjab and none in Madras. The

> institution of the B.Sc. degree in 1907 [in Calcutta] gave a fresh impetus to the study of Science. A candidate for a Science degree was now relieved of the heavy handicap of taking up English literature as one of his subjects, and he was in a position to devote more time and attention to Science. He had on the other hand to go through a systematic training on the practical side.[64]

Lieutenant Governor's Response to Sircar

With this background into Temple's own thinking, we return to the letter written on his behalf on 3 May 1875 in reply to Sircar's letter of 8 April 1875. The reply pointedly refers to a "spontaneous and unaided effort on the part of the natives themselves to promote the spread of practical science among the people of Bengal." The use of the term "unaided" suggests that Temple had no intention of financially supporting Sircar's scheme. The mention of practical science is Temple's way of pointing out where his own preferences lay.

Conceding for the sake of politeness that "Science may be pursued for its own sake in the abstract and for the mental pleasure it affords" and "there doubtless are many native gentlemen in Bengal who will thus pursue it," the Lieutenant Governor went on to painstakingly argue that "Science also may be made to add immeasurably to the national wealth and so to afford lucrative employment to numberless persons according to their qualifications and acquirements…". "Moreover by these means not only will many new industries be introduced into Bengal, but almost every one of the old established arts and manufacturers of the country may be rendered more useful and remunerative than at present." (Bengal and indeed the whole of India today could advantageously use Temple's blueprint prepared 120 years ago!). (Kochhar 2008a: 1028-1029)

Temple wanted the scheme's "details be settled by yourselves without any specific guidance from the State." He expressed confidence that Sircar and his supporters "will be able to elaborate plans calculated to redound to the material benefit of your countrymen." The letter closed with Temple's "cordial and earnest wishes for your practical success." The use of terms like material benefit and practical success leaves no doubt about the direction Temple wanted the native initiative to take. But he was not ready to confront the Calcutta middle class. He therefore decided to enlist native support for his own scheme. More specifically, he tried to dovetail his scheme to the ongoing municipal factional politics.

If colleges were churning out a large number of unemployed and unemployable young men whose discontent was a major cause of worry for the colonial government, there were also now after 50 years of English education, a significant number of well-educated, articulate bright young men who could look the empire in the eye and who now wanted a community leadership role. This leadership was currently in the hands of the landed class through the British India Association which had been formed in 1851 in time to influence the 1853 charter to be granted to the East India Company by the British Parliament. Though an organization of those entitled to privileges by accident of birth, it still had a place for the upwardly mobile members of the middle class. The arrangement was mutually beneficial. The upper crust could use the middle class' intellectual prowess and the ability to write and argue.[65] The middle class in return received social prestige, built contacts and acquired a forum. The 50-rupee-a-year membership of the British India Association was a proof, because proof was needed, of having arrived. But now this middle class was ready to strike out on its own. Fortunately, for it, the government for its own reasons was keen to reform the extant municipal corporations. So far, the native representation had been through nominated members. The government appointed justices of peace from among the "Hindu property-owners and British tradesmen" who in turn constituted the corporation.

Municipal Corporation

In 1875, an act was passed providing for a partially elective corporation for Calcutta. The self-made professional class now saw a bigger role for itself. Only it was not quite clear within its own ranks as to what was to be done with the past baggage as represented by the landed class. One faction led by Sisir Kumar Ghose, the owner of *Amrita Bazar Patrika* (who had moved to Calcutta in 1871), and Dr Sambhu Chandra Mookerjee (1839–1894), editor of the *Mookerjee Magazine*, founded a political organization, Indian League, on 25 September 1875. This faction wanted a clear break with the past elitist leadership. The other faction which had old family and social ties with the old guard was more moderate and favoured a smooth transition (it included Anand Mohan Bose, Surendra Nath Banerjee and others). It is this latter section which was by the side of Sircar. It eventually prevailed politically with the founding of the more representative Indian Association on 26 July 1876.

Since the Indian Association leadership was supporting the Science Association, Temple decided to enlist the support of the rival Indian League to further his polytechnic plan. The conflict between the Indian League and the Indian Association leadership was a factional fight untainted by any economic ideology. The Indian League leaders may have been upstarts compared to those of the Indian Association[66] but the former's support for Temple's polytechnic was certainly not driven by any commitment to the cause of the artisans. The Indian League was supporting the Lieutenant Governor not technical education. It was opposing the people behind the Indian Association; it was not supporting the polytechnic.

The fact that the Lieutenant Governor had decided to operate through a section of the native middle class rather than take a public stand himself lent intensity to the enrolment campaign in favour of the Association. Temple's letter was published in the press and commented on editorially. The influential *Hindoo Patriot* (15 May 1875) which had consistently supported Sircar exhorted the Bengali Babus to donate liberally for the Science Association project, since "Mohamedans of N. India have already raised Rs 200,000/-for their Anglo-Oriental Fund."[67] At the same time, it urged the government to give a grant-in-aid. Newspapers such as *Indian Public Opinion* and *Punjab Times* advocated "practical and professional orientation for the new science movement."[67]

The Second Subscribers' Meeting

The second subscribers' meeting was held on 20 November 1875 which appointed a provisional committee under the chairmanship of Father Lafont to work out the plans for the Science Association. Its report along with "a sketch of the scheme" by Sircar was considered on 16 December 1875. Sircar's sketch stated that

> The object of the Association is to enable the natives of India to cultivate Science in all its departments, with a view to its advancement by original research and (as it will necessarily follow) with a view to its varied applications to the arts and comforts of life.[68]

Obviously, reference to the arts and comforts of life was an afterthought added for form's sake as a concession to Temple's stated views.

The provisional committee was still banking on support from the government and its sense of noblesse oblige:

> Sir Richard Temple has already evinced the most lively interest in the project, and it will not be too much to believe that Lord Northbrook will do the same. And when the Rajas, Maharajas and Princes, who will gather in this our capital to honor the royal visitor, will learn this, they will, if we are not much mistaken, very gladly join, as one of them the Maharaja of Patiala has already long ago joined, in founding and endowing an Institution which, while, it will be the most fitting memorial of the Prince that can be conceived, will grandly fulfil the mission of England, the restoration and elevation of the people of India.[68]

Third Subscribers' Meeting

The campaign for more donations continued and the third subscribers' meeting was called on 15 January 1876 under the chairmanship of Temple. In the meantime, Temple had been active on his own agenda. The Indian League was formed on 25 September 1875. It called a public meeting of Native Gentlemen, Chiefs and Rajas on 25 December 1875 under the chairmanship of Temple where a resolution was passed "to found an Institution for instructing in the various branches of the Physical Sciences in the name of His Royal Highness the Prince of Wales, to commemorate the visit of His Royal Highness." Interestingly, the resolution was proposed by Sircar's ardent supporter Lafont.[69] In his presidential address, Temple made a far-sighted remark. He advised the organizers:

> I do hope that if the large sums you expect are realised, the money will not be spent in building a structure. A structure is a very good thing in its way, but what is of more essential importance is the means of paying the salaries of the lecturers. You must remember that the lecturers and students form the living part of an Institution like this. To that purpose the money should be primarily devoted; that is, money should be invested, and the proceeds devoted to the payment of the salaries of lecturers.[70]

As it turned out the Indian League never reached a stage where it could follow or flout Temple's advice. Sircar could have benefited from this valuable piece of advice but he chose to invest in the structure than in the living part.

Since the date for the third subscribers' meeting would have been fixed in advance in consultation with Temple, there can be no doubt that he contrived to make sure that the practical sciences school meeting was held earlier. Indeed, at the 15 January 1876 subscribers' meeting, in his presidential remarks, Temple declared that he "would be glad if any individual influence could be the means of drawing together a similar Association formed in the city under other auspices." Temple took this opportunity to reiterate his own thesis. He declared that the objects of both the initiatives

> are ultimately the same, namely, the improvement of the rising generation to the Western knowledge of science, while it will also afford those who cannot find a living in the public service and the Bar, a means of earning a good livelihood by practical pursuits, such as those of a scientific forester, a gardener, a civil engineer, a surveyor, a chemist and the like. I am sure you will agree with me that the learned professions, as they now exist in Bengal, are not sufficiently extensive to furnish employment to all those educated men who are annually, constantly seeking for employment. There is, there-fore, nothing for these young men, if they wish to live respectably, but for them to put their shoulders to the wheel - the wheel being the cultivation of the practical sciences.
>
> *(Biswas, 2003, 152)*

Temple's remarks were greeted with "loud cheers" but did not bring about any change of heart.

The meeting formally resolved to set up the Indian Association for the Cultivation of Science with Temple as its ex-officio chairman. The matter however did not end there. A joint meeting of the subscribers to the Science Association and to the Indian League's polytechnic was held on 28 January 1876 with Temple in the chair to examine the possibility of the merger of the two schemes. The idea was formally given up when of the present only five voted for amalgamation and 32 against. But far more significant than the vote count were the arguments.

In the early days of the British rule over Bengal, the social relationship between the British officials and the native leadership was quite cordially ce-mented as it was by mutually beneficial financial transactions. More basi-cally, the British in Bengal were dealing with a social class they themselves had created, enriched and socially elevated.[71] In this setting, Indians had no difficulty in playing second fiddle while learning English language, literature and law. But by the 1870s, the Empire had hardened and the native leader-ship had also gained in confidence. Given its class characteristics, it was not willing for the second round of apprenticeship that technical education en-tailed. The well-respected scholar Dr Rajendralala Mitra asserted that

> no nation on earth had shown a higher appreciation of learning for its own sake than the Hindu. For three thousand years and upwards their ancestors had cherished Sanskrit learning for its own sake, and need it be doubted that their descendents would not be equal to the sciences of the present day?.[72]

There could not have been anybody in the audience to remind the learned orator that 3,000 years ago the production of wealth was based on frozen empirical technologies which did not require any formal learning while the 19th century production of wealth required learnt skills. Learning for its own sake had appealed to the Brahmins then and had an equal fascination for the new social class British rule in Bengal had created. However, farmers and artisans would have benefited from modern science. Thus, while Europe was artisanizing science, it was sought to be Brahminized in India in keeping with the caste composition of the middle class.

Mitra warned Sircar: "do not attempt to make your institution a school of technical education in the industrial arts… nor attempt to make it self supporting by producing remunerative art work in your laboratories. If you do, you will disappoint your pupils."[72] (p. 150) Mitra's admonition had a history behind them. In 1854, a School of Industrial Art was set up under the auspices of a newly established Society for the Promotion of Industrial Arts, with Mitra as the secretary and a British engineer Colonel H. Goodwyn as the president. The school hoped to offer three-year training to about 30 students in "the arts of engraving, modelling, printing, architecture design, ornamental pottery and porcelain manufacture, etc." so as to open "new branches of employment for middle and educated classes" (Ghosh, 2002: 56). The idea was "to lead these classes… to regard with respect and honour the manual labour necessary for the practice of these arts." The school was taken over by the government in 1862. Its report for the year 1866–1867 is rather discouraging. Noting that the majority of students came from "the middle and poorer classes of the Natives," the Principal, H.H. Locke, lamented that

> several instances have occurred of parents being compelled to withdraw students from the School and relinquish their intention of obtaining them a professional training as draughtsmen, owing to the necessity for their procuring some kind of office or other employment.

He suggested that

> If Government or any of the native gentlemen…would offer one or two scholarships…to induce students to remain at their studies a year or two longer than at present, it would ensure the complete education of a few well qualified draughtsmen.

No support either from the government or native leadership seems to have been forthcoming. The school did succeed in diffusing the lithographic technology but by the time half-tone block prints were introduced, the school had changed its colour.[73] Under the leadership of E.B. Havell and Abanindranath

Tagore, it became a fine arts institute, since re-named the Government College for Art and Craft.

Father Lafont bluntly stated that the pro-polytechnic Indian League wanted "to transform the Hindus into a number of mechanics requiring for ever European supervision."[74] If the Indians drawn from artisan castes had been consulted, they would not have minded their utter inferiority to the foreign rulers for one or two generations as a price for upgradation of their traditional skills. But the native leadership was in the hands of upper castes well known for their disdain of manual work. It had taken them two generations of study of Western law and literature to claim equality with the rulers. They wanted science to be cultivated at the same level. Since this class knew Shakespeare as well as if not better than the British themselves, it believed that its edifice of science should be supported by and be an extension of the British effort. Science application was to be left to Europeans; science cultivation was for the Indians.

European missionaries acted as a bridge between the colonial rulers and native upper-class interests. In 1886, there was a suggestion afoot from Charles Henry Tawney, the acting director of public instructions, backed by the government that technical education should be introduced at the school level and the institutions which would not arrange technical education would cease to receive government aid. Father H. Neut (1845–1921), the then Rector of St Xavier's and a colleague of Lafont's, opposed the scheme saying that "To begin the technical studies in the school itself is to prepare a generation without elevation or grandeur."[75]

Exercising his executive powers and independently of the Science Association, the Lieutenant Governor resolved to establish a number of surveying schools observing that "the foundation of these schools will only be a preliminary step towards establishment of technical schools for the teaching of handicrafts and the improvement of several kinds of manual industry." The editorial comment in the influential *Hindoo Patriot* (31 January 1876) was on predictable lines: "This will of course improve the condition of the masses, but will not affect the educated classes."

Finally yielding to the demands of the educated classes, the Lieutenant Governor gave his approval to through a notification gazetted on 23 February 1876. The notification itself is dated 21 January 1876, which is a week before the joint meeting. Unless the official date is a misprint, the notification must have been back-dated because it could not possibly have been issued before the outcome of the joint meeting was known. Through this notification, the Lieutenant Governor noted that "the realization of so large an amount of donations as that promised would indicate munificence on the part of many native gentlemen for the good of their countrymen." Making it clear that "the members should depend on their own independent exertions for the attainment of success,"[76] the government decided to purchase a suitable building (for Rs 40,000) and make it available free of charge for the Association. It is noteworthy that the government saw the Association as a science college. As the Annual Report on Public Instruction for 1875–1876 in Bengal put it (para 451):

> The objects of the institution are to provide lectures of a superior kind in science, especially general physics, chemistry and geology, mainly for students who have already passed through school or college or have otherwise attained some proficiency in these respects.

By another minute dated 18 April 1876, Temple considered the proposal of the Indian League for the establishment of a technical school.

> The promoters of the institution having agreed to invest two lakhs of rupees (expected as donations) in Government securities, so as to produce an income of Rs 8000 p.a., an equal grant of Rs 8000 was made by His Honor.

It was officially noted that "Among the donations, one of Rs 40000 by Rai Luchmipat Singh Bahadur of Asimgunge has already been invested in Government securities" (Annual Report of Public Instruction in Bengal for 1875–1876, para 453). Interestingly, *Hindoo Patriot* (26 February 1876) pointed out that Luchmipat's contribution was made to the government for the Berhampore College and "he merely agreed for the diversion of funds to the Indian League at the request of Sir Richard Temple." As is well-known, nothing came out of the Indian League's officially supported initiative for a technical school while the Science Association was inaugurated by Temple on 29 July 1876 (see Table 9.1 for a summary of chronology).

Lectures

Within a month of its inauguration, the Science Association embarked on its regular lecture series. Much important documentation related to Sircar's scientific activities is compiled in Biswas (2000, 2003), including the extant annual reports. In 1880, Sircar published in a book form the essays (as he called them) on the Science Association along with "the opinion of the Press thereon." The book contains prefaces written by Sircar in March 1872, December 1875, January 1877 and April 1880. The contents of the book minus the prefaces find a place in Biswas (2003). The prefaces, not reprinted before, have recently been reproduced.[77] Apparently, the oldest published annual report of the association is of the seventh meeting read in 1884. It would be instructive to see if earlier, presumably unprinted, reports are extant anywhere. Not surprisingly,

TABLE 9.1 Indian Association for the Cultivation of Science: Chronology 1869–1876

1869	Dec 8.	Dr Mahendra Lal Sircar published "On the desirability of a national institution for the cultivation of science by the natives of India" in his Calcutta Journal of Medicine (nominally dated Aug. 1869).
	Dec 13.	*Hindoo Patriot* welcomes the proposal.
	Dec 20.	Article published as a pamphlet.
	Dec 29.	*The Englishman* comments encouragingly.
1870	Jan 3.	Prospectus issued in *Hindoo Patriot*, soliciting donations
	Jan 29.	First two donations received
1872	Feb	Sircar lectures at Bethune Society and at Uttarpara Hitkari Sabha
1875	Mar 10.	Sircar meets Lieutenant Governor Sir Richard Temple
	Apr 4.	First meeting of Science Association subscribers
	Apr 8.	Sircar writes to Temple
	May 3.	Temple replies to Sircar
	Sep 25.	Indian League established
	Nov 20.	Second meeting of subscribers, attended by Temple. Board of Trustees appointed.
	Dec 16.	Report of Provisional Committee; Sircar sketches the scheme.
	Dec 25.	Indian League meeting with Temple in chair proposes to set up a school for practical sciences.
1876	Jan 15.	Third meeting of subscribers, with Temple in chair
	Jan 28.	Joint meeting of the Science Association and the Indian League
	Feb 23.	Lieutenant Governor's minute gazetted (nominally dated 21 Jan.) sanctioning the Science Association.
	Apr. 6	Temple contributes Rs 500 to the Association fund.
	Apr 18.	Lieutenant Governor's minute sanctioning the League's polytechnic.
	Jul 26.	Indian Association formed
	Jul 29.	Indian Association for the Cultivation of Science inaugurated.

the first lecturer was Lafont in physics who continued till 1893 (in the following when factual statements are made giving the year the source is the relevant annual report). Sircar began in 1878, while a chemistry lecturer, Tara Prasanna Roy, could be found only in 1879, who continued till about 1885. His assistant, Ram Chandra Dutta (1851–1899), otherwise a chemical analyst in the Medical College and one of the earliest disciples of Ramakrishna Paramhans, took over from Tara Prasanna and continued lecturing till his death in 1899 (Biswas, 2000: 96, note 7). The newly appointed Presidency College physics professor, J.C. Bose, began practical classes in 1885 but discontinued them by 1888 end.[78]

In 1887, lectures in mathematics and geology were introduced. The mathematics lecturer was Asutosh Mookerjee (1864–1924), the son of a successful medical practitioner who was a personal friend of Sircar's.[79] Asutosh obtained his MA in mathematics in 1885 from Presidency College. The next year, he received the prestigious Premchand Roychand studentship and another MA in physics (Sinha, 1966: 7. Pres. Col. 100 does not list physics as a subject for MA but natural and physical science. It does not mention Asutosh as passing out in 1886. Presumably, he wrote the examination privately.)[80] While still a student, he published some mathematical research papers which were well received. In 1887, the Director of Public Instruction, Sir Alfred Croft, offered him an appointment as an assistant professor carrying a monthly salary of Rs 250 (like P.C. Ray). But Asutosh wanted to be placed in the superior European scale (as J.C. Bose had been). Since this was not possible, he decided to leave mathematics for law, it seems, on the advice of Sir Gooroonath Banerjee (1844–1918) who also had a university degree in mathematics but made a successful career in law (Sinha, 1966: 13). Asutosh obtained bachelor's degree in law in 1888 from City College and started his practice the same year after serving his articleship under Rashbehary Ghose (1845–1921). Because of his own love for mathematics and family relations with Sircar, he began lecturing at the association in 1887 on mathematical topics and continued till 1891. Characteristically, his lectures included some new material also. During this period, he published as many as 13 research papers in the *Journal of the Asiatic Society* of Bengal, Part 2 (Sinha, 1966: 179–180). In 1893, he published his book *Geometry of Conics*. Meant for the "beginners of the subject," it was "highly received" and "ran into many editions" (Sinha, 1966: 176). A last-ditch attempt was made to keep Asutosh in mathematics. Gooroodas Banerjee, by now (that is during 1890–1892) the Calcutta University's first Indian Vice-Chancellor (1890–1892), failed to collect even such sum as would give Asutosh a modest income of Rs 4000 a year (Sinha, 1966: 11). Mathematics lost Asutosh forever. He went on to get a doctorate in law in 1894 and became a high court judge in 1904. It is not possible to speculate on what Asutosh might have achieved as a mathematician but history remembers him as a great educationist. His association with the Calcutta University began in 1889 when he was nominated a fellow of the Senate. He served as the honorary vice-chancellor for four consecutive two-year terms during 1906–1914 and then again during 1921–1923.

India's first geologist Pramatha Nath Bose lectured at the Science Association during 1887 and 1888. Teaching in life sciences was introduced in 1894. All lecturers were honorary. Whatever gate money was collected went to the association. The gate money was more symbolic than substantial; it could be as low as four rupees (Biswas, 2000: 65). These lectures attracted science-hungry students from private colleges. Thus during 1881–1882, P.C. Ray, a regular student at the Metropolitan Institution (since renamed Vidyasagar College after its founder) attended lectures not only in Presidency College but also at the Science Association for additional instruction. Presidency College's ability to attract out-students irked Sircar. He even "made a representation to the Government requesting it to discontinue allowing students from private colleges to attend lectures at the Presidency College as otherwise the Science Association lectures would be more or less empty" IACS (176: 121) makes a rather strange claim:

> From 1891 or so the attendance started falling due largely to the organization of science departments in colleges of Calcutta. Instead of feeling discouraged, Dr Sircar regarded it was a good sign, for now, he thought, it would be possible to concentrate more and more on discourses of a graver nature giving the results of recent discoveries.

It is not clear on what basis Sircar's inner thoughts have been articulated. The "admissions were getting larger year to year and B course (Science) growing to be popular" (Ray, 1932: 77–78). As private colleges opened science classes of their own, the Science Association lecture rooms became "almost deserted" (Ray, 1932: 149). The annual report for 1892 noted "with satisfaction" in 1892 that "some of the lady students from La Martiniere Institution and the Doveton College attended the lectures regularly" while "The practical demonstrations in Chemistry were attended by two lady students, both of the Calcutta Medical College." But at the same meeting, taking note of the increasing redundancy of the association because of the laboratory facilities created by the colleges, Sircar proposed to institute "two classes of lectures, one elementary for instruction of the masses, and advanced for the enlightenment of those who have already passed through the portals of the University, or any how have mastered the discovered facts of physical science." (The exact sequence and chronology of the introduction of science teaching in individual colleges and the impact thereof on the Science Association needs to be studied in detail.)

Bowing to the ground reality in 1893, the association got itself affiliated with the Calcutta University in physics and chemistry up to the first examination in arts. In 1899, this affiliation was secured for the B course of the BA degree. From 1895, a small number of students from private colleges were permitted to work in the association laboratories to prepare themselves for the MA degree at Calcutta University. The Science Association decided in 1907 to seek disaffiliation from Calcutta University "as the Association had now some funds and abilities for pursuits of original research, and as the task of science-teaching could now be left to the competent authorities of the private colleges" (Biswas, 2001: 129). Thus, sadly the Science Association's rise as a research institute meant its demise as a college laboratory.

In 1896, Sircar's lecture on heat was attended by about 200 persons, most of them being students of the Bangabasi College. The audience included the principal also (Biswas, 2000: 308). In November 1899, when Sircar called on the Lieutenant Governor, the latter enquired how the "college" was doing, meaning the Science Association. Sircar's reply was: "not satisfactorily" (Sircar's diary entry dated 27 November 1899; Biswas, 2000: 345).

An active member of the executive committee of the Science Association was Keshub Chunder Sen whose daughter was married into the house of Cooch Behar. Sen helped Sircar by "securing donations from the Cooch-Behar Raj and other rich magnates" (Bagal, 1955: 7). In 1890, the Maharaja of Cooch Behar started contributing Rs 100 every month in aid of a permanent professorship which was earmarked by the Association for chemistry. However, since the amount was too small for a full-time appointment, it was used to remunerate the chemistry lecturer, Ram Chandra Dutta, who had been gratuitously teaching for years; see above (IACS, 1976: 24).

Sircar was very clear in his mind that "the Association cannot carry out its work with honorary lecturers" (Biswas, 2003: 303). "There ought at least to be two professorships" each requiring an endowment of 100,000 rupees. Although he dubbed the amount "modest," he knew it would not be forthcoming spontaneously. He therefore enlisted the support of the Viceroy and did not mind attributing the authorship of the idea to him. While inaugurating the new building in 1884 (see below) in the presence of a vast gathering comprising "upwards of seven hundred European and Native gentlemen" in addition to the association members, Lord Ripon "cheerfully and readily" agreed to lend his name and even contributed Rs 1000 towards the endowment. He light-heartedly referred to the rather "disagreeable" situation of paying to get his name perpetuated (Biswas, 2003: 306).

Sircar had naively believed that the targeted amount would be collected "before the year expires." But Ripon left office in 1884 itself. Sircar sought support for the professorships in the Viceroy's name. At the eleventh annual meeting held in 1888, he said:

> If ever there was a project which deserved the enthusiastic reception of the people of this town it was one projected for their benefit by Lord Ripon; twice urged on their attention in public by him, subscribed to by him, and to be called after his name.
>
> *(Biswas, 2003: 337)*

But three years' labour yielded no more than Rs 19,950. In 1891, Sircar hoped that "the country, of which Lord Ripon is such a true friend, will not allow the project of the first professorship, which it was resolved to name after the noble Lord, to remain a myth to our lasting disgrace." The disgrace lasted half a century. It was only in 1937 that a Ripon professor (Sir Lewis Leigh Fermor) could be appointed (Biswas, 2000: 306–307).

The Ripon professorship fiasco however failed to deter Sircar (we learn from the annual report of 1884 that following the Viceroy's lead Maharaja of Darbhanga subscribed Rs 10,000; Nizam of Hyderabad Rs 3000; and his deputy Nawab Salar Jung Rs 1000. A general grant of Rs 1000 from the first prince of Indore was unilaterally assigned to the Ripon fund. In all, a total sum of Rs 17,050 was said to be subscribed. The annual report further informs that "Of this amount the sum of Rs 2,050 has already been realised" (Biswas, 2003: 313). Yet the annual report for 1888 states that a sum of over Rs 13,000 was subscribed in 1884; while Rs 5000 was added in 1885 and Rs 1500 in 1886 (Biswas, 2003: 337). As per later annual reports, the fund showed only Rs 2,210 in 1892, while by 1932 end it stood at Rs 17,000 (Rajinder Singh, personal communication). Quite obviously, the funds were transferred from one head to another. It is thus not possible to trace the growth of the fund). In August 1896, on the occasion of David Hare's 54th death anniversary, the association resolved to establish Hare professorship and duly invited public subscriptions with predictably negative results (Biswas, 2000: 306–307). Finally, on the death of Queen Victoria in 1901, a new professorship was announced in her name but "there were only two donors" (Biswas, 2000: 403). Sircar had better luck with buildings and instruments.

Instruments and Buildings

When Sircar was trying to win support for his association in competition with the government-supported Indian League, it was necessary to make the subscription base as broad as possible. But once the institution had been established, Sircar turned to the wealthier sections of the society to which his profession and proximity to the government gave him access.

The Science Association began with a corpus of about Rs 80,000. Out of this, a sum of Rs 20,000 was earmarked for instruments. To this sum was added the handsome contribution of Rs 25,000 by Kally Kissen Tagore in 1878 (Biswas, 2000: 46). Several instruments were purchased locally. For the rest, money was placed in the hands of Father Lafont who was proceeding to France for health reasons. One of the new equipment was a state-of-the-art instrument, an 1878 invention, Crookes tube, a proto-type of all future cathode ray tubes. When high voltage was applied across the tube the rarefied gas inside glowed. Obviously, some sort of rays were being emitted by the cathode. It was generally believed that the rays were waves. Sircar however discounted the wave nature of these rays and believed them to be ions. On 18 March 1880, the Viceroy Lord Lytton came to the Science Association to attend Sircar's lecture-demonstration on Crookes tube and invited him to perform at the Viceregal residence on 31 March 1880 before a select audience. For the Britishers in India, Sircar became a window on the latest on the scientific front back home. Sircar approvingly quoted the *Hindoo Patriot* to say that "The Viceroy's visit marked an epoch in the history of the Association," adding that "The founders and supporters of the Institution have now the best encouragement for their undertaking" (Sircar, 1880: i). Eventually, using Crooke's Tube, J.J. Thomson in 1897 showed that the rays were in fact particles since named electrons. Kariamanickam Srinivasa Krishnan (1898–1961), Raman's collaborator and later successor, "used to say that Mahendra Lal came very close to the discovery of electron" (Biswas, 2000: 46 does not cite any source for this assertion).

The Viceregal invitation to Sircar "made some sensation in its time," but it was the interest taken by the next Viceroy, Lord Ripon, that launched Sircar into a higher orbit "and is remembered by many up to this day [1904]" (Banwari Lal Chaudhury, quoted in Biswas, 2000: 165).

Hindoo College, Calcutta, had started as a private body in 1817 but opted six years later to accept government control in lieu of financial aid. In contrast, the Science Association started with government aid but jettisoned it four years later.[81] In September 1881, the Association purchased its premise from the government for Rs 30,000 and expended another Rs 15,000 in adding a 500-capacity lecture theatre, and building a tower for housing an astronomical observatory. In 1880, Kumar Kanti Chandra Singh Bahadur presented the association with a seven-inch diameter equatorial telescope made by Merz in Germany with mounting by Browning. The association spent Rs 6000 to buy a "number of appliances to demonstrate astronomical phenomena" (Biswas, 2000: 92). But "Astronomy had a very brief existence at the Association" (IACS, 1976: 18). The telescope lens would be later used by Raman in his Nobel Prize-winning experiment (Biswas, 2001: 72).

The foundation stone of the new building was laid by Ripon on 13 March 1882 who returned two years later to the day for the inauguration.

Vice President's Resignation

Within a month of the foundation stone ceremony, that is on 12 April 1882, Mitra handed over his resignation to the Association President, the Lieutenant Governor Sir Ashley Eden, putting on record a number of valid objections.

The purchase of the building from the government meant the end of any government control and the transformation of the association into a private club (Mitra, 1882; reprinted as Appendix III).

Mitra charged Sircar with thoughtlessness in purchase of costly equipment and opaqueness in the conduct of examinations and award of scholarships. The association's emphasis should have been on "systematic teaching" instead of public lectures. Mitra rightly felt that money would not have been spent on buildings but used to hire full-time staff.

According to Mitra, as long as the association was located in a building provided by the government, its "educational work" was "open to inspection of Government officers." "It was soon, however, discovered that such inspection would not be beneficial to the Association, and the house, therefore, was purchased..." Mitra alleged that the grant of scholarships was not on the basis of any proper examination and no records were kept. "The secretary reported so-and-so should have the scholarship and the prizes, and the committee acted upon the recommendation."

Mitra's resignation letter was reproduced by the newspapers and elicited some comments. Privately, Sircar called Mitra "the malicious Doctor," but he and his friends decided not to react in public. Mitra's resignation does not figure in the association's official records (Biswas, 2000: 49).

Wealthy patrons donated to the association because of networking. On 8 June 1882, Kally Kissen Tagore paid Sircar as much as Rs 2,500 for medical attendance. He also donated Rs 1,500 to the Association Building Fund and promised another Rs 5,000. This was in addition to Rs 25,000 already contributed. Sircar asked Kally Kissen not to announce his donation before Sircar got one from Kally Kissen's kinsman the more famous Maharaja Jatindra Mohan Tagore "as in that case the Maharaja might not subscribe at all" (Biswas, 2000: 81). Sircar was keen to benefit from rivalries within the Tagore clan but was at the same time careful not to be harmed by the jealousies. In 1882, Sircar was a member of a delegation that called on Ripon. Another member was the Maharaja of Darbhanga whom Sircar was able to touch for Rs 5000. The most substantial contribution to come Sircar's way emanated from the Maharaja of Vizianagaram through the medical route. The Maharaja was a patient of Sircar's homeopathic mentor Babu Rajendra Dutt, who persuaded the Maharaja to give Rs 50,000 during 1889–1890 for the construction of a laboratory, named after him. In the annual report for 1892, Sircar called the Vizianagaram offer "unsolicited" which it certainly was not. It is this laboratory, backed by a workshop, which would become known the world over as the seat of Raman's world-famous research (Ghose, 1935: 56). Many accounts of the Science Association are coloured by Raman's Nobel Prize, but it should be kept in mind that the prize came 50 years after the opening of the Association. The Glory for Science Association came years after the demise of its founder who died a rather disappointed man.

The government monitoring that had ceased in 1880 with the Association buying the government building was restored in 1935 when a government representative was provided with a seat on the management council in return for an assured government grant (IACS, 1976: 68).

Dr Sircar had loftily declared in 1875 that the "primary object of the Association" was "the restoration and elevation of the people of India to the rank among nations which they have lost and which they might be made to attain" (Biswas, 2003: 131). A quarter of a century later, Sircar was a bitter man. The association's annual meeting on 4 September 1902 was Sircar's last. Addressing it he lamented:

> I do not know how to account for this apathy of our people towards the cultivation of science. And therefore I am forced to confess that I made a mistake in starting the project of founding a Science Association at all, and that I have wasted a life, as I have told you, in attempting to make it a national institution. If I had rigorously applied myself to the practice of my profession, though homeopathic, I am sure I could have left as a legacy an amount of money equal to that I have succeeded in collecting in over thirty years.
>
> (IACS, 1976: 25)

Responding, *New India* editorialized on 11 September 1902:

> We cannot ignore the sad fact that while on the one hand, the Science Association stands as a memorial to Dr. Sircar's energy and his profound love for his own country and own people, it is a disgraceful commentary on our national character on the other. As long as the Viceroys and Lieutenant-Governors openly supported this movement, money came from all quarters to its funds, but with the practical withdrawal of official patronage, the purse strings of the wealthy public tightened at once, which not even the magic of Queen Victoria's name could reopen.
>
> *(Biswas, 1969: 64)*

The reference here is to Sircar's unsuccessful proposal for instituting a new professorship in the name of Queen Victoria on her death in 1901.

Sircar's address elicited an editorial from Bombay-based *Voice of India* edited by Dadabhai Naoroji. It was probably he himself who wrote on 27 September 1902 (Biswas, 1969: 64–65).

> So my good friend Dr. Mahendralal Sircar has grown despondent... But from whom did the promoters expect substantial aid for the Association? From a short-sighted and a slovenly foreign Government? Or, from an apathetic and besotted aristocracy in the land? Or, from an illiterate and half-starved peasantry? The educated progressive class in the country ought to have been their main support – the professional, commercial, industrial aristocrats of India those have made their fortunes through, and who have been able to enjoy them under, a settled rule. Has this particular class been duly reached by Dr. Sircar? I should like him to make one supreme effort in this direction; if he succeeds, he may yet shame the authorities into recognizing the claims of the Association in an adequate measure.

Anyway, Sircar was now too old and tired to make another effort. In retrospect, it is not surprising that the Association did not quite succeed in enthusing the intelligentsia about science. In his time or later, the well-heeled in Bengal owed nothing to science. The Science Association was not seen as a societal or economic need but was indulged as a personal fad of a prominent citizen who was in the good books of the high-ups. In one important respect, Rajendralala Mitra had been right. If the Science Association had focused on the laboratory rather than the lecture theatre, modern scientific research might have taken root in India in the 1880s itself. Maybe in the first flush of excitement, he spent the collected money on buildings hoping that the inflow would continue. His hopes were badly belied. The upper classes were ready to financially support Sircar in his pursuits because he was one of them. But they were not ready to give money to create employment for others. One wonders why Sircar did not become a researcher himself. He was eminently qualified to do so. His association was well-equipped with the state-of-the-art instruments from Europe. He could easily have become a discoverer. But he preferred to be a high-profile demonstrator. The high point of Sircar's social life was an invitation from the Viceroy to display the spectacle of the newly invented Crookes tube (Ghose, 1935: 253). It was a toy for India but a research tool in Europe. In 1897, Father Lafont assisted by a Tagore boy (Maharaja Jatindra Mohan Tagore's son Pradyot Kumar) took the X-ray image of the Viceroy Lord Elgin's hand decorated with a ring and won a photography prize for the effort (Biswas, 2001: 272). The sporadic scientific work carried out by Dr Sarasi Lal Sarkar and under Dr Chunilal Bose in the Association labs did not amount to much (Biswas, 2001:120).

The Science Association however succeeded in introducing the Bengali youth to the attractiveness of science as a career option in preference to public service or law. One is inclined to agree with the assessment offered by Sircar at the 1899 annual meeting. He was broadly justified in claiming that he had made

a beginning at a time when even the very name of science was scarcely heard of in this country... It is not too much to say that it was mainly through the influence of the founders of the Science Association that examinations in scientific subjects were gradually introduced for the conferring of University degrees.

(IACS, 1976: 25)

India may have begun its flirtation with modern science in the last quarter of the 19th century itself but it was not yet ready for a serious affair. The Empire was still in full glory. A nod from the Viceroy's provided more excitement than anything in the laboratory could.

In many ways, the Science Association represents missed opportunities. It would have been ideal for Calcutta to have a polytechnic in place of a pure science institution, but given the class composition of the Bengal educated class, this would have been unthinkable. Even, within the upper-caste framework, it would have been desirable to continue the Science Association as a government-aided institution. However, questions of personal ego and control dominated over long-term social and educational benefits. The Association failed to initiate scientific research under Indian auspices. But it did serve a useful purpose. It made science a desirable career option among Bengal youth and compelled the government to induct science into its educational mainstream.

Appendix

Rajendralala Mitra's letter dated 12 April 1882 to the Lieutenant Governor sending his resignation as Vice President of Science Association, published in The Statesman, Calcutta, 27 May 1882.

From Rai Rajendralala Mittra, Bahadoor, LL.D., C.I.E., to the Honorable Sir Ashley Eden, K.C.S.I., C.I.E., President of the Indian Association for the Cultivation of Science, dated Manictolah, Calcutta, the 12th April 1882.

Honorable Sir,

I beg leave to place in your hands my resignation of the office of Vice-President of the Indian Association for the Cultivation of Science.

I have taken this course, as I feel I cannot continue to hold the office with justice to myself and to the public before whom I have to appear as the Chairman of the Managing Committee of the Association.

When the Association was first established, I had hoped that it would soon be in a position to redeem at least a part of its promises, but a few years' experience has convinced me that there is no prospect of that hope being realized within a reasonable time, and what has hitherto been done is by no means satisfactory.

The professed object of the Association is to help the practical cultivation of science by those who have already acquired the rudiments of science elsewhere, and of profoundly attaching them to their several branches of enquiry, in order to lay the foundation, among the higher classes of intellect, of an accomplished scientific character. As yet nothing has been done to realize this object.

The first requirement for the purpose is a staff of tutors; but the Association has not the means at hand to employ it. The lecturers who now work are unquestionable able men; but as they are volunteers, the Association cannot command or control their actions, and has as yet laid down no programme of the courses of tuition. The lecturers select their subject on each occasion according to their choice, and the result has been that some of the lectures have not been consecutive and progressive beyond the standard fixed for primary instruction in the Presidency College as they should have been, while others have been quite desultory. They may have been well calculated to teach isolated facts; but taken together, they cannot be called courses of systematic teaching.

In newspapers frequent announcements are made of a "practical class," and if a well organized class of this kind had been got up, it would have been of immense benefit. The microscope in the hand of the young botanist or physiologist; the goniometer or blowpipe in those of the mineralogical student; the various contrivances for reflecting, refracting, polarizing, and depolarizing light, and for the optical examinations of crystals; a well furnished laboratory for the working chemist, all such implements and appliances rendered easily and always accessible for instruction to willing learners under competent superintendence and advice, would be an acquisition the advantage of which could hardly be overrated. But as yet nothing worth naming has been done in this respect, The scholarship-holders (some eight or ten), who are practically the only pupils the Association has, dabble a little in acids and gases to help the lecturers in illustrating their lecturers; but that can scarcely be called practical teaching in the sense in which the Association originally used the phrase.

The next requirement is a supply of typical and most frequently used instruments. A sub-committee was originally appointed to prepare a list of such instruments, but it was never consulted; and the only information the committee of management got of instruments purchased was when drafts had to be met. Altogether about thirty thousand rupees have been written off on account of instruments; but I have failed, after repeated attempts during the last two years, to get for record in the office, an inventory of the instruments purchased and their detailed prices. The reply I always got in committee was that the lecturers had their onerous professional duties to attend to, and had no time to prepare an inventory. From what I have seen, I am of opinion that the selection has not been made with that care, discretion, and regard to the requirements of an educational institution and its resources, which I had a right to expect from the parties concerned. The principal instruments in the laboratory of the Association are the most costly, the most showy, and best adapted for public exhibitions; but as a collection (writing without a list before me) they are neither typical nor serially arranged for a practical course of tuition. There are several instruments of some kinds (for instance, five electrical machines and three air-pumps, when one of each kind would have sufficed), while some branches of physical science are entirely unrepresented. A year ago I wanted to see a complete set of lenses, but the assistant in charge had them not to show. Had the sub-committee been consulted, and a list been prepared before making any purchase, I feel certain that Rs 30,000 would have given the institution a pretty complete set of instruments for all ordinary requirements.

On two occasions I asked the committee to let me have a sight of the questions and the answers on which resolutions were come to grant scholarships; but they were not forthcoming; I could not even ascertain how many students had been examined, and how many had been plucked. There were not even detailed reports to come to an intelligent resolution. The secretary reported so-and-so should have the scholarships and the prizes, and the committee acted upon the recommendation.

The Government of Bengal originally granted the Association the use of the house at Bow Bazaar without any condition. Subsequently the only material condition proposed was that the educational work of the Association should be open to the inspection of Government officers. It was soon, however, discovered that such inspection would not be beneficial to the Association, and the house, therefore, was purchased at a cost of Rs 30,000. Under a recent resolution, a further sum of Rs 15,000 has been voted for a lecture hall fit to accommodate 500 persons. Had these two sums been retained in hand, their interest, along with that of the sum which the Association now has, would have sufficed to secure the services of three paid teachers, whose lectures would have placed the Association in such a position as to enable it to redeem its promises to a great extent, and remove all apprehension of the Government taking back the house from it. Looking to the scale of pay which obtains in Government colleges, the interest on about a lakh of rupees might at first sight appear insufficient for three teachers; but if it be borne in mind that at Cambridge 15 Sandlerean lecturers receive £45 each, that the lecturer of Natural Sciences in Emmanuel College received £67.10, that Sir Thomas Adams, Professor of Arabic, gets £72, the Lucasion Profession of Mathematics £137, the Professor of Moral Philosophy £195, and the Parliamentary grant for the Professor of Chemistry is £96, and that with the exception of some rich endowments, the average of stipends, apart from fees, is about £125 both at Oxford and Cambridge, I see no reason why indigenous lectures in Bengal should cost more. We cannot provide at present more than one lecture a week from each teacher, and for that I hold a hundred rupees ample. There are teachers in Government schools and colleges in Bengal, who devote an hour or more daily to private tuition for a smaller remuneration, and Baboo Taraprosanna Roy, the gentleman who delivers lectures gratuitously at the Association, gets Rs 100 from the Oriental Gas Company for his services as its analyst. Half the funded capital of the Association having now been spent and there being no immediate prospect of new subscriptions replacing it, the idea of paid lecturers cannot now be realized, and the Association must be satisfied with rich instruments and a big house with none to teach there except volunteers.

The anxiety recently evinced about a theatre for 500 can be explained only on the supposition that as in the case of the instruments, so in that of the house – show and ostentation have been preferred to honest, diligent work.

The prospect of getting 500 students in Calcutta to attend to tuitional lectures on abstruse scientific subjects is very remote; and if the Association had them (it has a very small number now), it could teach them in a single class, Mr. Tawney, the other day, deposed before the Educational Commission that the power of human lungs for satisfactory teaching by lectures was limited to 50, and could not exceed a hundred or at the outside 150. If there be any truth in this opinion, - and I believe it to be perfectly correct, - the plan of the Association to teach 500 at each lecture cannot be expected to result in much good. Lectures may be made interesting to an audience of 2000 or more persons, but such lectures are not tuitional.

There are other serious defects in the management of the Association; but this letter has already become long, and I shall not take up your Honor's time by recounting them. The defects have all arisen from the circumstances of the committee not having the means of employing paid teachers, and being obliged to submit, without any discretion, to the wishes of the volunteer lecturers to keep up appearances; and the state of things cannot be mended at present. As far as I am personally concerned, I find that action as Chairman of the Committee I am called upon to announce to the public that to be progressing satisfactorily, which, in my humble opinion, is not doing what it professes to do, and to make myself morally responsible for the due appropriation of public subscriptions; and these I cannot conscientiously do. I feel therefore that the only course left me is to sever my connection with the Committee of the Association.

Notes

1 Ray, 1932, 94–95.
2 Pres. Coll. 100, 1956, 53.
3 Cal. Univ. 100, 1957, 96.
4 Pres. Coll. 100, 1956, 11.
5 Pres. Coll. 100, 1956, 16.
6 Pres. Coll. 100, 1956, 16.
7 Sehgal & Mahanti, 1994: 22.
8 Ghose, 1935.
9 Amrita Lal Sircar, 1904, reprinted in Biswas, 2003, 513.
10 According to Natesan, 1929, 4, however, Sircar and family came to live in Calcutta only after his father's death.
11 Natesan, 1929, 11.
12 Cal. Univ. 100, 1957, 101.
13 Ghose, 1935, 6.
14 Ghose, 1935, 9.
15 Ghose, 1935, 365.
16 Biswas, 2000, 28.
17 Ghose, 1935, 333.
18 Biswas, 2000, 81.
19 Buckland, 1906, 391; Ghose, 1935, 245.
20 Ghose, 1935, 247.

21 Cal. Univ. 100, 1957, 461.
22 The *Calcutta Journal* article has been reprinted in Biswas, 2003, 40–44. There are very minor differences between the journal article and the pamphlet.
23 Report of the 17th meeting of British Association for the Advancement of Science, 1847, p. 349.
24 Sen, 1901, 325.
25 Complete Works of Mahatma Gandhi, Vol. 1, p. 192. https://www.gandhiashram sevagram.org/gandhi-literature/mahatma-gandhi-collected-works-volume-1.pdf
26 Biswas, 2000, 151. Author very self-consciously writes the word *nalachalaa* in Bengali script so that all but the most persistent readers will gloss over it.
27 Biswas, 2003, 79–80.
28 Biswas, 2003, 84–90.
29 Biswas, 2003, 216.
30 Biswas, 2003, 125.
31 Biswas, 2003,132.
32 Sircar, 1880, xii.
33 Lipner, 2005, 229.
34 Berman, 1976, 2.
35 Morrell & Thackray, 1981, 256.
36 List in Biswas, 2003, 213–217.
37 Biswas, 2000, 17.
38 Biswas, 2000, 80.
39 Chinnici, 1995/1996, 94.
40 *Nature*, 1908, 33, reprinted in Biswas, 2003, 567.
41 Cal. Univ. 100, 1957, 463.
42 Cal. Univ. 100, 1957, 441.
43 The Xaverian, 2, 308–310, reprinted in Biswas, 2003, 204.
44 Chinnici, 1995/1996, 106, note 24.
45 Chinnici, 1995/1996, 95.
46 Jesuit archives may be able to confirm this hypothesis and provide other useful information.
47 Biswas, 2000, 27.
48 Biswas, 2003, 213–217.
49 Biswas, 2000, 402.
50 Biswas, 2003, 108–109.
51 Biswas, 2003, 112.
52 Kennedy, 1910, 290.
53 Bom. Edu., 1958, 462.
54 Hunter, 1876, 2, 303.
55 Mukherjee, 1975, 294–296.
56 Mukherjee, 1975, 297.
57 Tayler, 1871, 26.
58 British Library IOL MSS EUR C144/17.
59 Chattopadhyay, 2007, 23. Calcutta University was transferred from the government of India to the Bengal government in 1921; Chattopadhyay, 2007, 44.
60 Bom. Edu., 1958, 329.
61 Temple, 1896, II, 26.
62 Dongerkery, 1957, 26.
63 Dongerkery, 1957, 273.
64 Ray, 1918, 29.
65 Chandra, 1971; Furedy, 1979.
66 Furedy, 1979.

67 Biswas, 2000, 43.
68 Biswas, 2003, 125–126.
69 Biswas, 2003, 134–144.
70 Biswas, 2003, 144.
71 Kochhar, 2008c.
72 Biswas, 2003, 149.
73 General Report on Public Instruction in the Lower Provinces of the Bengal Presidency, for 1866–1867. Appendix A, pp. 576–580.
74 Biswas, 2003, 162–163.
75 Biswas, 2001, 89.
76 Sircar, 1876, [S40-41].
77 Kochhar, 2008a, Appendix II, 1055–1062.
78 Biswas, 2000, 109.
79 Sinha (1966).
80 Pres. Coll. 100, 1955, 90.
81 Government grant and say in management would be revived half a century later.

10

SCIENCE UNDER INDIAN AUSPICES

J.C. Bose and P.C. Ray burst on the world scene in 1895 as India's (and non-Western world's) first mainstream modern scientists. At the 12th session of the Indian National Congress held at Calcutta in December 1896, barrister and noted public figure, Anand Mohan Bose, moved a resolution against the reorganization of the Education Service. At the time, Bose was in England, where "the general press and the public were struck by him as the first Indian to win distinction through investigation in science — in the most strictly Western of all its departments, and at that time also the most progressive."[1] A.M. Bose declared:

> Why, Sir, we know the London *Times* has only the other day borne testimony to the fact that that the year 1896 is an epoch-making year as regards the intellectual advance of India. We know that the grand researches of an Indian Professor [J. C. Bose] in the field of invisible light, in the sublime and giddy heights of ethereal vibration, have led to discoveries which have filled the mind of Lord Kelvin, the highest authority which England has produced, literally with wonder and admiration. ... We know of the discoveries which ... have rewarded the genius and the patient toils of another countryman of ours [P. C. Ray] in the realm of Chemical Research.[2]

Ananda Mohan also referred to Atul Kumar Chatterjee's "great and wonderful feat" in having come first in the ICS examination in which most candidates were British.[2] Combining oratorical skills with purple prose, Ananda Mohan declared that 1896 was the year when

> India has shown that she has not forgotten the traditions of her glorious past, when the Indian mind has awakened to the consciousness of the

DOI: 10.4324/9781003466406-10

great destiny before it, and ... has taken the first practical steps towards obtaining its recognition from the generous scholars of the West.[2]

Science certified by the West was seen as vindicating India's glorious past and at the same time contributing to nationalism.

Bose and Ray were trained in Britain and were professors in a government institution, Presidency College, Calcutta. Both had idealist fathers who, because of their failed enterprises, ran into heavy debts which the sons dutifully cleared. But here the similarity ends. Ray strove to succeed where his father had failed, while Bose, coming from a higher social background, maintained that industrial money was unclean.

Ray discovered a new chemical compound, mercurous nitrite, in December 1895. Though Ray's personal contribution to science is not as creative as Bose's, his role in institution-building in the academe and industry has been far more influential. Bose studied the properties of short-length radio waves, introducing numerous experimental innovations in the process. He however abandoned radio physics altogether in about 1902 and there were no trained students to continue his line of research. Thus, in spite of Bose's epoch-making research, technical physics could not be institutionalized in India. His impact on India is more psychological than material. He was the first tangible and dramatic proof that the natives of a slave country could be the equals of their European masters. His appeal and message went beyond the science that made him famous.

J.C. Bose

Bose passed his BA in 1880 from St Xavier's College, Calcutta, where he was taught by Father Eugene Lafont. Left to himself, Bose would have sat for the ICS examination but his father, though a government official himself, was dead set against the idea. Bose was sent in 1880 to University College, London, at family expense to study medicine. But because of recurrent fever (now believed to be Kala Azar), aggravated by chemicals in the lab, he decided to abandon medicine and transfer to physics at Cambridge. His stay at Cambridge involved three stages. In the 1881 Lent term (January–March), he was admitted as a non-collegiate student, meaning that he was not attached to any college. On 24 January 1882, he became a pensioner, that is, a fee-paying student at Christ's College. He became a scholar on 24 January 1883, meaning that he started receiving financial support. Finally, he passed BA (Natural Science Tripos) in 1884 in the second division.[3] Note that when Bose moved to Cambridge, he did not have any scholarship in hand. He used his Cambridge credentials to obtain in 1883 BSc (Honours) from University College, London, under the name Jagadish Chunder Basu.[4] Almost always, but wrongly, the date 1884 of his Cambridge BA is assigned to his London BSc also.[5] Sometimes, even 1885 is mentioned.

One of Jagadish's teachers in Cambridge was Lord Rayleigh who remained his lifelong well-wisher and promoter. Bose was now "eager for a career" and made use of the network of Anand Mohan Bose who was married to his eldest sister. Ananda Mohan had been a student at Christ's College and had the distinction of being India's first Wrangler. He struck a very cordial relationship with his economics professor, Henry Fawcett, for whose election as a Member of Parliament from Brighton, he actively canvassed. Ananda Mohan arranged for Jagadish to call on Fawcett, who was now the Post Master General. Fawcett in turn consulted Lord Kimberley, Secretary for State for India, who advised Bose to go home to India and see. Armed with an introduction from Fawcett, he met the Viceroy, Lord Ripon, at Simla on his journey home.[6] The Viceroy promised to nominate him for the Imperial Educational Service and sent his recommendation to the Government of Bengal. When Bose called on the Director of Public Instruction at Calcutta, the latter expressed his displeasure saying: "I am usually approached from below, not from above." The Director offered Bose an appointment in the Provincial Service, which he refused. He was next offered a position in the Imperial Service. However, there was a rule by which "a native officer is only allowed to draw two-thirds of the pay that would be drawn by an English officer doing the same duty." Bose accepted the appointment but insisted on full pay. By way of protest, he did not draw his salary for three years after which the government yielded and paid the back arrears.[7]

Bose began his appointment in 1885. After nine years of rather uneventful professional life, Bose turned into a researcher.[8] Electric waves (since known as radio waves) were discovered by Heinrich Rudolf Hertz (1857–1894) in 1888. At the time of his death on 1 January 1894, a leading expert on these waves was Oliver Lodge who had improvised a detector which he called coherer. In June 1894, he was invited by the Royal Institution to give a memorial lecture on "the Work of Hertz and some of his successors." Lodge took this opportunity to talk about his own work also. Lodge's lecture was summarized in *Nature*. It was also serialized in successive issues of *The Electrician*. The lecture text was revised and published as a book.[9] The work was frequently revised and expanded. All the editions received wide currency. The book "provided very simple and precise instructions whereby such detectors could readily be duplicated, even by unskilled hands." It succeeded "in disseminating an understanding of the properties of Hertzian waves beyond the small circle of mathematical physicists to whom the subject had appealed hitherto."[10] It was Lodge's publications, most probably his book, that introduced Bose to the exciting new world of radio waves. The results that Bose obtained were quick, spectacular and beyond his own wildest imagination.

He set up his own private lab in the college. During 1894–1995, Bose gave a lecture on "Electrical Radiation" under the auspices of the Society for the Higher Training of Young Men.[11] This was, in a way, an announcement of his research interest. Bose presented his first results at the Asiatic Society on

1 May 1895 which published them in its journal on 18 July 1895. According to P.C. Ray, Bose "had not then realized the importance of the new line of research he had hit upon." Bose sent a reprint to Rayleigh who immediately saw its worth and got it republished in *The Electrician*.[12] This was Bose's introduction to the West. Bose sent his next paper to Rayleigh who communicated it to the Royal Society on 20 October 1895. It was published in the *Proceedings of the Society* on 12 December 1895. This marked Bose's entry into the high club of English science. His next piece of work served two purposes. It was submitted as a thesis to University College, London, and the University of Cambridge which, respectively, awarded him a DSc and MA, both in 1896. The paper itself, routed through Rayleigh, was received at the Society on 2 June 1896 and published in the *Proceedings* on 1 January 1897.

In 1896, Bose reprinted his five 1895 papers in a 50-page book. Only one copy has been traced; it is at the Glasgow University Library as part of a special Kelvin collection.[13] Obviously, Bose wished to keep Kelvin informed about his work. It might have been connected with his DSc and MA degrees.

In England, 1896–1897

Rayleigh wrote to Bose "that a visit occasionally to Europe would be of great service to your work." In June 1895, Bose applied for a six-month study leave to attend the meeting of the British Association for the Advancement of Science and visit chief laboratories in England and Europe.[14] Given support from Rayleigh, his DSc, and an impressive list of publications, the government was favourably inclined. Sanction was received from the Secretary of State and the Government of Bengal issued office orders on 14 August 1895. He was to go on deputation and receive an allowance but would pay his own passage.[15] From England, he sent a request, on 29 October 1896, for the "grant of pecuniary assistance" and also a three-month extension of deputation. Both these requests were accepted.[16] He returned to the college on 20 April 1897.[17]

At the 66th meeting of the British Association held at Liverpool, on 21 September 1896, he read a paper titled "On a complete apparatus for the study of the properties of electrical waves." The other speakers at the session were Lord Kelvin and Ernst Rutherford. The paper was very well received. Next, on 29 January 1897, he gave the prestigious Friday Evening Discourse at the Royal Institution to a receptive audience. During this period, he visited France and Germany also. His next visit to Europe was a longer one, from July 1900 till late 1902. Subsequently, there were other visits also in 1907 and 1914–1915.

In 1897, Kelvin along with the President of the Royal Society, Lord Lister and others sent a memorial to the Secretary of State for India suggesting the establishment of a Physical Laboratory in India. The Indian Government however had no objection in helping individual scientists to a small extent but had no intention of institutionalizing basic research.

Public Demonstration of Wireless

It has been said that Bose gave an informal demonstration of wireless telegraphy in his college; radio waves were generated in P.C. Ray's room and received in the next one occupied by Dr Alexander Pedler. This sounds plausible but there is no confirmation. Ray does not mention the event in his autobiography.

Bose gave a public demonstration before leaving for Europe. Geddes, Bose's authorized biographer, wrote in 1920 that Bose demonstrated wireless in a public lecture in 1895 at Calcutta with the Lieutenant Governor in the chair.[18] An anonymous bio-sketch, published in 1921, identifies the venue as the Town Hall.[19] The source for the account seems to have been Bose himself who gave it in his Bengali essay, *Adrishya Alok* (Invisible light), written about the same time. Bose wrongly gives the first name of the Lieutenant Governor, Sir Alexander Mackenzie, as William. But there are other problems.

The *Amrita Bazar Patrika*, the leading English language newspaper of the day, carried a news item on Monday, 24 February 1896, saying that

> Friday last [i, e., 20 February 1896] witnessed a most gratifying scene, viz, a splendid conversazione at the British Indian Association Rooms, at which His Honour Sir Alexander and Lady Mackenzie together with other high officials of the European Service and members of the Legislative Council were most cordially entertained by the leading members of the Calcutta Native Society.

The report added, "Professor J. C. Bose's electric performances added a most enjoyable air of scientific pastime which was thoroughly liked by all present."[20]

Mackenzie took office only on 18 December 1895. If he presided over the experiment, it could only have been after that date. This would mean that he attended two Bose events within a brief span of two months. While this is not impossible, it is extremely unlikely. It should however be an easy matter to resolve. Lieutenant Governor's public engagements would have been covered by the Press and figure in official records. Placing the venue in the Town Hall and making the event exclusive and Bose-centric bestows on it a dignity that was not visible at the time. There however is no doubt that Bose's demonstration of the wireless telegraphy, be it in December 1895 or February 1896, is chronologically the world's first. The *Amrit Bazar Patrika* account was ignored and for 25 years, Bose's experiment-demonstration did not become part of the discourse. The Calcutta of the day was not scientifically or intellectually equipped to appreciate the significance of Bose's experiment. For it, wireless was amusement rather than an international scientific breakthrough. Ananda Mohan's December 1896 Congress Resolution spoke about Bose's foreign testimonials but made no reference to his Calcutta event earlier in the year.

About the time Ananda Mohan was talking about Jagadish Bose, Bose was talking to an American journalist, Henry Jackson Wells Dam who published the interview in the March 1897 issue of *McClure's Magazine*,[21] an influential journal of its time. Bose told him the technical details of his Calcutta demonstration. "My radiator [transmitter] was a small platinum ball between two small platinum beeds, connected with a two-volt storage battery. By pressing a key, the ball was made to spark and start an electric wave." The receiver was in a room 75 feet distant, separated by three brick and mortar walls, 18 inches thick. "The electric waves thus induced penetrated the walls and traversed the distance with sufficient energy to be able to fire a pistol and ring a bell." He described "wave-telegraphing in Calcutta" as "simply an incident in the course of a popular lecture, an illustration of the ability of electric waves to penetrate wood and brick." Bose's interest was in setting up "apparatus for the verification of the laws of reflection, refraction, selective absorption, interference, double refraction, and polarization of these waves."[22] Dam introduced Bose to his readers as the "immediate predecessor" of Marconi. "It should be said at once that Dr Bose has no interest in the new telegraphy," even though he has been named as its discoverer. His interest was not in sending waves but in studying their properties. In contrast, Marconi, whose interview followed Bose's, focused on the transmission of radio waves, picked up ideas and things from here and there, and succeeded in sending them over longer and longer distances.

Bose worked with waves of extremely short wavelengths. For this "he had to invent a large number of new apparatus and instruments," all "distinguished by simplicity, directness, and ingenuity."[23] Invention and innovation are two different things. Invention is the result of the creativity of an individual. It becomes an innovation only when it is incorporated into the system. For the West, Bose's pioneering work fulfilled a felt need.

British Navy

In 1891, the British Navy was seeking some means of communication by which a torpedo boat could announce its approach to a friendly ship. It occurred to a naval officer, [Sir] Henry Jackson, to employ electromagnetic waves for the purpose. In 1895, he heard about Bose's coherer and succeeded in communication from one end of the ship to another. He first met Marconi on 1 September 1896. For a year, the two "gave each other much mutual assistance."[24]

Andaman

Since the cyclones that affected the Bay of Bengal arose near Andaman, telegraphic communication with these islands would enable the government to get more timely and more accurate information on the approach of cyclones and "thus be the means of averting some frightful disaster to shipping."[25] The Chief Commissioner of the Andaman and Nicobar Islands, Colonel Richard Camac Temple, while on leave in England studied the Marconi system of telegraphing with special reference to its application to connectivity between the Andamans and India.

For his England lecture-demonstration tour, Bose took with him an electric apparatus "made with such help as Calcutta could afford." He got a duplicate made by the best firm of instrument makers in London which "expressed a wish to make copies of the same instruments for supply in the laboratories of Europe and America."[26] Bose's second innovation was more fundamental. Europe was happy to work with metal to make radio detectors. But since metal rusts in the damp climate of Bengal, Bose experimented with a whole new class of "natural substances" including even jute. His work on galena was especially of great intrinsic value to the world of science. It is the ecological aspects of his physics that made his work universal.

The *Spectator* described him as "a Bengalee of the purest descent possible",[27] implying kinship with Europeans on the basis of Aryan Race theory. Bose spoke in Paris in 1897. The former President of the French Academy of Sciences, Alfred Cornu, who chaired the session, exhorted Bose: "You should try to revive the grand traditions of your race, which bore aloft the torchlight of art and science and was the leader of civilization two thousand years ago."[28]

The appreciation that Bose got in Europe enthused India. Rabindranath Tagore, whose own world fame was still into the future, wrote to Bose in England on 17 September 1900: "We need not understand what you have achieved ... we shall simply help ourselves to all the credit when *The Times* publishes words of praise from the lips of Englishmen."[29] Continuing in the same vein, Tagore wrote to Bose on 4 June 1901: "I bow my heart at the feet of the God who has chosen you as the instrument of removal of India's shame."[30] Those indeed were the days when God operated through the West. In 1901 itself, Tagore wrote a poem in Bengali, titled *To Jagadishchandra Bose*, which dramatically opened with the lines: "Young image of what old Rishi of Ind/Art thou, O Arya savant, Jagadis? Towards the close, the poet says: 'So may our India, Our ancient land, unto herself return.'".[31] For the English-educated Indians, modern science was not a solution to current problems but a revival of old textual traditions. In retrospect, rishification of Bose was a hindrance in appreciating science as an agency for production of wealth.

The *Electric Engineer* expressed "surprise that no secret was at any time made as to its construction, so that it has been open to all the world to adopt it for practical and possibly money-making purposes." Bose however was clear in mind that "whatever offerings his life could make should be untainted by any considerations of personal advantage."

> Moreover, he was painfully impressed by what seemed to him symptoms of deterioration, even in scientific men, by the temptation of gain; and so at this time he made the resolve to seek for no personal advantage from his inventions.[32]

In 1901, Dr Alexander Muirhead (1848–1920), like Bose a doctorate in science from London University and a manufacturer of telegraphic equipment, met Bose in London and suggested that Bose patent his discoveries and share profits with Muirhead. Bose rejected the suggestion outright and with contempt.

US Patent

The same year a patent was filed in the USA in Bose's name, assigning half of the royalty to Sara Chapman Bull, better known as Mrs Ole Bull after her Norwegian husband.[33] But a stubborn Bose refused to encash it. Bose had no objection to accepting industrial money from the West (that is Mrs Bull) but would not generate it himself. There is an irony that has often been missed. Bose though a physics professor in a college was still a product of an orientalized East; accordingly, he was repelled by the idea of making money from his inventions. On the other hand, Sister Nivedita (born Margaret Noble, 1867–1911) though a spiritual person was still a child of Western industrial culture; she was all for patents and royalties. In fact, in her enthusiasm for creating an aura around Bose, she went overboard. In a 1903 letter to Rabindranath Tagore, she wrongly declared Bose to be "the discoverer of the Etheric waves that penetrate minerals." She also referred to the prevalence of "a strong race-feeling of jealousy to combine with the natural and scientific opposition."[34] Inspired by this, there have been attempts in recent times to project Bose as a victim. It has been claimed that Marconi cheated Bose and that Bose should have received the Nobel Prize.

The British relationship with the Indians was far too complex to be discussable in terms of a single parameter, racism. There is no doubt that the British in India as a body practised discrimination against the natives and lost no opportunity to put them in their place. But, Bose personally had no reason to complain on that count. Bose was placed in the European grade by The Viceroy himself interceding on his behalf. True that he had to agitate for three long years to get equal pay, but he did succeed finally. At the professional level, Bose received due encouragement and recognition from the West. He was even offered a new professorship at a renowned university.[35]

It is true that Marconi made use of the concept of a coherer Bose had devised and described. But there was no stealth because Marconi used information that was in the public domain. The criticism of the West would have been justified if Bose had been in competition for the prize and had been deliberately sidelined. By the time of Marconi's Prize, Bose was an ex-physicist. Had Bose continued with his radio work, someone in Europe or North America might have nominated him. But he had since waded into uncharted waters. A prize for him would have been construed as recognition of his plant work. As for Bose himself is concerned, given a choice between the Nobel Physics Prize and mainstream recognition of his plant research, he would have probably opted for the latter.

Prizes are decided by a committee on the basis of nominations. Committees do not work in a vacuum. Any decision by them is open to influences. In the cases of both Raman and Tagore, there was canvassing or campaigning by the candidate or on his behalf. The Nobel Physics Prize was denied to Jocelyn Bell, the discoverer of pulsars; the reason cannot be racial because she is English. Fred Hoyle did not get a share in the Nobel Physics Prize even though his co-author, William Fowler, did, for work on stellar nucleo-synthesis. The reason for his neglect was that his later ideas were considered maverick. By way of explanation, Harry Kroto, the 1974 Chemistry Nobel Laureate, noted that the Nobel Prize is not just an award for a piece of work, but a recognition of a scientist's overall reputation.

If Bose had taken out patents, the history of Indian science and industry would have been different. As Ray reminded his audience on the occasion of Bose's knighthood (1916), Bose would have made millions for himself as royalty. Even more importantly, he would have become a role model for the production of wealth through science. As it is, Bose abandoned radio physics altogether and there were no trained students to continue his line of research. Thus, in spite of Bose's epoch-making research, technical physics could not be institutionalized in India. An ancient rishi could indulge in speculation in a surplus economy based on agriculture and animal husbandry. If a scientist be a modern rishi, he should strengthen the economy. Bose could have accepted royalties and placed the amount in a public trust.

Bose's career as an internationally recognized pioneering experimental radio physicist ended more or less with the closure of the 19th century. He spent the remaining years of his working life investigating topics such as responses in the living and the non-living. There is a better appreciation of this work now, but at the time it was considered to be pseudo-science. Bose could not get it published in any Western journal and had to publish it himself. It was in fact seen as an embarrassment and delayed his election to the Royal Society (till 1920).

In India, the Western recognition Bose had won for his radio work was amalgamated with his later investigations. In the 1950s, when we were in school in a far-off place in Himachal Pradesh, we were told this story about Bose, which we discovered later was extant throughout the country. Sir J.C. Bose is in England on a lecture tour where he sets out to experimentally demonstrate how the plants respond to external stimuli the same way as humans do. To make his point, he sprinkles a poisonous substance on the plant but nothing happens. The audience bursts into ridiculing laughter. Touched to the quick, Bose swallows the substance himself. Nothing happens to him either. The hall is momentarily stunned into silence and then bursts into thunderous applause. Somebody (an Englishman?) had maliciously replaced the real poison with a harmless powder to spite Bose but the great Indian scientist gets the better of him. The story is apocryphal. Still, it is significant because it tells us that Bose's international stature was part of national consciousness. However, in his own country, he was perceived as an original modern thinker/researcher on issues that jelled with ancient Indian philosophy rather than as a part of the European science machine to which he owed his name and fame.

Victimhood

A 100 years after Bose, India seems to have come to the painful realization that it is unlikely to make any path-breaking scientific inventions any more. It has therefore decided to bestow victimhood on Bose.

In his time, Bose was cocking a snook at the European profit-oriented academe–industry–business alliance and occupying a high moral ground. His countrymen now are complaining that the West did not give him what was his due.

Marconi was an inventor, patentee, entrepreneur, and businessman, unconstrained by any ethical considerations. If he had mentioned Bose's name in his Nobel scheme as a radio pioneer, India's sense of inadequacy would have diminished somewhat, but otherwise, it would not have made any material difference. India charges the West with having been unfair, discriminatory, and racist. But, India practised racism in reverse, by indulging in culturism. Bose occupied high moral ground and condemned as greedy the European academe–industry–business coalition to which Europe owed its pre-eminence. The West offered royalties to India, but India wanted testimonials.

P.C. Ray

Ray graduated from the Metropolitan Institution (since renamed Vidyasagar College, after its founder Ishwar Chandra Vidyasagar). The Gilchrist scholarship brought Ray to Edinburgh University from where he obtained his DSc in 1887. He now spent a year as a Hope Prize Scholar (like Aghornath). He was elected as one of the two Vice Presidents of the Edinburgh University Chemical

Society and presided over its meetings in the absence of the President. Ray returned in 1888 but had to remain jobless for about a year. Pedlar had earlier recommended the appointment of an additional member of the faculty in chemistry. The position was sanctioned and in July 1889 Ray was appointed to it. His appointment was in the Provincial Education Service.

Ray "went straight" to Darjeeling to ask the Director of Public Instruction, Sir Alfred Croft, for placement in the Superior Service. Rather rudely, Croft told him: "Nobody compels you to accept the appointment." Subsequently, Ray discovered that Croft's anger was not so much directed at Ray as at the limitations of his own administrative powers. Croft did recommend Ray for the higher grade but without success. How Ray learnt about this tells us about the channels natives utilized for learning about goings on in the government. A distant relative of his was acquainted with a clerk in the Secretariat who copied relevant lines from "a report by the head of the Education Department" and passed them on to Ray.[36]

The placement of European appointees above the Indians irrespective of the latter's credentials was an all-India phenomenon. Earlier in 1872, in Bombay, when the post of Professor of Sanskrit fell vacant at Elphinstone College, it was not offered to [Sir] Ramchandra Gopal Bhandarkar (1837–1925) who eminently deserved it but to a 25-year-old Scotsman, Peter Peterson (1847–1899) who had graduated from Oxford University just a year previously.

John Arthur Cunningham

A young idealistic Cambridge-educated Irish young man, John Arthur Cunningham (1877–1911), joined Presidency College in 1903, after obtaining his BA in physics and chemistry the previous year. In 1906, he was given the additional appointment of Meteorological Reporter to the Government of Bengal and Second Assistant Meteorological Reporter to the Government of India. He was made a Fellow of the Calcutta University in 1905. Openly sympathetic to Indian aspirations, he often said in his lectures to the students that it was a curious anomaly that a junior like him should rank higher than an internationally acclaimed chemist like Ray. He would have probably gotten away with such radical utterances, but his breach of official discipline provided the authorities with a pretext to punish him. In 1909, he was banished to Chhota Nagpur as Inspector of Schools.[37] He plunged into his new appointment "with characteristic earnestness and thoroughness." "The most distant and inaccessible of jungle schools was a matter of as keen an interest to him as the best equipped of model schools. From one of these journeys he returned ill, and passed away with agonizing quickness." He took an interest in the establishment of Bengal Chemicals and advised Asutosh Mukherjee on University matters. A tablet to his memory was unveiled at the Baker Laboratory of Presidency College on 24 November 1914. The refusal of the administration to place Indians in the higher Education Service had always rankled them, but open advocacy of native cause by a British Professor brought discrimination against educated Indians into sharper focus. Gopal Krishna Gokhale (1866–1915) drew attention to this anomaly in a public speech in 1911 with a pointed reference to Ray's case.[38]

Chemical Lab

The very first research problem Ray took up was socially relevant. He set out to address the problem of adulteration of ghee (clarified butter) and mustard oil, the two main sources of fat in Bengal. "The composition of butter fat derived from the Indian cows differs somewhat from that of the British cows and hence the analysis of the latter as published in the English works on Foods could not be relied on." The results of this painstaking research, which took three years, were published in 1894.[39]

The Presidency College already had a chemical lab since Pedler's appointment which however was without proper ventilation and exhaust and was thus a health hazard. Ray's first task was to persuade the College Principal to initiate steps for building a new one. Very farsightedly, Ray had brought with him the details of the new laboratory built in Edinburgh. Pedlar on his part obtained some plans for German laboratories as well. In July 1894, a state-of-art chemical laboratory became operational. Bose's physics lab was private and was dismantled when his research interests shifted. In contrast, thanks to the existence of a college lab, chemical research was institutionalized. The lab served as a training ground, and ushered India into internationally competitive chemical research. In December 1895, Ray reported the isolation of mercurous nitrite in a paper read before the Asiatic Society of Bengal, which published it in its journal in January 1896.[40] His path-breaking work was duly noticed in *Nature*[41] and by eminent European chemists and learned societies.

Ray was not content with merely teaching modern science; he wanted to demolish old taboos too. "I used to place on the table samples of burnt bones, which had now nothing to do with the sources they came from; they might have been derived from the sacred cow, or the horse or the human skull." The burnt bone was a pure chemical compound, that is calcium phosphate, and a nerve tonic. Ray would chew the bone himself, "and even swallow it wholesale," and invite his students to follow suit. While some of them "hesitated and could not shake off their orthodox notions," there were others who readily emulated their radical teacher. Those days it was customary for forward-looking scientists to delve into ancient India. Ray found time to publish in

1902 and 1908 his work on the history of chemistry in India, self-consciously calling it *History of Hindu Chemistry*. While concluding it, Ray wrote:

> The Hindu Nation with its glorious past and vast latent potentialities may yet look forward to a still more glorious future, and if the perusal of these lines will have the effect of stimulating my countrymen, to strive for regaining their old position in the *intellectual hierarchy* [italicized in the original] of nations, I shall not have laboured in vain.[42]

Ray exhorted the youth to take inspiration from past scholars; yet, his own world-class researches were made possible by the fact that he had a state-of-the art lab at his disposal.

Ray's commitment to research transcended any desire for promotion in the official hierarchy. In 1897, he was asked to go to Rajshahi as Principal of the College, but he "respectfully submitted" to the Government that he be permitted to remain at Presidency College so that he could continue his research. The Director of Public Instruction, Dr Martin, aware that "Dr Ray is a distinguished Chemist engaged in original research in the Presidency College" "decided that the idea ought to be abandoned."[43] Even before he embarked on his theoretical research, he started manufacturing and marketing chemicals and drugs.

Bengal Chemical

It was left to Ray to initiate chemical and pharmaceutical manufacturing activity in Bengal with "the idea of wiping out the reproach that the Bengalees were good for nothing in business affairs."[44] It was important for him to succeed. He was born into an old wealthy, landed and cultured family but his idealist but impractical father managed to impoverish the family. While Ray was still in school, his family "estates began to be sold one after another." Soon, the father was transformed from a creditor into a debtor. Ray could never forget

> the pathetic scene of my mother sobbing and with tears in her eyes, signing away the landed property, which was purchased in her name with the proceeds of the sale of her ornaments and which really belonged to her as stridhan [dowry].

To clear off the debts left behind by his father on his death in 1894, Ray and his brother sold off the remaining, heavily mortgaged ancestral property, and undertook to repay the still outstanding debt from their own earnings. And yet Ray was extremely proud of his father whose debts were debts of honour which he willingly undertook to repay. Witnessing the loss of family wealth converted young Ray into an entrepreneur. Ray's father brought out a revised

edition of H. H. Wilson's celebrated *Sanskrit English Dictionary* at a heavy
cost which he could not market at all. Years later, Ray and his elder brother
styled themselves as booksellers and managed to sell some copies, the pro-
ceeds of which went into meeting their school education expenses.[45]

Ray was clear in his mind from the start that he wished to start industrial
production utilizing "the thousand and one raw products" available in
Bengal. While his academic training would come in handy, he was conscious
that his impressions about manufacturing in Britain would be quite irrelevant
in the local conditions. Without hesitation, he enlisted the support of Pedlar's
lecture assistant, Chandrabhushan Bhaduri, who had assisted him in per-
forming classroom experiments, but was otherwise much lower than Ray in
the professional hierarchy. After some false starts such as extracting citric
acid from lemon juice (commercially unviable) and manufacturing carbonate
of soda (less pure and more expensive than the imported stuff), Ray succeeded in producing large quantities of phosphates of soda and superphos-
phate of lime using the easily available cattle bone as the raw material. This
was particularly satisfying because the bones were being exported abroad for
processing. He happily used the roof of his residence to dry animal bones,
much to the chagrin of his neighbours and suspicion of the policemen.

About 1891, Ray purchased a crude acid plant against his future earnings
from University examination work but failed to turn it around. It had to be
sold off at a loss, "but the experience thus gained proved to be a valuable
asset, which was turned to good account several years later." In 1892, Ray
set up a private firm with the long but descriptive name Bengal Chemical and
Pharmaceutical Works.[46] The Company took to making various syrups and
tinctures according to the British Pharmacopoeia specifications. To get the
flavour of the time, we may look at excerpts from an advertisement prepared
by Ray himself and published in 1894 in *Sanjivani*, the widely read Bengali-
language newspaper:

> With the help of Dr. Prafulla Chandra Ray, D. Sc. (Edin.) and the well-
> known medical practitioner Dr. Amulya Charan Bose, M.B., in this allo-
> pathic manufacturing concern some three hundred medicines have been
> prepared and are for sale. Our preparations are made according to the
> latest scientific methods ...Syrup of Hypophosphite [sic] of Lime for colds,
> coughs, catarrh, asthma, phthisis, bronchitis and other lungs-diseases: A
> never-failing remedy. It is sweet and agreeable to the taste and of beautiful
> rose colour. Trial of last two years has proved that because it is freely
> prepared, its efficacy is superior to that of the imported article. The lead-
> ing physicians of Calcutta are prescribing it.[47]

In April 1901, Bengal Chemical was converted into a public limited company. The idealism and hard work notwithstanding, the company was not

doing too well, shortage of capital being the main reason. When a shareholder called for his dividend of ten annas (that is five-eighth of a rupee), "the coffers of the Company were so empty that the paltry sum had to be borrowed from the durwan [porter]."[48]

At the outbreak of the First World War, the President of the London Chemical Society wrote to Ray asking for his help in the war effort. Responding positively, Bengal Chemicals not only increased its production but also introduced new processes and products. Additional chambers were erected for sulphuric acid; caffeine was extracted from tea dust; fire extinguishers and surgical bandages were manufactured; and photographers' hypo was produced on a large scale.[49] Also, chemical balances were manufactured for the first time in India. More generally, for the nascent and struggling Indian industry, be it chemicals or alcohol or iron and steel, the First World War came as a godsend.

There had been rumours that Ray's factory was supplying the revolutionaries with knowhow for making bombs. The rumours were strong enough for the police to investigate. In 1912, when Ray was made Companion of the Indian Empire, he jokingly told the CID official in a school boyish style that he could not touch Ray now because while he was merely CID, Ray was now alphabetically superior to him by being CIE.[50] The contribution to the war effort washed away all his sins, and in 1919 Ray was knighted.

Traditional Plant Medicine

In India, the British had to take note of indigenous drugs for their own sake and the sake of good governance. Imported medicines were very expensive and ran the risk of deterioration during the long transportation times. Most plants and shrubs described in London and Edinburgh Pharmacopoeias were not to be found in India. The problem became more acute during wars: when the stock of imported medicines was depleted. Many Indian patients who came to European doctors had previously been treated by local practitioners with indigenous preparations or drugs known only by their vernacular name. Also, the doctors were called upon to attend to cases of bites by snakes and other animals. For legal and medical reasons, the doctor had to know about available poisons as well as malicious poisoning of cattle.

Synthesis of molecules was still into the future and the West also depended on medicines obtained from the vegetable kingdom. Europe and the USA were thus interested in Indian plants, their traditional use, and the British physicians' experience with them in India. The British Indian medical men scanned Persian, Sanskrit, Tamil, and other texts for information; interacted with practising Indian physicians and other knowledgeable persons; frequented shops selling "bazaar drugs;" correlated local names with the Latin ones; and kept records of their own findings.

The first British Indian medical publication was John Fleming's 1810 *A Catalogue of Indian Plants with their Names in Hindustani and Sanskrit Languages*. It was a guide book intended for European doctors on their first arrival in India. Many other, more important, books followed; they were all very useful because they covered different geographies and ecologies. Their printing was facilitated by the government, but the initiative had been the author's.

The government's own initiative came in 1838 with the appointment of an official committee to assess the possibility of using indigenous medicines in government dispensaries. Its active member was the Medical College Chemistry Professor and chemical examiner William O' Shaughnessy. In 1839, he brought to the notice of the West the therapeutic use of cannabis. He published *The Bengal Dispensatory* in 1841 and followed it in 1844 with *The Bengal Pharmacopoeia*.

Colonial expertise on native drugs came to be appreciated by the Indians also. In 1856, Dr Edward John Waring, Madras army surgeon, was appointed Durbar Physician to the Maharaja of Travancore. In 1860, he published in English and Tamil *Remarks on the uses of some of the bazaar medicines and common medical plants of India*. The book was translated into South Indian languages and remained in use for half a century, with the sixth edition appearing in 1901.

Those days, when a colonial official came back home to England on furlough or forever, he took the opportunity to network, draw attention to the significance of his achievements if not already known, and catch the eye of influential persons. When the British Pharmacopoeia (BP) marking a sharp break from the past was first issued in 1864, Waring was in England. Immediately, he proposed the bringing out of Indian Pharmacopoeia (IP). The International Exhibition held in London barely two years ago, in 1862, where Indian drugs were displayed, had already created a favourable climate. The proposal was accepted and a committee formed by the Secretary of State for India, with Waring as the editor. The compilation was carried out in London, and an official *Pharmacopoeia of India* was issued in 1868. In addition to all the entries in BP, it included 40 drugs indigenous to India.

Earlier Indians had served only as informants and assistants. Things changed when Indians were trained in Western medicine and employed in the medical service though at lower levels. They now became associates, collaborators, and independent researchers. IP was the first publication which explicitly asked for contributions from Indian doctors. Of the various names acknowledged in IP, three sub-assistant surgeons are noteworthy for their latter contributions: Kanny Lall Dey, Moodeen Sheriff and Uday Chand Dutt.

Kanny Lall Dey obtained his diploma from Calcutta Medical College in 1853 and was posted as assistant to chemistry professor and chemical examiner at Calcutta Medical College. Preparation for the 1862 London Exhibition imparted great impetus to systematic investigations into Indian materia medicas. On instructions from the government, Kanny Lall Dey sent a consignment of assorted indigenous drugs (including metallic preparations) and medicinal oils to London. For wider circulation, he even brought out from Calcutta a 14-page pamphlet titled *A Brief Report on Indian Drugs as contributed to the London Exhibition of 1862*. Dey's collection was the largest among that of individuals and was well received. He won medals for it. In addition, it brought him professional recognition in the form of 1863 election as an honorary member of the Pharmaceutical Society London. In 1867, he contributed "a collection of Native Drugs" to the Universal Exhibition at Paris accompanied by a "Descriptive Catalogue," which in turn became the basis of his celebrated work *The Indigenous Drugs of India*, published in 1867 from Calcutta.

Kanny Lall was the Empire's man on indigenous drugs. He sent collections to foreign institutions (including the University of Virginia, in 1870). He was asked in 1874 to make a collection of Bengal drugs for the museum at Netley hospital "for the benefit of surgeons joining the Indian Medical Service." In 1877, he prepared five complete sets of the indigenous drugs of India for the five medical schools of Bengal. Towards the end of his life, in 1896, he brought out, with assistance from William Mair, an enlarged and completely rewritten edition of his *Indigenous Drugs* in the hope of it being used as a textbook. Expectedly, he won suitable colonial titles and honours (Rai Bahadur 1872, CIE 1884).

While Kanny Lall's inputs went into the Indian Pharmacopoeia, Moodeen Sheriff added great value to IP after it was published. Sheriff, the "Native Surgeon of Triplicane Dispensary" in Madras painstakingly brought out in 1869 his *Supplement to the Pharmacopoeia of India*, which ran into 700 pages and gave synonyms of about 400 IP plants and drugs in 15 languages in their own characters, including Latin, English, Arabic, Persian, Sanskrit, Burmese and Sinhalese. The work won high praise, with one reviewer declaring that without it, IP would be "a dead letter." In 1869 itself, he was given the honorary rank of Surgeon (otherwise reserved for Europeans) and created a Khan Bahadur in 1878. He retired in 1889 and died two years later. His *Materia Medica of Madras* was edited and posthumously published in 1891 by David Hooper, government quinologist, Ootacamund.

In 1877, Uday Chand Dutt [Odoy Chund Dutt] extracted a materia medica from Sanskrit medical texts. He gave only those details which arise as "a result of observation and experience," and omitted those that are "the outcome of an erroneous system of pathology and therapeutics." During the heyday of the colonial empire, Indians were very keen to validate their traditional knowledge in the Western eyes.

IP's glory lasted less than two decades. There were many drugs in it whose efficacy remained unproven. There was no standardization of names or quality. In addition, adulteration was rampant. The British pharmaceutical industry was also unhappy with IP; if the government bought indigenous drugs in bulk, the export of costly British medicines to India would dwindle. The third edition of BP which came out in 1885 included all drugs of Indian origin that were considered to be of proven value. BP was now declared to be "the sole authority on all matters relating to pharmacy" and IP banished. In other words, the Government of India could buy only those medicines that carried the BP stamp.

Some years later, in response to pleas made by its own officer, Dr George Watt, Reporter to the Government of India on Economic Products, and by Kanny Lall, the government declared that it was willing to buy indigenous drugs beyond its brief list "if they could be obtained pure, of a stable character, and at a price not exceeding that at which they can be imported." Towards this end, a Central Indigenous Drug Committee was set up with Watt as the secretary and with Kanny Lall as the only Indian member.

Following the Indian Medical Congress held in Calcutta in 1898, a strong representation was made by its Council, at the instance of "Kanai Lall Dey, who was then almost on the verge of his grave," urging the official recognition of some of the drugs being made by Indian pharma companies, and "the British Pharmacopoeia authorities were at last prevailed upon to find a back seat for some Indian drugs in the Addendum," published in 1900.[51] The achievement was no doubt symbolic but it also had a commercial angle. Once included in BP, these Indian preparations could be sold to government depots. As for IP, it would be revived in 1955, within a decade of the departure of the British. Ray's interest in traditional medicines was academic as well as commercial. He received from traditional physicians (kavirajs) a number of Ayurvedic "formulae and recipes" whose efficacy "had been proved beyond doubt by their universal use in the households of Bengal." These included the extracts of Kalmegh (*Andrographis paniculata*) and syrup of Vasaka (*Adhatoda vasica*). "All that was needed was their active principles should be extracted according to scientific up-to-date methods and that they should receive the imprimatur of the practitioners."

Chaulmoogra

Traditionally, in India, China, and elsewhere, the oil extracted from the seed of a tree known as chaulmoogra had been used in cases of leprosy and other skin diseases. It was first noticed by William Roxburgh in his *Flora Indica*. In 1854, Frederic John Mouat, an English doctor working in Calcutta, reported the possible utility of chaulmoogra oil in treating leprosy.[52] The tree was correctly identified in the early 20th century as *Hydnocarpus wightianus*, and in 1909 a patent was obtained for its ethyl esters (by Ludwig Taub) for injectible use against leprosy. The oil is no longer in use against leprosy because of the

TABLE 10.1 Colonial Notice of Traditional Medicines

Year	Author	Name of Work	Comments
1795	Sir William Jones	A catalogue of Indian plants comprehending their Sanskrit and as many of their Linnaean names as could with any degree of precision be ascertained.	Lists 419 names alphabetically; Asiatic Researches, 4, 229–236.
1795	Sir William Jones	Botanical observations on select Indian plants.	Describes 78 plants; Asiatic Researches 4: 237–312.
1810	John Fleming, MD Bengal	A Catalogue of Indian Medicinal Plants and Drugs with their names in Hindustani and Sanskrit Languages	Intended for European doctors on their first arrival in India. First published in Asiatic Researches.
1813	Whitelaw Ainslie	Materia Medica of Hindoostan, and Artisan's and Agriculturist's Nomenclature	To facilitate purchase of articles of British Materia Medica in the "Bazars of Hindoostan"
1841	William Brooke O'Shaughnessy MD	Bengal Dispensatory	Published on orders of the Government
1844	William Brooke O'Shaughnessy MD	The Bengal Pharmacopoeia, and General Conspectus of Medicinal Plants: Arranged According to the Natural and Therapeutical Systems	Published on orders of the Government
1867	Kanny Loll [sic] Dey, Additional Chemical Examiner to Government	The Indigenous Drugs of India: or, Some Descriptive Notices of the Medicines, both Vegetable and mineral, in common use among the natives of India	The expanded version of the catalogue of native drugs sent to the exhibition in Paris
1868	Edward John Waring, MD	Pharmacopoeia of India	Prepared on the authority of Secretary of State for India, to take note of substantial changes in British Pharmacopoeia. In addition to all the contents of the latter, it included 40 materia medica indigenous to India

Year	Author	Title	Description
1869	Moodeen Sheriff, 'Native Surgeon'	Supplement to the Pharmacopoeia of India	Gives synonyms in 14 Indian languages, including Arabic, Persian, Burmese and Cingalese, to entries above.
1877	Uday Chand Dutt, Chief Medical Officer	The Materia Medica of the Hindus, compiled from Sanskrit Medical Works	Patterned after above. Carries a Glossary of Indian Plants by George King, MB, Supdt of Botanical Garden, Calcutta
1896	Kanny Lall Dey; assisted by William Mair	The Indigenous Drugs of India: Short Descriptive Notices of the Principal Medicinal Products met with in British India	The second edition of Dey's 1877 work, revised and entirely rewritten. Includes a biographical sketch of Dey by Mair.
1922	Uday Chand Dutt	The Materia Medica of the Hindus (rev. ed.)	With additions and alterations by three traditional physicians (Kaviraj) Binod Lal Sen, Asutosh Sen and Pulin Krishna Sen.

availability of synthetic drugs. There is however renewed interest in the external use of chaulmoogra oil and its derivatives for the treatment of pigmentation problems of the skin and other cosmetic uses, as can be seen from the patents obtained.

"Natives" in Colonial Service

Indians were placed at the lowest rung of government service. Except in the rarest of rare cases, no Indian was placed above a European. Indians were given titles like Rai/Khan Bahadur which would enhance their prestige in their society, but would not affect the official hierarchy. Many officers (but not all) wanted their Indian subordinates to remove their shoes before entering the office. Also, the officer would beforehand get all extra chairs removed so that the subordinate would have to keep standing.

A universal way of showing Indians their place was the Anglicization of their names. Dey's real name was Kanai Lal Dey which was used in official and legal records. In his professional career beginning with the 1862 London exhibition, both his personal names were anglicized to Kanny Loll. His reaction came towards the end of his life when the revised edition of his *Indigenous Drugs* appeared. The first name Kanny had become internationally too well known to be dispensed with, but now he wrote Lall in place of Loll.

Sheriff's first name is spelt as Mohideen in the Medical College records. Throughout his service years, it was anglicized to Moodeen. He reverted to the correct spelling after retirement as can be seen in his posthumous *Materia Medica of Madras*. It should however be appreciated that when Kanny Lall and Moodeen, two universally respected Indian authorities, brought out their books in the 1890s, they were assisted by Europeans.

Chemistry at Dacca

While the work of Ray and his students at Calcutta is well recognized, Dacca's contribution deserves to be better known. Unlike in Calcutta where nationalism was the driving force, the pioneer at Dacca College was a British Professor, Edwin Roy Watson (1880–1926). After his education in Cambridge, Watson came to Calcutta in 1904 as a chemistry professor at Shibpur Engineering College. In 1906, he was transferred to Dacca College. In 1921, he was appointed the Principal of the newly opened Government Technological Institute, Kanpur, subsequently (1926) named after the Lieutenant Governor, Harcourt Butler.[53] Not only was he "able to prepare the students for their degree examination in science" but was also "gradually successful in creating an atmosphere of research among his more advanced students." When in December 1908, the first batch of students passed the MA examination in Chemistry from the Dacca College, he hand-picked Anukul Chandra Sircar from among them, and jointly began doing research work. Two others joined afterwards. This was the beginning of research in Chemistry at Dacca College which focused on Watson's primary interest, dyestuffs.[54]

A capable British scientist in India was put to various uses. In 1907, Watson on order from the Government of India, published a monograph on indigenous manufacture of iron and steel in Bengal.[55] More in line with his professional expertise, he published on the relative fastness of natural and synthetic dyes as seen in the case of cotton and silk. Natural dyes were purchased from him from Calcutta bazaars by Bipin Behari Das, a research student of the Civil Engineering College, Shibpur.[56] The trigger for this work was the Kashmir Durbar's 1906 decision to impose a hefty (45%) duty on synthetic dyes to prevent their use. While the tasks assigned to Watson in India were oriented towards commerce, England used his professional expertise during the First World War. Stationed at the University of Leeds, he carried out confidential work on dye manufacture on behalf of British Dyestuffs Ltd.

In India, however, he was asked to help his colonial economy. In 1908, he published "The exact determination of the fastness of the more common indigenous dyes of Bengal, and comparison with typical synthetic dye-stuffs," in two parts dealing with printing on cotton and silk.

T.K. Gajjar

Chemistry followed a trajectory in Western India different from Calcutta and Dacca. Here the emphasis was on industrial chemistry. Tribhuvandas Kalyandas Gajjar (1863–1920) led Kala Bhavan, Baroda, from its inception in 1890 till 1896; he inducted synthetic dyes into the Indian textile industry, established a Techno-Chemical Laboratory at Bombay in 1900 and successfully got it integrated into the University academic programme, and guided the establishment, in 1907, of Alembic Chemical Works at Baroda. While Bengal Chemical's focus was on pharmaceuticals, Alembic concentrated on alcohol. In the course of time, Bengal Chemical turned sick and had to be nationalized, while Alembic is flourishing in private hands.

By and large, the fruits of Western education went to upper castes. But, Gajjar strove to extend these benefits to members of artisan castes to one of which he himself belonged. He was born in Surat in the Suthar caste, traditionally associated with carpentry.[57] His wealthy and well-regarded father Kalyandas (1829–1915) owned two large timber shops in Surat and Ahmedabad and was a noted civil engineer. He compiled and published a number of books on *Shilpa shastra*, the traditional science of architecture. As a high school student at Surat, he would often take broken pieces of laboratory equipment home, reassemble them and do experiments. He very successfully combined formal Western education with family tradition. While he learnt mechanical drawing in the school, he "acquired skills of carpentry using tools and implements in my father's workshop." After passing his matriculation examination in the first division in 1879, he joined Elphinstone College Bombay and earned the BA degree in Chemistry in 1882, standing first in the examination. On his future course of action, he was subjected to contrary pulls by his friends. He toyed with the idea of studying law or Sanskrit and Philosophy. It is noteworthy that by this time Sanskrit was no longer the preserve of the Brahmins. Finally, he opted for science and did his MA in Chemistry in 1884. His first efforts were to set up a polytechnic in his home town but the plan failed to materialize. In 1886, he joined Baroda College as a professor of Chemistry. Established in 1881 for art subjects alone, the College had that year started science classes but without success; all the students who wrote the first BSc examination in 1887 failed. The young Maharaja Sayajirao Gaekwad (also spelt Gaekwar) (1862–1939) was an enlightened ruler to whom Gajjar had access through his friend, Yashvant Vasudev Athalye, known as Bapusaheb (1863–1894) who was the Deputy Diwan.[58] Accepting Bapusaheb and Gajjar's proposal for a polytechnic institute, Gaekwad founded Kala Bhavan in 1890 with Gajjar as the principal. "A good deal of money was spent in engaging competent German and other teachers, in giving scholarships and assisting students. Bapusaheb and Prof. Gajjar had to empty their pockets for the cause in hand." In May 1895, on Gajjar's recommendation two *mistris* from Kala Bhavan, Lallubhai Mansukhram and Bhaichand Chelabhai, were sent to London to participate in the Empire of India exhibition organized by the Society for the Preservation of Indian Art. Bapusaheb's death in 1894 robbed Gajjar of valuable support: "[d]ay by day the conviction began to grow on his mind, owing to various circumstances, that Baroda was not the proper place for his work."[59] Accordingly, Gajjar resigned from his post in 1896 and moved to Bombay.

The Kala Bhavan offered practical training in a number of areas: civil, mechanical and electrical engineering, drawing and printing, architecture and photo engraving, textile chemistry including dyeing, bleaching, sizing and printing, oil and soap making, etc. Incidentally, one of the earliest students at Kala Bhavan was Dadasahib Phalke (1870–1944) recognized as the father of Indian cinema. In 1896, out of the 204 students, 39 (19%) belonged to the artisan castes and another 44 (22%) were sons of farmers and cultivators. In 1907–1908, the Kala Bhavan had 570 students on its rolls, out of which 70% were from Baroda state, as many as 18% from Bombay Presidency, and the remaining from other states.

To Gajjar goes the credit for introducing synthetic dyes into the Indian textile industry. As he recalled in 1907, "When our vegetable colours were driven out from the world's market, which they had held for centuries … there was no recourse left but to make use of these new colours." The world leader in synthetic dyes was Germany with three firms dominating the scene: Bayer, Hoechst and BASF.

When Gajjar was carrying on correspondence with some German colour firms, they offered him their agency. Those were the days when nation-building ranked higher than personal fortune-building. Committed to the "spread of technical education and of modern industries in his motherland," he declined the lucrative offer. The European gentleman who then secured it was able to make some lakhs of rupees by means of that agency.[60]

Germany, the home of these chemical dyes, was anxious to secure a market in India. Our mill industry also needed healthy growth and development. Gajjar suggested to Bayer "to train students and instruct native dyers in the use of their [German] dyes if they desired India to become one of their great customers." Bayer financially supported the establishment of a laboratory in Surat and appointed Gajjar the firm's consulting chemist. The German firm also sent (and funded) several experts to the school, such as a technician named Schuhmacher and a professor of chemical technology, Dr Ehrhard. Training centres for dyers were opened in Ahmedabad, Delhi, Cawnpore and Amritsar under Gajjar's supervision. Many of the students were later employed by Bayer in its India business. Gajjar sent a trained dyer to Madura who was seen as a blessing by the "47000 Sorathi settlers." The Glasgow turkey-red yarn manufacturers had to send their agents to Madura to enquire why all the imports were stopped and what were the methods of dyeing adopted there.

When Mr. J. N. Tata heard about this, he at once communicated with me and made up his mind to append a dye-house to his mill, with the help of dyers trained in my private laboratory at Baroda. Even a costly laboratory set of dyeing apparatus was presented to his mill through me by the German manufacturers.[61]

Techno-Chemical Laboratory, Bombay

On moving to Bombay, Gajjar joined Wilson College as professor of Chemistry and almost immediately won professional and official recognition in a spectacular manner. In October 1896, someone disfigured Queen Victoria's marble statue by smearing it with tar with the result that it had to be removed from public view and "boarded up." Many European experts tried to remove the stains but failed. Gajjar rose to the occasion and removed the stains which to others had appeared indelible. For this service, he was given a prize of Rs 2,000 in 1897.[62] He was certainly an innovative chemist. He developed a new process to clean up pearls that had turned yellow. His lasting contribution however is his gearing the Bombay University Chemistry curriculum towards industry. In 1900, in consultation with and consent from Justice Mahadeo

Govind Ranade (1842–1901) and friends such as M.G. Deshmukh, MD,[63] he became the proprietor and director of a training institute named Techno-Chemical Laboratory in Girgaum which trained graduates and undergraduates "to enable them to think of starting new factories." Such a private initiative would probably not have succeeded anywhere else in India than Bombay. Next, Gajjar in co-operation with the Jesuit Father Professor Dr H. Kemp of St Xavier's College persuaded Bombay University to make its courses for the degree in Chemistry "more practical and useful."[64] His own laboratory was recognized by the University for MA in Chemistry in 1907.[65] An entrepreneur himself, Gajjar did not wish to risk other people's capital in new ventures. He therefore "with his own money started new factories through his students."

The most notable of his private students was Anant Shridhar Kotibhaskar (d. 1910) who went on to secure First Class Honours in MA and win the Chancellor's gold medal in Chemistry. His initiative led to the establishment of Alembic Chemical works. Another trainee at the Laboratory was Bhailal Dajibhai Amin (1878–1950) whose forte was business management and who eventually became the sole proprietor of Alembic. In 1903, Gajjar started a small factory called Parel Laboratories, after the location in Bombay, for the manufacture of spirit and "pharmaceutical products, toilet preparations and certain chemicals" based on it. Soon, it was found necessary to have a factory for the large-scale production of spirit alone. For this, it was considered advisable to go out of British India, "as the Government of Bombay did not seem to be inclined to grant any concessions." Kotibhaskar approached the Maharaja of Gaekwad as well as his Dewan Ramesh Chandra Dutt. Accordingly, a factory for the manufacture of spirit was started in Baroda in 1905. The name Alembic, broadly meaning distillation apparatus, was chosen to indicate "that the works were principally started for the manufacture of spirit and its products." Alembic acquitted itself well at the 1906 Calcutta National Exhibition where its products were examined by "reputed Chemical Experts" such as Dr David Hooper, curator of the Indian Museum and Dr Rai Chunilal Bose Bahadur, chemical examiner to the Government of Bengal who certified them "as possessing the highest chemical purity."[66]

While Kotibhaskar looked after "the management of scientific and manufacturing work" with the assistance of three chemists, the "management of business" was placed in the hands of Mr K.B. Mavhankar [sic, Mavlankar?] about whom nothing is known.[67] Amin was not yet a part of the enterprise.[68] He was looking after the lac factory Gajjar had personally set up in Nadiad "to serve as an outlet for use of spirit produced by the Alembic Works." This unit had to be closed down,[69] and Amin now got associated with Alembic. As Amin himself wrote in 1939: "As the business of the enterprise increased,

Prof. Gajjar and Prof. Kotibhaskar realized that in the interest of efficiency, the technical and the business sides should be put under separate management." While Kotibhaskar continued to look after the technical side, Amin was appointed Business Manager.[70] Alembic came into existence on 30 July 1907 as a joint stock company. It was registered first in Bombay and then in Baroda. On 7 December 1907, it appointed the partnership firm of Messrs. Kotibhasker, Amin & Co. as its Managing Agents. Gajjar's minor son was one of the four partners of the firm.[71] Thus contrary to popular perception, the future owner Amin was not associated with Alembic when the work started in 1905 but entered the picture only in 1907 at the time of the registration of the company. Amin described Gajjar as a friend, guide and philosopher; Kotibhaskar as commander-in-chief; and himself as quarter master general.[72] An important difference between Bengal Chemicals and Alembic should be noted. The former was established by a professor while the latter was set up by students under guidance from their professor.

Alembic's first big-time venture was a significant development on the technical front but a colossal failure on the financial. It took a three-year contract beginning April 1910 from the Baroda Government's Excise Department to supply potable liquor. Although the raw material was the traditional mahura (or mahua) plant, the Company decided to process it in a scientific way. Kotibhaskar went to Europe in 1909 to obtain some experience in distillery and pharmaceutical work and returned with a French still. Kotibhaskar's death in 1910 was not a severe setback because Gajjar was at hand to take up the responsibilities of the technical director.

If the Company had stipulated in the contract the quantity of spirit that it would supply to the Baroda state, it would have made a neat pile of money from the deal. However, as the contract stood, Alembic was obliged to supply "excessively large" quantities of alcohol way beyond its own production capabilities. As a result, the Company lost heavily on the contract. Although Gaekwad "graciously" granted Rs 30,000 as compensation, the amount was less than one-tenth of what the Company had lost.[73] Alembic was saved from a "severe financial collapse" by a substantial loan of Rs 200,000 sanctioned by the Gaekwad-supported Bank of Baroda.

Like Bengal Chemicals, Alembic also profited from the First World War. Baroda's modern distillation facilities received an enthusiastic welcome from Europeans based in India who could no longer get imported foreign liquor. "Brandy, Whisky, Rum, etc. began to be manufactured in the factory, and found ready sales." In the four-year period of 1915–1918, the Company's foreign liquor business showed an increase of 2700%, from Rs 28,000 to Rs 761,000. In this period, the pharmacy, foreign liquor and rectified spirit businesses taken together showed a ten-fold increase from Rs 104,000 to Rs 1,022,000.[74]

An account of Alembic products and Gajjar's "rational preparations" in 1915 was put out by their sole representatives for South India, Messrs S. Vaidya and Co. Alembic "are manufacturers of chemical, pharmaceutical and toilet requisites, and they are distillers of rectified spirits, essential oils, and attars." Professor Gajjar's "remedies are for such diseases as typhus, typhoid, and malarial fevers, plague, and cholera…good results have been obtained in cases of pneumonia, phthisis, and consumption." It was further pointed out that "Several gold and silver medals have been awarded to the proprietors for many of his specialties."[75]

Speaking at Alembic Works on the occasion of Gaekwad's visit on 30 October 1912, Gajjar pointed out that while "the original scheme of the Bangalore Institute as drawn up by Sir William Ramsay provided for the establishment of small model factories attached to the Institute itself, the project as finally adopted was only for pure research work." In contrast, Gajjar noted with apparent pride that Alembic had laboratories attached to the factory which turned out research work that "compared favourably with that attempted at the Indian Institute of Science, Bangalore."[76]

Ray noted with a tinge of envy that while his Bengal Chemical was perennially short of capital, Gajjar's Alembic could call upon Gaekwad for its capital needs.[77] The phenomenon however was far more complex. Given the general anti-entrepreneurial Bengali mindset, Ray's industrial initiative was a swim against the tide, while Gajjar's was part of the flow. Thus, more than access to the royal purse, it was the general industrial culture that set Western India apart from Bengal.

Srinivasa Ramanujan

The most untypical example of Indian response to modern education is the First Arts-failed creative mathematical genius, Srinivasa Ramanujan (1887–1920), whose introduction to modern mathematics at the age of 15 began and ended with *Synopsis of Pure Mathematics* written by George Shoobridge Carr (1837–1914), first published in 1886 as a study guide for those preparing for the Cambridge Tripos mathematics examination. This book was borrowed by a friend for Ramanujan from the library of the Government College at Kumbakonam. Fortunately, there were men of science around who though incapable of judging Ramanujan's work had the sense to put him in touch with knowledgeable persons. Ramanujan arrived in Cambridge in 1914 at the invitation of G.H. Hardy and remained here for five years. In 1918, he was elected a Fellow of the Royal Society, the first Indian to be so honoured in the 20th century. Later in the year, he became the first Indian fellow of Trinity College. Madras University endowed him with a research studentship in addition, and early in 1919, still unwell, but apparently considerably better, he returned to India. One wonders as to what a Ramanujan would have done if he had been born a 100 years earlier. Ramanujan was not a scientist in the usual sense of the term, and could not have served as a role model, his mysticism and aura enthused all aspiring Indian scientists.

Calcutta University College of Science

At long last, Indians were able to be hired by Indians themselves. The educated Indians viewed the cultivation of modern science as an extension of their nationalist movement. By the beginning of the 19th century, the English-knowing Bengal middle class had become articulate and assertive and come to occupy responsible positions in the colonial establishment. The first successful attempt to transform Calcutta University from a merely affiliating and examining body into a science research and education centre was made by Sir Asutosh Mookerjee, a mathematician turned jurist. In 1912, he initiated a vigorous drive for the establishment of the University College of Science, beginning with munificent donations from two lawyers, Rashbehary Ghosh and Tarak Nath Palit – it would have been a rather easy task for a judge to persuade lawyers. As a young lawyer, Asutosh had served his articleship under Rashbehari.

The foundation stone of the college was laid in 1914 which became functional in 1916. Saha passed his MSc in "mixed mathematics" in 1915 from the Presidency College Calcutta. [S.N.] Bose (of Bose–Einstein statistics, 1924) was his class fellow. Both were appointed lecturers in mathematics in 1916, but since they were unable to pull on with their professor, Goarakh Prasad, they were transferred to the physics department the next year. Two physics professorships were created. The experimental physicist C.V. Raman would join as Palit professor and head of the department in July 1917. The other professorship, named after Ghose, was offered to the England-educated, well-connected, Debendra Mohan Bose (1885–1975), in 1914, who in addition was awarded a two-year European travelling fellowship. He chose to go to Berlin, where he had to remain till the war ended. His internment in Germany proved to be very beneficial for Indian physics. In the absence of the professors, the task of designing the courses and delivering lectures dwelt on the two young lecturers, Saha and Bose, who themselves had not studied advanced physics as students. They taught themselves physics to be able to teach their students and in the process became world-renowned researchers themselves.

Saha and Bose

In the 1920s, both Meghnad Saha (1893–1955) and Satyendra Nath [Satyen] Bose (1894–1974) published Nobel Prize-level work which was immediately recognized. Though they were both part of the British Empire, professionally they were children of Germany. Their physics education came in two instalments, from German-language books in private libraries, one belonging to a German in India and the other to a Germany-returned Indian.

Paul Johannes Brühl

Professor Paul Johannes Brühl (1855–1935) was born in the village Weifa in the Bautzen district of the Sachsen state in Germany and made India his home for reasons of health (TB). During 1878–1881, he travelled through central Europe, Turkey, Asia Minor and Armenia collecting plant specimens and arrived at his destination, Bengal, in July 1881. Even though his world fame rests on his contributions to botany, he was a versatile scientist. In an era when most senior positions in the colonial education service were filled by "third-rate Scotsmen,"[78] a knowledgeable and dedicated non-official European was a great asset to colonial and nationalist science and education. Being an outsider, he was far more accessible to Indians than British professors in general. In 1882, he was absorbed in the provincial (and not Imperial) education service and appointed professor at Rajshahi College (now in Bangladesh). He married an English woman, Annie Betts Fox, in 1883. In 1887, Sir George King (1840–1909), the director of the Calcutta Botanic Garden, arranged for Brühl's transfer to the Bengal Engineering College, Shibpur, Calcutta, with a view to utilizing his botanical expertise. In 1896, the two published the *Century of new and rare Indian plants*. This influential illustrated text would undergo 18 editions till 1971. Brühl taught physics and held charge of the library, officiated as the principal in 1895, and served as part-time lecturer in geology at Presidency College during 1902–1903. Upon his retirement from government service in 1912, he was made Companion of the Indian Empire. He spent a few months during 1912–1913 at the Indian Institute of Science, Bangalore, learning chemical geology. In 1913, he accepted the post of the Calcutta University registrar which he held till 1918. He was extremely unhappy at the drudgery of the post. In early 1914, he complained to Sir David Prain, Director of the Royal Botanic Gardens, Kew, that before he accepted the post, he had been informed that he would have opportunities to do some research work. But that was not the case. He made up his mind in June 1914 to leave India for good and move to England to do botanical research at Kew.[79] Fortunately for India, he was thwarted by the war, and then the conditions changed for the better. In 1918, he was appointed professor of botany which post he held till 1928. To mark his services, his former and current students raised money to institute a Paul Johannes Brühl Memorial Medal, a triennial award for contributions to the study of Asiatic botany, to be awarded by the Royal Asiatic Society of Bengal of which he was a prominent member.[80] If Brühl had left for England in 1914, he would surely have taken his extensive personal library with him. He now made it available to Saha (who already knew some German) and Bose. Among the books they borrowed and read were the works by Maxwell and Boltzmann and the more recent ones such as Planck's *Vorlesungen über die Theorie der Wärmestrahlung* (1906) and von Laue's *Relativitätsprinzip* (1911).[81] According to Bose, Brühl himself might not have read many books he owned. It is not clear why and how Brühl acquired books he did not really need for himself.

D.M. Bose

D.M. Bose returned to Calcutta in 1919, bringing with him a large number of books, including the latest German publications. Saha and Bose now continued their self-education in D.M. Bose's library. Among the books they read was the special issue of *Naturwissenschaften*, brought out on 26 April 1918 as a Festschrift on Planck's 60th birthday, containing articles by many eminent authors.[82] In 1920, Saha and Bose brought out, from Calcutta University Press, the world's first-ever English translation of Einstein and Minkowski's papers on relativity, written during 1905–1916. Reviewing it, *Nature* wrote in 1922 that it "will be of service to those who are unfamiliar with German, and wish to grapple with the pioneer works, some of which are rather inaccessible." The inaccessibility was due to the war. The restoration of full European scientific activity and knowledge exchange would take some years. During this short period, India became the inheritor of German theoretical physics scholarship and extended it further. Physics was young then. With research papers, textbooks and popular accounts complementing one another, it was easy to identify outstanding research problems. Both Saha and Bose were mathematically well-equipped to address and solve them. Saha learnt about the spectral confusion from Agnes Mary Clerke's 1903 *Problems in Astrophysics*, while Bose could immediately see the inner inconsistency in the derivation of Planck's Law and set out to impart rigour to it.

Saha's Equation

By the 1910s, a vast amount of data on solar and stellar spectra had been obtained. The spectra were classified empirically. The scheme was obviously meaningful but lacked theoretical basis. It had even been suggested that light came from elements that were present in distant celestial bodies but not known to Earth (an example is the postulated element nebullium). It was inevitable that sooner or later the theoretical basis for spectral classification would be found. History chooses the hour, and the hour produces the hero. The only surprise was that the hour was seized not in any established research centre in the West but in far-off Calcutta which was nowhere on the world research map. The work was immediately recognized as laying the foundation of quantitative astrophysics. Saha showed that astronomical spectra of all kinds, notwithstanding their seeming complexity and diversity, can be rigorously explained in terms of known laws and chemical elements, by simply invoking different physical conditions. Saha's work thus had great philosophical significance also; it transformed the cosmos from an exotic outfield into a science lab.

Saha set out his theory in a number of papers published in British journals during 1920–1921. Saha's first two papers, including the one that gave the ionization formula, were published before he left for Europe for the first time. Much to his annoyance, an impression persisted in the West that Saha did his pioneer work while in England, implying that "an Indian was incapable of making breakthrough discoveries without western training or western assistance."[83] On return from Europe in late 1921, Saha was made Khaira professor, but the personal elevation left basic issues unaddressed. Nationalist science faced a dilemma. Not enough money was forthcoming from Indian donors. In the West, science was the means of production of wealth, a part of which was ploughed back to support science. Science, however, played hardly any role in the Indian economy. Sporadic and limited funding for science came about because the individuals collecting money enjoyed social and official prestige and were well-networked. This model was unsustainable in the long run. The colonial government was ready to help with grants but demanded administrative control in return, which the Indian side was not willing to concede. A similar thing had earlier happened in the case of the Indian Association for Cultivation of Science. The government was ready to fund it as a science college under the education department, but its leaders were not ready to let go of control (Ch. 10, p. 196).

Saha would have liked to carry out further observational and experimental work suggested by his theory, but University funding was not forthcoming. On this count, he fell out with the head of the department, Raman, who as an experimentalist himself was in need of funds. Saha moved to Allahabad University in 1923, where he remained till 1938 when he returned to Calcutta University to occupy the professorial chair once held by Raman. He retired in 1953 on reaching 60 years. In 1923, Saha turned to the USA for a grant to set up a spectroscopic lab. The grant might have been forthcoming if Raman had not given a negative report to Millikan on Saha's experimental abilities.[84] One can understand the turf war between Raman and Saha when they both were competing for funding from the same source. But, Raman thwarting Saha's efforts to obtain a research grant from Rockefeller philanthropy shows pettiness of mind. Raman and Saha, both important Indian science leaders, maintained a lifelong mutually antagonistic relationship. Saha had wanted to join the government service but was refused permission because of his pronounced anti-British stance. For the same reason, the British government would have liked The Royal Society to exclude Saha. It goes to the credit of the Society that it ignored the pressures and the hints, and elected him a fellow, in 1927. This recognition brought him an annual research grant of £300 from the Indian government followed by the Royal Society's grant of £250 in 1929.[85] But the aid came too late.

Saha's father was a very poor shopkeeper in rural East Bengal, now Bangladesh. As a high school student, he won Rs 100 as first prize in an all-Bengal Bible competition organized by the Dacca Baptist Mission. I think the motivating factor was not so much Christianity as 100 rupees. In the peculiar Bengal social hierarchy, his caste was ranked low (though higher than the erstwhile "untouchables"). Caste humiliation scarred Saha for life. Casteism in a rural setting, which he experienced when he was young, would not have hurt as much as when it was practised in Calcutta.

He was not permitted to eat at the main table at the Government Eden Hindu hostel nor allowed to participate in the annual worship of Sarasvati, the goddess of learning, who would have considered him his favourite child. Perhaps, the upper-caste boys, irked by his brilliance, wanted to show him his place. After two years of stay at the hostel, he along with a handful of his upper-caste friends moved out of the hostel to a private mess [board and lodge]. Even half a century later, he had neither forgotten nor forgiven. In the late 1950s, when inmates of the Eden Hindu hostel called on him to invite him to preside over the annual function, he refused bluntly, recalling for their information his college-day humiliation. At the time, he was an elected member of the Indian Parliament from Calcutta, having defeated a nominee of Nehru's ruling Congress Party. Saha was quite close to Jawaharlal Nehru in the years preceding Indian independence, but the distance increased subsequently.[86] Nehru, India's charismatic Prime Minister during 1947–1964, had a soft corner for sophisticated, suave, upper-crust people. Bitter and angry, confrontational rather than persuasive, Saha, unlike Homi Jahangir Bhabha (1909–1966) and Shanti Swarup Bhatnagar (1894–1955), did not become part of big science under Nehru (Anderson 2010). Normally, an activity begins modestly, reaches a peak, declines somewhat, and settles on a plateau. By a fortuitous combination of factors, Indian physics began at the top, but did not have the wherewithal to sustain itself; it had no place to go but down. Given his intellectual prowess, teaching abilities, restlessness, social background, and political inclinations, Saha remained active throughout his life in various fields. But at the end of the day, as far as world science is concerned, Saha's individual brilliance remained individual.

S.N. Bose

Unlike Saha, Satyen Bose was a well-adjusted person, at peace with himself and the outside world. When the Dacca University was established in 1921, he joined there on promotion as Reader. In 1924, he formulated the statistics of a class of elementary particles since named bosons. He sent his paper to Einstein who translated it into German and got it published in the August 1924 issue of the leading journal of the time, *Zeitschrit fur Physik*. In it, the name of the author was given as Bose (without initials), Dacca University, India. Einstein went on to expand S.N. Bose's work, but in two successive papers, dated September 1924 and February 1925, he erroneously attributed the ground-breaking work to Hrn [Mr] D. Bose. This Bose was Debendra Mohan Bose (1885–1975), himself a well-established physicist, who was already known in the Berlin circle.

In September 1927, an International Congress of Physics was held in Como, Italy. It was attended by about 60 invited participants, including 11 Nobel laureates drawn from 14 countries. From India one of the two invitees was Saha. The other intended invitee was S.N. Bose, but the organizers were shocked to discover that a wrong Bose had landed! Apparently, the Como organizers picked up the invitee's name from Einstein's paper rather than Bose's own. That is how D.M. Bose came to Como in place of S.N. Bose. Boson particles are indistinguishable from one another. Seen from Europe of the day, the various Boses in Bengal were indeed bosons. The truth was publicly revealed not by the beneficiary D. Bose, but by the aggrieved S.N. Bose, whose next visit abroad was to occur 27 years later, in July 1954.

Indian science never became self-assessing. In 1926, when Bose was in Europe on a scholarship, he applied for a professorship at Dacca. Since he did not have a doctorate, his friends advised him to get a letter of recommendation from Einstein. Einstein was surprised at the request; because Bose's internationally acclaimed work should have been its own recommendation. This part of the story is well known. What is not is that in spite of Einstein's recommendation, Bose was not selected for the post which was offered to D.M. Bose, and S.N. Bose was placed on the waiting list. It was only when D.M. Bose decided to stay put in Calcutta that S.N. Bose was made a professor, in 1927. Bose transferred to Calcutta University in 1945 as a Khaira Professor.

When the noted physicist, Paul Adrien Maurice Dirac (1902–1984), who coined the term boson, visited India in the late 1950s, he was shocked to discover that Bose was not an FRS. The omission reflected poorly on the Society. On Dirac's initiative, Bose was elected FRS belatedly in 1958. At the time, there were already a number of Indian Fellows, but none of them had ventured to propose Bose's name. To borrow an analogy from astronomy, asteroids collide among themselves in their desire to go around the Sun. More picturesquely, we have here at work what we may call the Sultan's Harem Syndrome. The inmates of a harem compete with one another to catch the eye of the Sultan, in this case, the West. This syndrome became more and more pronounced when scientific research became merely above average rather than outstanding and could not speak for itself.

Subramanya Chandrasekhar

Subramanya Chandrasekhar (1910–1995), whose father was C.V. Raman's brother, was a science celebrity in his own right and winner of the 1983 Physics Nobel laureate for work done half a century earlier, needs to be noticed, even though he left India in 1930. He came of age at a time when nationalism was mildly asserting itself among the educated. In 1930, when Chandrasekhar was travelling from Delhi to Madras in the first class (his father's service in the railways entitled him to do so), an English memsahib loudly expressed to her husband her disgust at having to share the compartment, with a native, but added that at least he was in European dress. As soon as the train started moving, Chandrasekhar promptly went to the washroom and returned wearing the typical South Indian dress of shirt and *veshti*. The station master could do nothing more than suggest to Chandrasekhar if he would transfer to a second-class compartment. On his refusal, it was left to the lady and her husband to move.

Chandrasekhar missed classes to go and listen to Jawaharlal Nehru who was visiting Madras. The principal was shocked to find him among the "culprits." But this did not prevent the College from creating a scholarship to enable their most brilliant student to Cambridge for his doctorate. The government however would not create a job for him in India when he wanted to return. Chandrasekhar had already published a research paper in 1929, and on his long voyage to England, he did preliminary calculations laying the foundations of relativistic astrophysics. Because of the imperious and contemptuous attitude of Sir Arthur Eddington, Chandrasekhar became a persona non grata and had to migrate to Europe. On the eve of independence, he was invited to become the Director of the Kodaikanal Observatory, but, much to India's loss, things did not work out.

Jamsetji Tata and IISc

India's own technical university, the Indian Institute of Science, Bangalore, admitted its first batch of students on 24 July 1911. Jamshedpur produced its first iron on 2 December 1911 and steel in February 1912. The first hydroelectrical power was generated at Khapoli in Western Ghats on 8 February 1915. All these projects were envisioned by Jamsetji Nusserwanji Tata (1839–1904), who as per custom took his father's first name as his middle name. Jamsetji gave his projects definite form but died before they could be completed. Had Jamsetji died in the 1880s, he would have been described as a successful, well-respected, dynamic cotton mill owner, but not as a national hero.

Jamsetji was born at Navsari (some 30 km from Surat) to poor but respectable Parsi parents belonging to the priestly class. His father Nusserwanji was the first one to leave home to seek his fortune in business in Bombay. At the time, the export of opium to China was legitimate, profitable and in the hands of Parsis. Nusserwanji joined the party. Nusserwanji called his 13-year-old son to Bombay in 1852.

Jamsetji studied at Elphinstone Institution (school) from 1853 till 1855. In 1856, he moved to Elphinstone College[87] as a paid student meaning that on the basis of his school performance, his tuition fee was waived. In 1856, he received a stipend from The Clare Scholarship Fund, subscribed in 1835, in honour of the Earl of Clare, Governor of Bombay. In May 1857, Jamsetji was given a stipend out of The West Scholarship Fund, subscribed in 1828, in honour of Chief Justice Sir Edward West. It was granted for "proficiency in different branches of literature and science."[88] When did Jamsetji leave Elphinstone College? Unfortunately, old publications give contradictory chronology. In 1906, two years after Tata's death, his biographer Pestonji A. Wadia wrote, "He completed his academic education in 1859, after a four years' programme of study."[89] After 20 years, in 1925, F.R. Harris published a detailed chronology of Tata's life. Harris states that Tata's career at Elphinstone College came to an end in 1858: "He passed out as Green Scholar, which was then the equivalent of a degree." This version has been repeated by all biographers and historians. But it is problematic. Green scholarship is not attested anywhere nor is it known what its equivalence to a degree before the university system came into existence meant. It is a minor matter, but still exactitude needs to be established.

Jamsetji joined his father's far-east business and helped its expansion. The American Civil War 1861–1865 came as a boon to Bombay. Supplies of American cotton to England came to a halt, prices shot up, and orders were transferred to India. Immense profits were realized from cotton shipments to Liverpool. Had Bombay merchants conserved these profits, the financial history of India would have been different. But massive and quick wealth went into Bombay's head. It jettisoned financial discipline and took to recklessness. As soon as the Civil War ended, cotton prices crashed bringing all round ruination. The speculator-in-chief was Premchand Roychand who was also the partner of senior Tata. Providence however was kind enough to give the Tatas another chance to rehabilitate themselves.

Bombay was the base from where Sir [Later Lord] Robert Napier's 1868 military expedition against Abyssinia [Ethiopia] was launched to liberate Europeans held captive by the King. The contract for supplies for the expedition was obtained by a syndicate led by Nusserwanji. The cost of rescuing 30 British missionaries and diplomats came to £10 million, and the syndicate became richer by 40 lakhs of rupees. Nusserwanji now retired leaving things in charge of his son who had learnt his lessons from the earlier bubble burst. Caution became his watchword, and he decided to move from trade to manufacture.

He set up three cotton mills in his lifetime, at Nagpur (1877), Bombay (1888) and Ahmedabad (1903). They all brought him money. In addition, Nagpur made him aware of the mineral wealth of Central India and helped him embark on heavy industry.

Tata Iron and Steel

As early as 1882, Jamsetji expressed a desire to set up iron and steel works. The prevailing Indian regulations for mining and prospecting were "carefully devised to obstruct and prevent development."[90] However, it was noted that in the 1890s, India was importing more steel from Belgium than from Britain. German steel was also penetrating the Indian market. It was therefore considered necessary to change the existing policy with a view to encourage India to develop its own industry.[91] The question had been under consideration for some time, but it was Curzon in 1899 who signed the new policy of which Jamsetji was a beneficiary. Based on the government-sponsored geological reports, Jamsetji obtained a mining lease in the Chanda district in 1901. There was however hardly any progress and Jamsetji eventually surrendered the license. Curzon grew impatient at the delay, expected to see tangible results, and had no "sympathy with the slow and cautions methods adopted" by Tata. This and Curzon's misgivings about the proposed Tata University may well be the reason why Jamsetji was not included in the list of official invitees to the Imperial Coronation Durbar held by the Viceroy Lord Curzon in 1903 at Delhi to mark the accession of King Edward VII. Jamsetji however was a practical man. Ignoring the snub, he attended the Durbar "as a private visitor."

Already, in 1887, the Government geologist, P.N. Bose, had published an official report on iron ore in Dhalli and Rajhara Hills in Raipur district. Acting on this basis, the Tatas obtained a prospecting license for the area, but this choice also was not final. Bose took retirement in 1903 and joined the Mayurbhanj state as its geologist. On 20 February 1904, he addressed his famous letter to J.N. Tata recommending iron ore deposits in Gurumahisani Hill. The Tata accepted the suggestion and decided to set up their steel mill at a village called Sakchi. To make an impression on the investors, the Tatas grandiosely but inaccurately claimed in their 1907 prospectus of Tata Iron and Steel Mills that for four years "Mr J. N. Tata and his successors at their own expense conducted a private geological survey of considerable areas in India" and "discovered very large deposits of high grade iron" "in proximity to coal of suitable character." Bose immediately wrote to Padshah clarifying that both the Raipur and Mayurbhanj discoveries were made by him and it was he who emphatically declared the latter ore to be superior. In a prompt reply, Padshah agreed that though Bose's "statement of facts is perfectly correct" "[I]n a commercial document one is not always able to reserve place for giving due credit to everyone." He however promised to make amends in the final prospectus. It is not clear whether a final version of the prospectus was issued or not and what it said about Bose. Bose however was given due credit once the steel mill came into being. The capital requirements were met from within India, with the Parsis buying as many as 36% of the shares.[92] During the First World War, Tata Steel supplied steel rails to the British for use in Mesopotamia, Egypt, Palestine and East Africa. After the War, on 2 January 1919, the Viceroy Lord Chelmsford came to Sakchi to say thanks and announced the change of its name to Jamshedpur. Sometime later, the name of the adjoining railway station at Kalimati was changed to Tatanagar.

Hydropower

It was the considered opinion of a Bombay-based British engineer, David Gostling, that the configuration of land in the Western Ghats provided an excellent catchment area and the storage of rainwater could furnish a considerable portion of the energy required to drive the mills of Bombay. There were already two hydropower stations in India at Darjeeling and Mysore state, but they depended on natural waterfalls. The new proposal envisaged the use of artificial reservoirs. Gostling brought the scheme to Jamsetji who immediately saw its merit and began work on it. By the time of his death little had been done, except the preliminary spade work, "but the prestige of his name, and the tactful way in which he enlisted the sympathy of India Office, did much to lighten the labours of those who followed him." The Lonavala dam was begun in 1911, the Walwan dam in 1912, and in 1920 the final link at Shirawta was completed. On 11 February 1915, the Simplex Mill became the first mill to receive electric power.

As ultimately designed, the hydroelectric project required far more capital than was anticipated. The price the Tatas paid to tide over the cash crunch has turned out to be high indeed. During 1924–1926, the Tatas raised a loan of two crore rupees from Framroze Edulji Dinshaw, a landlord and advocate. In the 1930s, the loan was converted into 12.5% equity in Tata Sons. In 1936, Shapoorji Pallonji Mistry purchased the stake from Dinshaw's heirs. Mistry also purchased the holdings of JRD Tata's siblings whose grandfather was Jamsetji's cousin and owned shares in Tata Sons. The Shapoorji Pallonji Group now has an 18.37% stake in Tata Sons and the distinction of being its largest individual shareholder.

Indian Institute of Science, Bangalore

In September 1898, Jamsetji announced his decision to establish a technical university which he would endow with his own landed property worth about 30 lakh rupees yielding an annual income of Rs 125,000. To work out the details, a 23-member Provisional Committee was formed with Justice E.T. Candy, the Vice-Chancellor of Bombay University, as the Chairman, and Justice Mahadev Govind Ranade as the Vice-Chairman. Tata was an ordinary member, but his trusted lieutenant and ward Burjor Jamaspi Padshah (1864–1941) was appointed the secretary. On 13 December 1898, the Committee drew up a plan called "A research university for India," and made it public on 31 December. This was the day Lord Curzon landed in Bombay to take over as the Viceroy which post he held till 1905. Within two days of his arrival, he received a deputation from the Provisional Committee, which included Jamsetji. Had Curzon approved of the scheme, and promised a grant-in-aid, "further offers from Indian princes would be stimulated."[93] But the Viceregal approval was not forthcoming. Tata proposed the placement of his real estate in the hands of a trust. Of the income generated, the Trust would hand over half to Jamsetji while the other half would be utilized for the proposed institute. This was not acceptable to the government. Curzon in fact felt that Jamsetji was after a baronetcy. The general perception of the meeting was that the Viceroy was "throwing cold water on the scheme."

Tata eventually withdrew the Family Trust condition, enabling the matter to progress. In October 1899, the Government of India organized a conference at Simla to consider the proposal. It was chaired by Sir Thomas Rayleigh and included Tata and Padshah and many high officials. The Conference noted that the proposed University would be a "central institution" under a "central authority" to control its operations. The Gazette of India gave the following outline of the Tata University scheme. "It is proposed to found an institution which shall be or correspond to a teaching University for India, its primary aim being to teach, not to examine." Trombay was in serious reckoning as the site for the proposed Institute, but finally, the rather sleepy town, Bangalore was chosen, whose climate the Conference noted would suit the Europeans.[94] The negotiations were prolonged and not without acrimony. The financial details were worked out. Finally, 10 years after the proposal was first made, the Indian Institute of Science opened at Bangalore as a tripartite arrangement between the Tatas, the Government of India, and the Government of Mysore, with the British Resident in Mysore being made the ex-officio chairman of the Institute's Council.

Jamsetji had already "forged an enduring friendship" with the enlightened Dewan of the princely state of Mysore, Sir K. Seshadri Iyer (1845–1901). Through his efforts, the Maharaja of Mysore granted 370 acres of land. The interaction of Tata with Mysore led to a development which became significant domestically and historically. The Inspector General of Education in Mysore was a Parsi: Dr Hormusji Jehangir Bhabha. Bhabha had a daughter, Meherbai, and a son, Jehangir Hormusji Bhabha. In 1897, Meherbai was married to Jamsetji's elder son Dorab Jamsetji Tata (1859–1932). Jehangir, a successful Bombay lawyer, became the father of Homi Jehangir Bhabha (1909–1966). The Tata connection facilitated Bhabha's institution-building activities. This technical university established by the Tatas in the heyday of British imperialism was named Indian, whereas the research institute set up on the verge of India's independence, on the suggestion of Homi Bhabha, was named after themselves.

Tata's philanthropy in the cause of technical education was appreciated everywhere except in Bengal. Mahendra Lal Sircar could not help comparing Tata's scheme with his own. He told his subscribers in 1899 that the objects of both were the same, namely, "to fit and enable the natives of India to carry out scientific investigation for the discovery of new truths." And yet,

> while the ways and means proposed by Mr. Tata for carrying out that object are too extravagant for even imperial resources, the ways and means proposed by the founders of the Science Association are reasonably economical and quite within the resources of the people themselves, if they would mind contributing each according to his capacity.[95]

P.C. Ray claimed in 1899 that the proposed institute "would be waste of money and a diversion, and misapplication of energies." Ray felt that "It would be more conducive to the cause of science in India if the existing institutions in the different parts of India...were utilized to the fullest extent."[96]

The Bangalore institute represented the investment of Parsi money for a general cause and that too outside the Parsi mass base of Bombay. It started shakily. The success that later came to attend the Indian Institute of Science could not have been anticipated in its early years. The first three directors of the Indian Institute of Science were all British. The first one, Morris W. Travers, was appointed in 1909, but was asked to go in 1913; "no one can deny that he had not tried to do his best for the Institute." The first Indian director was also removed from office but in acrimony. Raman joined in 1933, but resigned in 1937, faced with a revolt from the Council which recorded that "Raman was unfit to continue as Director." He offered his resignation from the Institute itself and requested that a special retiring allowance of Rs. 100,000 be granted to him. This was accepted, but then audaciously, Raman reopened the matter by writing to the Viceroy. In retaliation, the Council withdrew the offer of special allowance and asked him to continue as a physics professor or quit with "such retiring allowance as he may be entitled to according to rules." Raman chose to stay put till superannuation. On retirement in 1948, Raman set up his own institute on a nearby piece of land partially donated by the Maharaja of Mysore.[97] One can imagine Raman's state of mind during the decade of his forced employment from the fact that in his own institute, he grew tall trees to obstruct the view of the tall tower of the Institute where he had worked for 15 years.[98]

First World War

The First World War (1914–1919) was very good for Indian industry. A vulnerable England was compelled to draw on Indian resources. A ten-member Indian Industrial Commission was set up in 1916, with three Indian members: Pundit Madan Mohan Malaviya, Allahabad; Sir Rajendra Nath Mookerjee of Martin and Company, Calcutta; and Sir Dorabji Jamsetji Tata. It dutifully submitted its report in 1918.

Commission or no Commission, the War brought Indian companies commercial orders. In fact, it was the war rather than the optimism and patriotism of the early Indian industrial enterprises that made them viable. In early 1914, the Mysore Government asked the institute to manufacture soap "which was sent by the Indian Red Cross Society to the troops in Mesopotamia."[99] Alembic benefited from import substitution, as already seen, and Bengal Chemical from export.

Tata Steel made a direct contribution to the war effort. It became impossible for England to send steel to Mesopotamia, Egypt, Salonika and East Africa. The task was therefore entrusted to Tata Steel Mill, which supplied 15,000 miles of rail and 300,000 tons of steel to the war front. In gratitude, the Viceroy, Lord Chelmsford, who visited the works in 1919 gave the name Jamshedpur to Sakchi. Similarly, the railway station of Kalimati was named Tatanagar.[100]

Indian Research Bureau (1935)

In 1912, a Government Test House was formed at Alipore in Calcutta as an attachment to the Indian Stores Department. After 20 years, it was decided to support industrial research. As a purchasing authority, the Stores Department would through "the inspection and examination of the articles" "indicate directions in which research should be undertaken in order to improve standards and qualities." The proposed industrial research authority should give the greatest attention to research which will yield practical results rather than research of a purely academic character.[101]

With effect from 1 April 1935, three "bodies" were set up in connection with industrial research under the control of the Indian Stores Department: (a) The Industrial Research Council; (b) The Industrial Research and Intelligence Bureau (subsequently, the name was shortened to Industrial Research Bureau) and (c) The Research Branch of the Government Test House. The Council was an advisory body established with a view to the coordination and development of industrial research. It included representatives and non-official nominees of the Central, the Provincial and the leading State Governments. The bureau was responsible for carrying out the policy laid down on the recommendations of the council and, in general, with the administrative work of the organization. The Research Branch of the Government Test House was formed in order to deal with the research programme drawn up by the Council and also with such minor problems as may arise from time to time from references made to the Bureau. N. Brodie was appointed the Director of the Bureau.[102]

The problems that concerned the government at the time can be seen from the items of research work approved for the Research Branch of the Government Test House. They included the investigation of the properties of different paint formulae in connection with the protection of structural steel and other painting purposes; the use of vegetable oils for the lubrication of internal combustion engines and as a fuel for internal combustion engines; the investigation of the behaviour of Indian and British cement when tested under Indian conditions in accordance with the proposed British Standards specifications; and the analysis of the different known Indian sands and felspars with the view to their utilization in the manufacture of glass.[103]

The bureau did not sponsor any research projects. It however awarded prizes to selected industrial papers for which purpose a sum of Rs 10,000 was set aside from the funds of the bureau.[104] For example, a 100-rupee prize was given on the subject "Manufacture of Photographic Plates in India."[105] While setting up the Research Bureau, the government conceded "that it is at present not a practicable proposition to endeavour to set up in India an industrial research organisation on the lines of the great research organisations which exist in some of the more advanced industrial countries," it held that something a "beginning should be made to lay the foundations on which a research organisation suitable for the needs of the country could later on be constructed." The Research Bureau was wound up in 1939. The initiatives after this were fashioned by the requirements of the Second World War and the plans for independent India's future.

Notes

1 Geddes, 1920, 62.
2 Ray, 1932, 1, 156.
3 Alumni Cantabrigienses, 1940, Part 2, Vol. 1, 327. I thank Catherine Twilley, Christ's College, for clarification.
4 https://archives.libraries.london.ac.uk/resources/UoL_Historical_Record_1836-1926.pdf. See p. 314.
5 Bhattacharyya & Engineer, 1997, 1, vi.
6 Geddes, 1920, 32.
7 Geddes, 1920, 38-39.
8 The Centenary Volume of Presidency College states, unmindful of recorded facts, that "[A]fter working silently for more than a decade on Hertzian waves he published his researches in 1895...'; Pres. Col. 100, 1955, 20.
9 Lodge & Oliver, 1894.
10 Garratt, 1994, 65.

11 General Report on Public Instruction in Bengal for 1894–1895, pp. 36–37. The Society was founded in 1891, and renamed Calcutta University Institute in 1896.
12 Ray, 1932, 1, 153.
13 Bose, 1896, https://eleanor.lib.gla.ac.uk/search~S6?/fsp+coll+kelvin+q34+b1863599/fsp+coll+kelvin+q34+b1863599/-3%2C0%2C0%2CB/frameset&FF=fsp+coll+kelvin+q34&1%2C%2C18/indexsort=-.
14 Mukherji, 1983, 36.
15 https://www.abhilekh-patal.in/jspui/handle/123456789/2728365.
16 https://www.abhilekh-patal.in/jspui/handle/123456789/2728380.
17 General Report on Public Instruction in Bengal for 1896–1897, p. 34.
18 Geddes, 1920, 62.
19 Natesan, 1921, 9.
20 https://www.frontierweekly.com/archive/vol-number/vol/vol-41-2008-09/vol-41-45%20May%2024-30%202009/note-41-45.pdf.
21 Dam, 1897.
22 Dam, 1897, 386.
23 Geddes, 1920, 59.
24 *Nature*, 1930, 125, 59.
25 Temple, 1900, 2.
26 Bhattacharyya & Engineer, 1997, 4, 312–313.
27 Bose, 1921, 220.
28 Bose, 1921, 221.
29 Maitra, 1959, 263–264.
30 Translated by Manmohan Ghosh; *Visvabharati Quarterly*, 1959, 24 (4), 258–259.
31 http://jcbose.ac.in/assets/uploads/8d6ce2cef73e06e0fff070e483d179e5.pdf
32 Geddes, 1920, 63.
33 Dasgupta, 1999, 92.
34 Gupta, 1970, 125–128.
35 Gupta, 1970, 38.
36 Ray, 1932, 1, 81.
37 Three letters written by him to Sir Joseph Larmor are archived in St John's College, Cambridge. Two, dated 11 July 1907 and 19 August 1908, were sent from Calcutta while the third one was written on 14 July 1909 from the Office of the Inspector of Schools, Chota Nagpur Division, Purulia. (I thank Fiona Colbert, Biographical Assistant, for her help.)
38 Ray, 1932, 1, 162.
39 Ray, 1932, 1, 84–85.
40 Ray, 1896.
41 *Nature*, 1896, 54 (28 June), No. 1387, 83.
42 Natesan, 1929, 145.
43 Ray, 1932, 1, 158–159.
44 Ray100, 1962, 299.
45 Ray, 1932, 1, 534–535.
46 Bengal Chemical 100, 2004, 10.
47 Bengal Chemical 100, 2004, 11.
48 Ray100, 1962, 173.
49 Ray, 1932, 1, 317–318.
50 Bengal Chemical 100, 2004, 19.
51 Ray, 1932, 1, 105.
52 Mouat, 1854.
53 The College was opened following the recommendation of Indian Industrial Commission, 1916–1918.

54 *Dacca University Journal*, 1927, March, 138–140.
55 Watson, 1907a.
56 Watson, 1907b, 28, note.
57 Mehta, 1985; Raina & Habib, 2004, 182–198.
58 Eastern Daily Mail and Straits Advertiser, 1907 May 20, p. 6.
59 Eastern Daily Mail and Straits Advertiser, 1907 May 20, p. 6.
60 Eastern Daily Mail and Straits Advertiser, 1907, 20 May, p. 6.
61 Gajjar, 1907, 9–10.
62 Indian Biographical Dictionary, Pillar and Co., Madras, 1915, p. 152.
63 Eastern Daily Mail and Straits Advertiser, 1907, 20 May, p. 6.
64 Amin, 1939, 2.
65 Bombay University Calendar, 1912, 1, 944.
66 Amin, 1939, 4.
67 Eastern Daily Mail and Straits Advertiser, 1907, 20 May, p. 6.
68 Eastern Daily Mail and Straits Advertiser, 1907, 20 May, p. 6.
69 The factory was functional at least till May 1907.
70 Amin, 1939, 5.
71 http://indiankanoon.org/doc/81894/ Apart from Kotibhaskar, Amin and junior Gajjar, the fourth partner was one Moreshwar Bhalchandra Bhatavadekar.
72 Amin, 1939, 7.
73 Amin, 1939, 45.
74 Amin, 1939, 56.
75 Playne, 1915, 711.
76 Amin, 1939, 34.
77 Ray100, 1962, 173.
78 Mehra, 1975, 120.
79 https://plants.jstor.org/stable/10.5555/al.ap.visual.kdcas289.
80 Biographical details are mostly from Banerjee, 1935.
81 Mehra, 2001, 504.
82 Mehra, 2001, 506.
83 De Vorkin, 1994, 156.
84 De Vorkin, 1994, 162.
85 De Vorkin, 1994, 164.
86 Sur, 2002.
87 Elphinstone Institution was established in 1840, though the name was given in 1845. From 1 April 1856, the Institution was divided into Elphinstone School and Elphinstone College. The College was affiliated to Bombay University in 1860.
88 Report of the Director of Public Instruction, Bombay, for 1856–1857. Table 14, pp. (80–81). His name is given as Jamshedji Nusarwanji. https://www.granth sanjeevani.com/jspui/viewer?searchWord=&viewType=single&doc=GP_ 00133311.pdf123456789/112485/2/&backquery=[sort_by=dc.date.accessioned_ dt&order=desc&rpp=100&etal=0&start=200]&itemHandle=123456789/ 112485.
89 Wadia, 1906, 69.
90 Harris, 1958, 150.
91 Headrick, 1988, 290.
92 Headrick, 1988, 291.
93 Harris, 1958, 126.
94 *Nature*, 1900, 61 (11 Jan.), No. 1576, 260–261.
95 Biswas, 2003, 459.
96 Ray, 1918, 9.
97 Venkataraman, 1988, 278–280.
98 Venkataraman, 1988, 518.
99 Subbarayappa, 1992, 92.

100 Dutta, 1977, 13.
101 Report of Indian Research Bureau for 1935–1936, p. 2.
102 Brodie, 1935.
103 Report of Indian Research Bureau for 1935–1936, pp. 4–5.
104 Report of Indian Research Bureau for 1935–1936, p. 5.
105 Report of Indian Research Bureau for 1936–1937, p. 1.

11

SCIENCE AFTER INDEPENDENCE

Till the Second World War (1939–1945), India's industrial backwardness was Indians' concern; the War made it Britain's handicap. The export of raw materials from and import of finished goods into India stopped. At the same time, India was called upon to take up the responsibility of "supplying the technical equipment of a modern army."[1] (xxiii) At the time, there were two mutually exclusive streams in Indian science: routine science under the government and nationalism-inspired research activity by the Indians in the universities. The twain met during the war. The government decided to tackle the problem of "shortages and substitutes and war requirements"[1] (xxiii) in two ways: conducting research under its own auspices and, more importantly, funding scientific and industrial research in centres outside the government system.

> It was a foregone conclusion that the British would leave India after the war. Indians were already in important positions in government as well as in industry and science. Though still working under British auspices, the Indians sought to dovetail their country's post-independence interests into the British exigencies of war.[1]

Throughout the world, all available scientific expertise was mobilized by the governments for their war effort. But as soon as the war needs were over, universities were re-energized. Not so in India. What was an outgoing foreign government's temporary compulsion became the abiding philosophy of a new nation. Independent India opted for government science labs at the cost of universities. In December 1939, Dewan Bahadur Sir Arcot Ramaswami Mudaliar, commerce member in the Viceroy's executive committee, visited Shanti Swarup Bhatnagar's laboratory in Lahore, was impressed by what he

DOI: 10.4324/9781003466406-11

saw and advised the Viceroy that Bhatnagar be appointed to head the government's war-time science effort.

S.S Bhatnagar

Panipat-born Bhatnagar was brought up under straitened circumstances by his Lahore-based future father-in-law. He passed his Matric in 1911 and Intermediate in 1913, both from the newly opened Dyal Singh College. In 1913, after finishing his intermediate examination in the first division, Bhatnagar joined the Forman Christian College. He was a bright student, up to date on scientific literature. This cost him an extra year. When in 1915, Bhatnagar sat for his BSc examination, he flunked in the subject his name is now associated with: chemistry. One of the questions dealt with the nature of X-rays, discovered 20 years previously. Bhatnagar, on the authority of the books he had read, wrote that X-rays could be reflected, refracted and polarized just as ordinary light. Either the examiner was not well-informed or considered bound by what was written in the textbook. He failed Bhatnagar who eventually got his degree in 1916, with honours in physics.

During the First World War, Bhatnagar did some personal consultancy. His chemistry professor referred to him a leading Lahore stationer who could not import gelatin duplicating pads from Germany. Bhatnagar solved the problem, earning in the process the welcome sum of Rs 150.[2] Post-BSc, Bhatnagar took up a job as a demonstrator in physics and chemistry at Forman Christian College and then moved to Dyal Singh College as a senior demonstrator in chemistry. In 1917, he started studies for his MSc as a private student. Then for the next two years, he worked from the Forman College, receiving instructions from professors of the Government College under the scheme of inter-collegiate post-graduate teaching. He obtained his MSc degree in 1919.

Bhatnagar, like his late father and father-in-law, was a Brahmo. The small Brahmo network stood by him. Professor Ruchi Ram Sahni arranged for the award of a scholarship to Bhatnagar from Dyal Singh Trust, of which he was a member. Bhatnagar spent the next two years, 1919–1921, at the University of London earning his DSc degree on surface tension of oils, under the supervision of Prof. F.G. Donnan, FRS. A travel grant from the British Department of Scientific and Industrial Research enabled him to visit France and Germany.

He returned to India in 1921 to take up a professorship at the Benaras Hindu University at the invitation of the founder Pandit Madan Mohan Malaviya. His stay at Benaras is noteworthy on two counts. He composed in Sanskrit the anthem of the University and gave a "good drubbing" to a fellow professor for plagiarism (the plagiarist later resigned). While bidding farewell to Bhatnagar, Malaviya remarked that "whoever leaves Benaras has a seat reserved for him in heaven." Bhatnagar retorted naughtily: "I agree with Malaviyaji in the sense that Benaras town being so dirty that whoever leaves Benaras feels that he is going to a heavenly place."[1] (xxii)

In 1924, 30-year-old Bhatnagar took over as the director of the newly opened University Chemical Laboratories, Lahore, having been chosen in preference to his rather ineffectual European competitor who had been Bhatnagar's teacher. The laboratories addressed problems in industrial and applied chemistry brought in by agriculturists and industrialists, such as Sir Ganga Ram, an engineer-turned neo-agriculturist; Lala Shri Ram of Delhi; J.K. Mills, Kanpur; and Tata Oil Mills. The most celebrated consultancy, of course, was the solution to the mud problem brought in by Messers Steel Brothers & Co., London. The company, prospecting for oil in Punjab, used mud to lubricate its drilling jigs. However, as soon as the mud came into contact with the underground salt deposits, it coagulated, bringing the operations to a halt. The other experts from the University, consulted by the company, suggested several "chemical" and "mechanical" methods which were all impractical. But "the theoretical chemist - Dr. Bhatnagar - insisted from the beginning that it was a simple problem in Colloid Chemistry."[1] (xxii) He added an Indian gum to the mud so that it would not harden on contact with salt. The company was so pleased with the result that it offered Bhatnagar a substantial sum of Rs 1,50,000. Consistent with the spirit of the times and his own idealism, Bhatnagar converted this personal offer "largely to the benefit of the University and research," in the form of six research scholarships for five years. Synergy with research has been the strength of the Indian chemical industry.[1]

CSIR

Accepting Mudaliar's offer, Bhatnagar moved to the government, with the stipulation that he should have at his disposal a laboratory for research and that in addition his Lahore-based research students, funded by Messers Steel Brothers, be permitted to come along. This was accepted and in August 1940 Bhatnagar took over as Director, Scientific and Industrial Research. He was based in Alipore, Kolkata, where the existing Test House Laboratory was refurbished for his use. The laboratory was shifted to Delhi University campus in December 1942, in view of the threat of Japanese invasion. In the meantime, on 1 April 1940, a purely advisory body, the Board of Scientific and Industrial Research (BSIR), was set up with Mudaliar as ex-officio chairman and a civil servant as the secretary. The board would receive research proposals from research institutions, universities, industries and trades and advise the government "whether these proposals were approved and if so what funds should be provided for carrying them out." A year later, on 14 November 1941, the government agreed to sanction an annual amount of Rs 10 lakhs for five years towards establishing an Industrial Research Fund for "fostering industrial development in the country."[1] (xxiv-xxv) What was now needed was a mechanism for utilizing this fund. Accordingly, on 12 March 1942, a legal entity called a registered society was set up in Delhi under the name Council of Scientific and Industrial Research (CSIR) with Mudaliar as the ex-officio founder-president. On 26 September 1942, the government transferred the control of the fund to the council, at the same time making the board an advisory body to it. The CSIR wrongly celebrates its foundation day on 26 September and not on 12 March, the date on which CSIR was registered as a society. In December 1943, the post of vice-president was created. Sir M.S. Akbar Hydari, ICS, served as the vice-president till 1946. Envisaging the great role of CSIR, Jawaharlal Nehru (1889–1964) made the Prime Minister its president (in this respect, CSIR is unique in the country). The first vice-president after independence was the Minister for Industry and Supplies, Dr Syama Prasad Mukherjee (1901–1953), who held office from 1947 till 1950.

By virtue of his position in the government, Bhatnagar was the key figure on the board and the council. In the early years, the formation of CSIR hardly made any impact. The setting up of BSIR was seen as a landmark because it was the first time official funding was systematically forthcoming for research being carried out by individuals and organizations outside the government system. The CSIR was seen merely as a clearing house. It was only much later when national laboratories were established that CSIR came to acquire its distinctive identity. Norah Richards' detailed and authorized 1948 biography of Bhatnagar does not make any mention of the CSIR. An important date in the history of CSIR is 29 February 1944, when the government declared that "Rs. 1 crore will be forthcoming towards capital expenditure on a chain of research institutions."[1] (xxvi) The chain comprised five laboratories. Their foundation stones were laid between December 1945 and April 1947 – the Central Glass and Ceramics Research Institute, Kolkata (CGCRI), 24 December 1945; the Central Fuel Research Institute, Dhanbad (CFRI), 17 November 1946; the National Metallurgical Laboratory, Jamshedpur (NML), 21 November 1946; the National Physical Laboratory, Delhi (NPL), 4 January 1947; and the National Chemical Laboratory, Pune (NCL), 6 April 1947. No laboratory was proposed to be established in the territory which later became Pakistan. For four of these, support was forthcoming from industry and trade. The house of Tatas gave a grant of Rs 8.3 lakhs for the NCL, with the reasonable condition that it be located in Pune, within the Mumbai industrial zone (the Tatas' suggestion that the laboratory be named after them did not find acceptance). For the NML, the Tatas donated 30 acres of land in their steel city Jamshedpur, backing the offer with a grant of Rs 11.7 lakhs. For the CFRI located in the central Indian coal belt, the Raja of Jharia, Babu Shiva Prasad Singha, donated about 100 acres of land, which lay near the colliery of the Tatas as well as the Model Town being built by them. The CGCRI received

Rs 10,000 each from the Bengal and the UP glass manufacturers' associations. The CGCRI was headed by Dr Atma Ram, who began his career in 1936 as a chemical assistant at the Industrial Research Bureau and later (1966–1971) rose to head the CSIR itself.

While the location for four of the five original laboratories suggested itself, there was controversy on the site for NPL. Finally, Delhi was chosen in preference to Kolkata, partly on the extraneous ground that this would enable the laboratory "to keep in touch with the government."[3] Its 1,000-seat-capacity auditorium was opened in time (14 February 1952) for a violin concert by Yehudi Menuhin, visiting India on Nehru's invitation. The auditorium also had the distinction of hosting Indrani Rahman's first dance performance in Delhi.

The Central Electronics Engineering Research Institute was set up in Pilani at the personal request of Ghanshyam Das Birla (1894–1983) whose birthplace it was. The Central Electrochemical Research Institute is located at Karaikudi in Chettinad, Tamil Nadu, because Alagappa Chettiar offered 300 acres of land and 15 lakh rupees. That such spurious arguments were being proffered and accepted for deciding the geographical location of scientific institutions only shows that India was not yet ready for these disciplines. While progress in physics-based industrial research was being made at a break-neck speed in the West, India was opening laboratories with a vengeance. Without linkage to a factory, a laboratory would merely be an office. Government science in general is more government than science.

The Punjab Government was keen to recall Bhatnagar after the war and make him the vice-chancellor of Punjab University, but the proposal fell through because of the disinclination of the Union Government to relieve him. The five laboratories sanctioned in 1944 were all opened between January and November 1950, led by NCL, Pune, which was inaugurated by Nehru on 3 January 1950, the occasion being provided by the holding of the Indian Science Congress.

The first laboratory planned after independence dealt with food and was housed in a palace, thanks to the gift from the government of what is now Karnataka, the Central Food Technological Research Institute, Mysore. It was ceremonially opened on 21 October 1950. The already existing Indian Institute of Fruit Technology was merged into it. In the five years 1950–1954, during Bhatnagar's tenure as the Director General (as the post was later renamed), as many as 14 laboratories were opened, acquired, or had their foundation stones laid (these include the five sanctioned before independence). The research carried out by Indians in the universities was basic in nature. The sudden creation of national labs without creating a pool of trained personnel beforehand robbed the universities of talent. It also blurred the distinction between applied and basic research. Also, because of rapid expansion, and dependence on existing institutions, new culture could not be introduced. Nuclear and space programmes were in mission mode, while

Bhabha was able to infuse his Tata Institute of Fundamental Research with a culture that was new to India.

View from America

The Indian Science Congress session held in New Delhi in early January 1947 was attended on invitation by delegations from Britain, Canada, the USA, China, France and the Soviet Union. The American delegation included Professor Alfred Francis Blakeslee (1874–1950) as a representative of the American Association for Advancement of Science. Blakeslee was a former Director of the Carnegie Institution and a well-respected botanist of his time. After the Congress, he visited the Forest Institute at Dehradun as well as universities and scientific institutions at Lahore, Lucknow, Benares, Calcutta, Darjeeling, Hyderabad, Madras, Bombay, Jodhpur and Karachi. On return, he published in February 1948, a short paper on his impressions of India in *Scientific Monthly*, which was reprinted the next year in *Science & Culture*.

In carefully chosen words, Blakeslee made a number of significant points on the basis of his own experience. Blakeslee and his colleagues were "besieged by students who wanted our assistance in securing admission to Americal universities. They even called at our rooms before breakfast." "[s]everal requests [were] made to me that I mention the work of certain Indians when I gave my lectures at their institutions" so that "pull" [his inverted commas] could be generated in their favour.[4] At the same time,

> the men who appeared to me to be doing the most original work in certain institutions had considerable difficulty in getting to me to talk about their work. In fact, sometimes I had the feeling that they were actually being kept from me.[4]

A perceptive visitor, coming to Indian science 70 years after Blakeslee, would agree that many of his impressions are still valid.

The well-known US-trained experimental cosmic ray physicist, and something of a misfit in Indian science establishment, Piara Singh Gill (1911–2002), sent Blakeslee's clipping to Jawaharlal Nehru, who "handed it over" to Bhatnagar. According to Gill, "Bhatnagar was greatly annoyed with me for pointing this fact to the Prime Minister."[5] This is ironic because more than a decade previously, in 1935, Bhatnagar had complained to P.C. Ray about the jealousy betrayed by some of his friends. Ray advised him not to be "bothered by such pettiness," pointing out that

> It is a characteristic feature of Indians - and I may add of orientals - that they want to drag down those who have acquired some sort of eminence to their own level - whereas in Europe, it is generally the custom to carefully study the ways by which one acquired eminence and try to emulate it.[6]

Jawaharlal Nehru

Mahatma Gandhi rejected modern science and machinery as part of the Western cultural baggage. During his ascendancy in Indian political science, the middle class' commitment to science weakened. Science came back into focus with the political emergence of Jawaharlal Nehru (1889–1964). As President of the Congress, he declared in 1936: "I believe in the rapid industrialization of the country and only thus I think will the standard of the people rise substantially and poverty be combated." (Nehru, 1946: 103) In 1937, on the occasion of the silver jubilee of the Indian Science Congress, he reaffirmed: "Even more than the present, the future belongs to science and to those who make friends with science and seek its help in the advancement of humanity." (Nehru, 1946: 292) The Congress did come to limited power in 1937 but resigned two years later. Nehru had to wait till independence in 1947 to implement his agenda of big science.

In 1936, the British Government conferred on Bhatnagar the Order of the British Empire. A disappointed Bhatnagar was consoled by his friends that in his case OBE stood for Oil Borer of the Empire. A bigger honour came his way in 1941 when he was made the Knight Bachelor. From a scientific point of view, great recognition of his work came with the 1943 election as a Fellow of the Royal Society of London. Independent India honoured him with a Padma Vibhushan in 1954. Bhatnagar concurrently held a number of posts in the government. In 1948 and 1949, he worked as Secretary to the ministry of education and educational adviser to the Government of India. He was chosen to become the first secretary to the Ministry of Natural Resources and Scientific Research, which was set up in 1951. He was also the Secretary of the Atomic Energy Commission and later became the Chairman of the University Grants Commission.

It must be said to the credit of the Indian administrators planning for independent India that they made all-out efforts to bring the noted astrophysicist S. Chandrasekhar back to India on his terms. He was offered the directorship of the Kodaikanal Observatory. Although his family and well-wishers in India pressed him to accept, he was not interested in an administrative post. The Vice-Chancellor of Banaras Hindu University, Sarvapalli Radhakrishnan, was keen to appoint him. The least attractive of the offers was from his overbearing uncle Raman for a position at the Indian Institute of Science. A positive offer came from Bhabha in 1951, which tempted Chandrasekhar but not sufficiently. In 1953, Chandrasekhar accepted US citizenship and was lost to India.

What course would Indian science and education have taken if Chandrasekhar had returned? No doubt, he would have trained a large number of researchers, who in the course of time would have occupied important positions in the Indian academy. Would Chandrasekhar's total commitment to science have become the guiding principle for his students also? Would his conscientious negation of administrative and executive powers have been emulated? To borrow a phrase used by him in a different context, one is left speculating on the possibilities. As it turned out, in his native land, Chandrasekhar became an icon, and a show boy, but never a teacher or guide or a role model.

Being the solitary scientific organization of its type, CSIR nurtured many initiatives. It supported three private initiatives, the Tata Institute of Fundamental Research, Bombay (1945), the Physical Research Laboratory, Ahmedabad (1947) and the Research Institute of Indian Academy of Sciences at Bangalore under Sir C.V. Raman – (1948). It also provided Homi Bhabha with an official forum for his initiative on atomic research.

Homi Bhabha

If Bhatnagar was the face of what was meant to be industrial science, Homi Bhabha came to symbolize the new nation's initiatives on prestigious science. He was born into an aristocratic family, had had a brilliant academic and research career, and was in addition related to the wealthy, philanthropic, and well-respected House of the Tatas. Bhabha's father's sister was married to Sir Dorab Tata. Nehru had a tremendous fascination for science and a soft corner for persons with an aristocratic background. He was more comfortable with a Bhabha than with a Saha.

Bhabha left for Cambridge in 1927, where he would remain for the next 12 years. He joined Gonville and Caius College which already had a Tata connection. Dorabji Tata had studied there for two years 1877–1879 (even though he obtained his degree from St Xavier's College, Bombay in 1882). In 1920, the College received a donation of £25,000 for starting an engineering laboratory. Bhabha passed mechanics tripos in deference to his family's wishes, and mathematics tripos two years later for his own interest. He next went on to complete his PhD in theoretical physics, in 1934. Given his background, wide-ranging interests and personal charm, Bhabha was the first Indian scientist to establish social relations with his Western counterparts.

We have it on the testimony of a leading nuclear scientist of the time, Otto Robert Frisch (1904–1979) that Bhabha at the time did not know how to use a Geiger counter, the most elementary gadget in experimental nuclear science.[7] He came to India in 1939 hoping to be able to go back to Europe after a brief holiday. Once in India, Bhabha's plans changed for good. In January 1940, Bhabha was appointed a Special Reader at IISc on an honorarium of Rs 2500 and gave a course of 25 lectures on cosmic rays during January and February. Here he made an important acquaintance. The American Nobel laureate in physics, Robert Andrews Millikan, was at the Institute for conducting experiments on cosmic rays near the magnetic equator.

Because of the war, Millikan could not arrange Bhabha's visit to the California Institute of Technology, but in Bangalore itself introduced Bhabha to experiments. In June 1840, the Dorabji Tata Trust (established in 1932) gave him a monthly honorarium of Rs 1000 for setting up a Cosmic Ray Laboratory as an IISc project. He was appointed Reader-in-Charge of the Laboratory, "with the title of Professor as personal distinction."[8] High-sounding titles apart, these were temporary arrangements. Bhabha did receive a number of offers of regular appointments. The Allahabad University offered him a chair in 1941 which Raman would have liked him to consider. Bhabha was however "only interested in research and not in teaching," which to him constituted "routine duties." It was followed in 1942 by an offer from the Indian Association for the Cultivation of Science Calcutta. Bhabha found the Mysore University's offer to create a special chair for him particularly attractive: "Moreover there will be no regular teaching attached to the chair, which for India is a very welcome exception."[9] Exceptional the offer was; welcome it should not have been. Before leaving for India in 1939, Bhabha had applied for a Reader's position at Liverpool, but was not selected.[10] The War was still raging, and various considerations might have been at work.

Bhabha was ready to teach in England, but not in India. He was a beneficiary of the British University system and was ready to serve it, but he would not extend a similar courtesy to an Indian University. In India, he preferred to preside over a domain of his own, indulgently carved out for him by the state. As director of a research institute, Bhabha could comfortably deal with people whom he had inducted into his social club. It would be tempting to speculate on the impact an aristocratic Bhabha would have made on the rank and file of Indian students in a classroom and vice versa.

Tata Institute of Fundamental Research

It was an easy matter for Bhabha to persuade the Tatas to set up an institute for him. The Tata Institute of Fundamental Research finally came into existence on 1 June 1945 at Bangalore in the Indian Institute of Science but shifted to Bombay within six months. Bhabha rented a portion of a bungalow named Kenilworth from his aunt, Mrs Coover Panday, whose residence it was (incidentally, Bhabha was born in this building). The institute was formally inaugurated by the Bombay Governor, on 19 December 1945. Its first year's budget was a modest Rs 80,000 comprising a contribution of Rs 45,000 from the Tata Trust, Rs 25,000 from the Bombay Government, and Rs 10,000 from the Government of India through the CSIR. At about the same time, the CSIR formed an advisory Atomic Research Committee under the chairmanship of Bhabha, which held its first meeting in May 1946. The TIFR and India's atomic energy programme grew together. In 1949, the institute moved to the Old Yacht Club building. Mathematics and theoretical physics departments as well as the library were accommodated in the main building, but experimental physics faculties had to be set up in the erstwhile servant quarters. The institute remained here for 13 long years, but the wait was worth its while. The permanent housing of the institute came at Colaba at a site explicitly vacated by the Indian Navy.

Indian Atomic Energy Commission

In August 1948, the Indian Atomic Energy Commission was set up under the Department of Scientific and Industrial Research, which had been established in June 1948 under Bhatnagar. On 3 January 1954, the IAEC decided to set up a new facility, called the Atomic Energy Establishment, Trombay, with Bhabha as director (subsequently, it was named Bhabha Atomic Research Centre). Finally, a separate Department of Atomic Energy came into existence on 3 August 1954, with Bhabha as its secretary. From this date, Bhabha can be said to have a science domain of his own. During 1955–1956, a tripartite agreement was signed between the Tata Trust, the Bombay Government, and the AEC, whereby the TIFR became a generously funded affiliate of AEC. To accommodate Bhabha's Institute, the Government of India took the unprecedented step of releasing seafront land belonging to the Indian Navy in the posh Colaba area. The foundation stone of the permanent building was laid by Nehru on 1 January 1954, who returned eight years later, in 1962, to inaugurate it.

Bhabha is important on two distinct fronts. He initiated India's foreign-policy-related big science and he changed the social setting of fundamental research. Bhabha headed both the TIFR and the AEC which thus enjoyed a good relationship. And yet, they were guided by different philosophies. While the atomic establishment was to be self-contained with its own rigorous man-power training programme, the TIFR was to be socially and intellectually integrated with the West. It is as if Trombay Bhabha was distinct from the Colaba Bhabha.

Earlier the interaction of Indian scientists with their Western counterparts had been through the pages of research journals and in the lecture rooms. Indians hoped to excel in their science while retaining their cultural identity. Raman was very proud of his distinctive turban, while Chandrasekhar would sit in a first-class train compartment as an equal of the Europeans but in his South Indian attire. In contrast, Bhabha insisted that Indian scientists integrate with the Western scientific community at the social level also.

Bhabha was a Parsi by birth. The Parsis (literally the Persians) fled Islamized Iran in the 8th century CE and came to the west coast of India as refugees. They were offered asylum subject to conditions including that they carry no weapons and accept the local language and dress. The conditions were not severe and the Parsis had no choice. The Parsis accepted the conditions and India the Parsis. Ever since they have remained out of controversy and on the right side of the rulers, and prospered. As soon as Bombay changed hands from the Portuguese to the English, the Parsis, attracted by the religious neutrality of the new rulers and the business opportunities they offered, transferred their loyalty to the British and their residence to Bombay. And now Bhabha wanted his scientists to be socially acceptable to the Europeans.

The research institute served as a finishing school. Young researchers were given western toilet training and taught how to use a fork and knife. The building was designed by a foreign architect to Bhabha's requirements. The toilets did not have running water and were so designed that the facility could never be added. In the initial days, the faculty was potty-trained. A person was hired to see from the outside whether the feet of the toilet user rested on the ground or not. If not, he would bang at the door.

The hostel was not provided with balconies lest the ugly sight of washings left out to dry hurt sensitive eyes. Bhabha insisted at least with the senior faculty that they come in a tie. Those without it were expected to avoid high visibility (this was akin to George Everest's orders on Bengali dhoti, in the 1830s; p. 32). Two separate canteens, aptly designated the west canteen and the east canteen were constructed for the upper crust and the lower crust, respectively. The European cuisine of the west canteen immediately became the talk of the town. In Bhabha's time, chapati and rice were banned from the west canteen. In a minor concession after Bhabha's death, rice has been permitted, but chapati still remains forbidden.[11]

At the professional level, TIFR had some very constructive features. Bhabha believed in identifying persons and building institutions around them. In contrast, Bhatnagar's CSIR first built buildings and then scrambled to somehow fill the posts. At least in the early years, the TIFR offered higher salaries than elsewhere in India. Bhabha's greatest asset however was that he lay outside the caste hierarchy and beyond regional or linguistic parochialism. He could thus build a truly Indian institution. Contrast this with the situation in the sisterly Indian Institute of Science Bangalore. "Early in 1943, there was a serious agitation by students against the construction of a common dining hall, since they preferred the already existing four different messes which were run almost on a regional basis."[12]

Space Technology

Just as the Second World War introduced India to nuclear energy, the Cold War brought space technology to India. Vikram Ambalal Sarabhai (1919–1971) was born in a wealthy Gujarati industrialist family and was sent to Cambridge where he obtained his tripos from St John's College in 1940. War years saw him back in India. He utilized this time to work at the Indian

Institute of Science, Bangalore, with Bhabha and others on experimental studies of cosmic rays. Sarabhai went back to Cambridge in 1945 to return to India in 1947 for good. Sarabhai's personal contribution to scientific research was not of the same calibre as Bhabha's nor did he build international contacts and friendships the way Bhabha did. But, like Bhabha, he did establish, in 1947, an institute on his home turf, the Physical Research Laboratory, Ahmedabad (PRL). It was headed not by him but by K.R. Ramanathan (1893–1984) who had just retired from the Indian Meteorological Department (IMD). Ramanathan would serve as the President of the International Union of Geodesy and Geophysics (1954–1957). Though privately owned, like the TIFR, in the legal sense, the PRL was seen as a national facility. It could thus easily draw on the services of CSIR architects for designing its building.

India was one of the 64 countries that participated in the International Geophysical Year (IGY) which lasted for 18 months from 1 July 1957 to 31 December 1958. Its activities were continued till 31 December 1959 under the heading International Geophysical Cooperation. India with its vast size, extant institutions, and scientific manpower turned out to be an important and enthusiastic participant. The IGY has been called "a poor man's programme" (Mitra, 1985: 18) in the sense that its scientific and technological requirements were quite modest and easily met by the industrial and educational India of the 1950s. While Bhabha or his institute had no role in IGY, Sarabhai and PRL were actively involved.

Space Programme

An entirely new vista was opened by the IGY. India was introduced to the new field of satellites. The Naini Tal Observatory (established 1954) was one of the 12 world stations which were equipped by the US Smithsonian Astrophysical Observatory (SAO) to optically track artificial earth satellites. Unlike the other satellite tracking stations that were under SAO's control, the Indian station would be "under the complete jurisdiction of local astronomers." (Kochhar 2008b: 815)

The non-scientific dimension of the project was lost on none. K.S. Krishnan, director of NPL, New Delhi, rather indelicately and to the embarrassment of the Soviet representatives remarked publicly that

> it was wonderful that the U.S. was taking the world into confidence on the satellite program so that all nations could cooperate. He said further that it was a shame that the satellite program of the USSR was so secret and he hoped they might follow the example of the U.S. (Kochhar 2008b: 815)

On its part, the USA was very sensitive that the project should be viewed as international and not American. The importance the USA attached to the satellite tracking programme under IGY can be gauged from the fact that the *New York Times* carried a news item datelined Naini Tal where the reporter made it a point to mention that both Soviet and American satellites would be tracked and the information "will become part of the treasury of scientific data" of IGY.[13]

It would be no exaggeration to say that the IGY experience paved the way for the Indian space programme under Sarabhai. He had already been interested in observational studies of the impact of solar activity on cosmic rays. The IGY exposure helped him expand his horizons. In 1962, an Indian National Committee for Space Research (INCOSPAR) was set up. The very next year there came up the Equatorial Rocket Launching Station at Thumba near Trivandrum. The Indian Space Research Organization (ISRO) was established in 1969, under the Department of Atomic Energy. Finally, an independent Department of Space was set up in 1972. Because of Sarabhai's connection, the PRL became an affiliate of the Department of Space, just as previously the TIFR had been linked to the Department of Atomic Energy. India's first satellite, named Aryabhata after the 6th-century Indian astronomer, was launched in 1975 from the Soviet Union and tracked at Naini Tal from the facility set up during the IGY.

Arnold Frutkin, who was the director of NASA's Office of International Programmes from 1959 onwards, has an interesting story to tell. The USA was planning the Satellite Instructional Television Experiment (SITE), which could broadcast to home receivers provided the host country set up some simple equipment. NASA wished to have a big country like India participate. The India desk in the State Department however declined to approach India, because India had earlier refused permission to Voice of America to set up its broadcasting stations. The fact that SITE was not propaganda but science cut no ice with the officials. Frutkin then decided to take matters into his own hands. He knew Sarabhai well as he had been dealing with Sarabhai on sounding rocket programmes. He phoned Sarabhai and persuaded him not only to arrange for India's participation but also to write as if the initiative was coming from India itself. The programme, which ran during 1975–1976, was such a great success from the Indian point of view that India unsuccessfully tried to get the availability of the US satellite extended for another year. India then decided to make use of commercial satellites. Eventually, India developed its own satellite network as part of the INSAT programme, with the first satellite INSAT-1A launched in April 1982.

India set up a Defence Research and Development Organization in 1958 and placed it under a separate government department in 1980. A missile is a rocket fired horizontally. Fear of the enemy is a greater driving force than the love of stars. When India found an Avul Pakir Jainulabdeen Abdul Kalam (b. 1931), he was transferred (in 1983) from the Space Launch Vehicle-3 project to a new Integrated Guided Missile Programme under the

Defence Ministry. His doctorate is merely honorary and should not be used as a prefix. As far as formal education goes, Kalam has the University degree of BSc. followed by a Diploma from the Madras Institute of Technology, the combination being recognized as equivalent to a plain B.Tech. degree. Recognizing Kalam's talent and utilizing it speaks very well of India's space and missile programmes.

Indians at large consider the nuclear, missile, and space programmes to be India's most notable successes in post-independence science. Strictly speaking, these programmes are not science; they are not even technology; they belong to the domain of engineering, that is they are no more than successful applications of known technologies. This is not to belittle the achievements but to place them in proper perspective. But then, production of electricity is also a simple exercise in engineering where India's performance has been highly unsatisfactory.

The missile and nuclear programmes and, to a smaller extent, the space programme also are directed at India's external defence and foreign affairs rather than at India itself. Partial success on the agricultural front also belongs to this category. The increase in food production has not been large enough to feed the whole country, but sufficient to obviate dependence on foreign countries. These programmes give India a sense of general well-being because they are seen as strengthening India's efforts towards emergence as a sub-superpower. They tend to mask the failure concerning the intellectual and, more importantly, the production-of-wealth aspects of science.

Notes

1 Kochhar, 2004a, xxiii–xxiv.
2 Kochhar, 2004b, 85.
3 Visvanathan, 1985, 136.
4 Blakeslee, 1948, 141–144.
5 Gill, 1992, 122.
6 Ray to Bhatnagar, 12 December 1935; Ray100, 1962, 296.
7 Frisch, 1979, 55.
8 Subbarayappa, 1992, 158.
9 Chowdhury, 2014, 1101.
10 Abraham, 1999, 41.
11 This paragraph is based on the information accumulated from the oral testimonies of a number of old TIFR hands as well as visitors, who all narrated these stories with relish.
12 Subbarayappa, 1992, 157, note.
13 Rosenthal, 1958.

12
DISCUSSION

It would perhaps have been better for Indian science if Raman had missed the Nobel Prize. The dazzle of the award has made it well-nigh impossible to subject Indian science to a dispassionate and critical analysis. Normally, an initiative starts modestly, rises, reaches a peak, declines a little and settles on a plateau. In the case of India, science started at the top and had nowhere to go but downwards.

The 120 years of Indian pursuit of science can be conveniently discussed by distinguishing between three successive phases: (i) from 1895 (the year of J.C. Bose and P.C. Ray's work) till Second World War, (ii) from Independence in India till the onset of globalization, and (iii) the globalization era.

Nationalist Phase

India has been hoping against hope that the early spectacular success story of Indian science would repeat itself. This has not happened, cannot happen, because the early achievements were not part of a pattern but were made possible by a fortuitous combination of circumstances.

(i) Modern science was young then. It was just a short step ahead of, or rather a continuation of, MSc-level studies. Thus, Raman could publish research papers in international journals while still a student and establish his credentials as a world-class experimentalist working part-time. There was hardly any difference between a classroom textbook and a research journal. Saha and S.N. Bose as young lecturers produced the first-ever English translation of Einstein's papers on relativity for use as

DOI: 10.4324/9781003466406-12

course material. Saha and before him, J.C. Bose could identify research problems by reading popular accounts.

(ii) Another very important feature of this phase was that the calibre of teachers was exceptionally high. Teaching was the best career option after the limited options in the civil services. Surendra Nath Banerjee after being unfairly dismissed from ICS became a college professor (he taught P.C. Ray English literature). Since Saha could not enter civil services because of his pronounced nationalist leanings, he became a university lecturer. Raman left a cushy civil job to become a professor.

(iii) As J.C. Bose noted, in his time, the Presidency College Calcutta was among the best equipped anywhere in the world. The infrastructural and technological requirements of experimental research were very modest and easily available at the level of college teaching. Ray had a BSc-failed assistant, Jitendra Nath Rakshit, who " [O]ut of a few bits of rejected glass – tubing" "could improvise an apparatus, which hitherto could be had from a firm in England or Germany after months of anxious waiting." Raman used to boast that his equipment cost only 200 rupees. Raman misses the point completely. What is important is not the cost but the fact that at the time the state-of-the-art labs could be easily set up in the country. It was the "science application" under the aegis of the British administration that made 'science speculation'" by the Indians possible. The technical support that basic science required was available in British India. But as science developed, India failed to keep pace with scientific applications, which cannot be maintained in a technological and industrial vacuum.

Now, Nobel-Prize-level work requires billions of dollars worth of equipment which needs continual upgradation. Basic science has increasingly become a child of high technology and the days of simple discoveries are long over. It was one thing to formulate Bose–Einstein statistics using paper and pen (as S.N. Bose did), but quite another to achieve the technological feat of isolating the predicted condensates, which was honoured with a Nobel prize in 2001. Had Satyendra Bose been alive, he would have shared the Nobel Prize. But he would have to be 120 years old. Before the Second World War, science was a baby India could feed. After the war, it soon grew into a giant, outside India's feeding capabilities.

The take-off stage of modern physics coincided with the enhanced sense of Indian nationalism. Making scientific discoveries requires a certain amount of defiance. The suppressed semi-articulated resentment against the colonial rulers provided that defiance. Paradoxically, while Indian achievements in science were perceived as part of the nationalist movement, at the same time honours bestowed by the colonial rulers were coveted and even flaunted.

In the early days when India was new to modern science, it was natural that recognition be sought from the West. But modern science in India never became self-assessing. Scientists have continued looking towards the West for guidance, encouragement, support and recognition.

International Phase

During the international phase, at least in the earlier part, nation-building was a recurrent theme. Attempts at industrialization, reverse engineering, irrigation dams, agricultural production, strategic science, healthcare and the desire for expansion of science and engineering all placed science (including technology and engineering) in a pivotal place. This rubbed onto basic scientific research also. Generally speaking, research was of lesser quality than before. This is understandable because in the interim science had developed faster than India had. Indian science depended on foreign collaboration and visits and had an eye on the manpower needs of the post-war West. Yet, it fitted in with the national desire to harness science for economic development and as an instrument of national prestige. Although political power is now vested in elected representatives, the distance between them and the middle class was still small. The distance has since increased to such an extent that the middle class has lost whatever sense of national obligation it had cherished earlier.

Globalization has transformed the Indian economy as well as the Indian middle class. The globalization era (till the COVID times) saw India enjoy a high growth rate, but it has been driven by the services sector, which is manifestly science-less. If the economy of a country becomes derivative, so will its culture. Science cannot flourish in a society whose economy does not require science. If the Indian economy has disowned science, the middle class has disowned India itself. Globalization has introduced Upper India to a consumerist lifestyle that is beyond the intrinsic strength of the Indian economy. This lifestyle can only be maintained by servicing the western economy.

Throughout the world, science provides the quickest, shortest, and the surest route for entry into the middle class and for upward social mobility. Indian science and engineering degree-holders are more than willing to do petty unintelligent jobbery for big companies for the sake of a salary, which though small in dollar terms translates into a hefty rupee bundle. If they want to pursue science they go to the USA, where a middle-class living is still an improvement over their Indian status. It must however be admitted that at a technical level, there is a cascading effect in the decline of science in India. There is an ever-increasing chasm between the best of Indian science and the best of world science. If any Indian wishes to make a mark in scientific research, they can as well go abroad, especially when the world is culturally far more homogeneous than ever before and travel and communication costs have come down drastically. Interestingly, while politicians, lawyers, and doctors want their children to follow their parental profession, Indian scientists would in general not like their children to become scientists in India! It may not be out of place to remark that Indian military officers do not generally want their sons to follow suit. It is the other ranks who have a burning desire to see their sons as officers.

If science is to survive in India, the catchment area for education must expand. Our education system must step out and embrace children of formally uneducated parents. For them, a science-related career in universities, defence, national labs, public sector undertakings, etc., would be a social step upward and therefore would be enthusiastically accepted.

We can distinguish between the three aspects of the development of modern science: the intellectual aspect, the production of wealth aspect, and the dominational aspect. The (non-white) non-west's view of these developments in the west has been blinkered. When science was being developed as a methodology and as an agency that was intellectually uplifting and quality-of-life enhancing, the non-west in general was not a party to the phenomenon. It is a measure of the success of orientalism that modern science was not seen as the latest stage in the continuum of human endeavour to comprehend natural phenomena but as western science set in opposition to the so-called eastern philosophy and way of life. This image of modern science was reinforced by its role as a producer of wealth. To the west, science was wealth; to the east, an agency that destroyed traditional manufacturing.

However, when the dominational aspects of science were being developed, the (non-white) non-west was fully aware of the process. It was in fact a participant. It contributed to the process by becoming its victim. Domination is a well-recognized old paradigm; modern science was merely an add-on. That is why of all the aspects of modern science, the dominational aspect has appealed the most to the formerly subjugated people of Asia and Africa, who have tended to decouple it from the other two aspects. Thus, the most modern weapons can be used to capture power in Afghanistan, but once the power has been obtained it is not used to bring in other aspects of modern science. Rather, it is used to impose a highly outdated mindset. Although India has been more comfortable with science than other former (non-white) colonies, its collective attitude towards science has been rather ambivalent, a mixture of acceptance and rejection. Thus, Ganesha's imbibing milk could be widely perceived as proof of the victory of "our" Ganesh over "their" science. The irony is lost that the news of this victory over modern science was flashed across the world using the latest gadgets of telecommunication. But, as we have seen, for historical reasons, there has been a latent and not-so-latent hostility towards production of wealth through science. The emphasis on the cultural, or Brahminical, aspects of science unsupported by a knowledge-based economy has harmed Indian science.

While in Europe, the industrial revolution artisanized the whole society, in India consistent with the caste composition and aspirations of the new middle class, science itself was Brahminized, that is, it was viewed as a cultural activity. After independence, consistent with the aspirations of a new nation, science has been successfully Kshatriya-ized. It still remains to be Mandalized, in the sense of creating a new technology-driven artisan class. Science can be enhanced only by those who harness it. Countries whose GDP does not depend on science cannot "make friends with science."

In the globalization era, Indian economy is being driven by the services sector which by definition is science-less. For science to develop in a society, it must form a symbiotic relationship with industry. The purpose of science is to generate wealth; the aim of this wealth is to support science. If a country's economy does not need science, science cannot flourish in such a setting.

REFERENCES

Abraham, I. (1999). *Making of the Indian Atomic Bomb: Science, Secrecy and the Postcolonial State*. Orient Blackswan.

Alder, G. J. (1979). The Origins of "The Pusa Experiment": The East India Company and Horse-breeding in Bengal, 1793–1808. *Bengal Past and Present*, 98(1), 10–32.

Alexander, J. E. (1827). *Shigruf Namah-I-Velayat of Itesmaddin*. London: Parbury, Allen.

Allen, D. E. (1989). Book Review of *The Life of Charles Ledger (1818-1901): Alpacas and Quinine, by Gabrielle Gramiccia*. London: Macmillan, 1988. *Medical History*, 33(3), 380–388.

Amin, B. D. (1939). *The Rise and Growth of the Alembic Chemical Works, Alembic Chemical Works*. Baroda, p. 2.

Andrews, C. F. (1929). *Zaka Ullah of Delhi*. Cambridge: W. Heffer & Sons Ltd.

Arnold, D. (2000). *Science, Technology and Medicine in Colonial India*. Cambridge University Press.

Bagal, J. C. (1933a). Radhanath Sikdhar. *Modern Review*, 53(4), 457–460.

Bagal, J. C. (1933b). More Light on Radhanath Sikdhar. *Modern Review*, 54(3), 281–293.

Bagal, J. C. (1955). *Pramatha Nath Bose*. New Delhi: Sushma Sen.

Bailey, M. (2016). Women and the RAS: 100 Years of Fellowship. *Astronomy & Geophysics*, 57(1), 1.19–1.21. https://doi.org/10.1093/astrogeo/atw037

Banerjee, Kalipada. (1935). *Current Science*, 4, 231.

Basu, P. (1943). *Oudh and the East India Company 1785-1801*. Lucknow: Maxwell.

Bedi, Baba Pyare Lal. (1940). *Harvest from the Desert, the Life and Work of Sir Ganga Ram*. Lahore: Sir Ganga Ram Trust Society.

Berman, M. (1976). *Social Change and Scientific Organization: The Royal Institution, 1799-1844*. Ithaca: Cornell University Press.

Bhalla, J. S. (1988). *History of the Remount and Veterinary Corps, 1794-1987*. New Delhi: Army Headquarters.

Bhaskaran, T. P. (1923). The 15-inch Grubb Equatorial of the Nizamiah Observatory, Hyderabad. *Popular Astronomy*, 31, 497–501.

Bhat, P. N., & Yadav, M. P. (2018). *Animal Husbandry Research, Education and Development*. Jodhpur: Scientific Publishers (India).

Bhathal, R. (2009). 150 Years of Sydney Observatory. *Astronomy & Geophysics*, 50(3), 3.26–3.30.

Bhatt, U., & Pathak, S. (2008). Asia ki Peeth Par Pandit Nain Singh Rawat Jeevan, Anveshan tatha Lekhan (Hindi).

Bhattacharyya, P., & Engineer, M. H. (Eds.). 1997. *Acharya J.C. Bose – A Scientist & A Dreamer*, Vol. 4. Calcutta: Bose Institute, Calcutta.

Birch, T. (1756). *History of the Royal Society of London*, 2 Vols. London: Miller.

Biswas, K. (1950). *The Original Correspondence of Sir Joseph Banks Relating to the Foundation of the Royal Botanic Garden, Calcutta, and the Summary of the 150th Anniversary Volume*. Calcutta: Asiatic Society.

Biswas, A. K. (1969). *Science in India*. Calcutta: Firma KL Mukhopadhyay.

Biswas, A. K. (2000). *Gleanings of the Past and the Science Movement*. Calcutta: Asiatic Society.

Biswas, Arun Kumar. (2001). *Father Eugene Lafont of St. Xavier's College, Kolkata and the Contemporary Science Movement*. Kolkata: Asiatic Society.

Biswas, A. K. (2003). *Collected Works of Sircar, Lafont and the Science Movement*. Kolkata: Asiatic Society.

Black, C. E. D. (1891). *A Memoir on the Indian Surveys, 1875-1890*. London: Arnold.

Blakesbee, A. F. (1948). Impressions of India. *Scientific Monthly*, 66(2), 141–144.

Blanford, W. T. (1865). On the Geological Structure and Relations of the Raniganj Coal Field, Bengal. *Memoirs of the Geological Survey of India*, 3, 1–196.

Blechynden, K. (1905). *Calcutta, Past and Present*. London: Thacker.

Blunt, W. (2001). *The Compleat Naturalist: A Life of Linnaeus*. London: Frances Lincoln.

Bom. Edu. (1958). *A Review of Education in Bombay State 1855-1955*. Poona: Government of Bombay.

Bose, J. C. (1896). *An account of experimental research carried out at the Physical Laboratory, Presidency College, Calcutta, in the year 1895*. Calcutta: W. Newman.

Boxer, C. R. (1963). *Two Pioneers of Tropical Medicine: Garcia d'Orta and Nicolás Monardes*. London: Wellcome.

Boylston, A. (2012). The Origins of Inoculation. *Journal of the Royal Society of Medicine*, 105(7), 309–313.

Brandon-Jones, C. 1997 Edward Blyth, Charles Darwin, and the Animal Trade in Nineteenth-century India and Britain. *Journal of the History of Biology*, 30, 145–178.

Brockway, L. H. (1979). Science and Colonial Expansion: The Role of the British Royal Botanic Gardens. *American Ethnologist*, 6(3), 449–465.

Brodie, N. (1935). Industrial Intelligence and Research in India. *Current Science*, 4(3), 138–139.

Bruce, J. F. (1933). *A History of the University of the Panjab*, Lahore: Registrar, University of the Panjab, 54.

Bruce-Chwatt, L. J. (1988). Three Hundred and Fifty Years of the Peruvian Fever Bark. *British Medical Journal*, 296, 1486.

Bryant, G. J. (1995). The Cavalry Problem in the Early British Indian Army, 1750–1785. *War in History*, 2(1), 1–21.

Buckland, C. E. (1906). *Dictionary of Indian Biography*. Bloomsberry: Swan Sonnenschein.

Burkill, I. H. (1965). *Chapters on the History of Botany in India*. Calcutta: Botanical Survey of India.

Burrard, S. G. (1904). Mount Everest: The Story of a Long Controversy. *Nature*, 71 (Nov. 10), 42–46.

Burrard, S. G., & Hayden, H. H. (1933). *A Sketch of Geography and geology of Himalayan Mountains and Tibet*, 2nd ed. Delhi: Manager of Publications.

Burrow, R. (1790). A Proof That the Hindus Had the Binomial Theorem. *Asiatick Researches*, 2, 388–395.

Calcutta Review. (1890). *The Calcutta Review*, Vol. 90. Calcutta: Thomas S. Smith, City Press.

Carey, W. (1814). *Hortus Bengalensis*. Serampore: Mission Press.

Carey, W. H. (1882). *The Good Old Days of Honorable John Company*. (Reprint, Riddhi-India).

Carpenter, K. J. (1986). *The History of Scurvy and Vitamin C*. Cambridge: Cambridge University Press.

Chandra, Sudhir. (1971). The Indian League and the Western India Association. *Indian Economic and Social History Review*, 8, 78–98.

Charlton, A. (1841). *Correspondence Regarding the Discovery of the Tea Plant of Assam*. Calcutta: Star Press. (Author's name is implied).

Chary, C. Ragoonatha. (1874). *Transit of Venus*. Madras: Indian Institute of Astrophysics Archives.

Chattopadhyay, B. (2007). The University of Calcutta: An Overview. *University News*, 45(4), 15–49.

Chaudhury, N. C. (1978). *Clive of India*. Bombay: Jaico.

Chinnici, Ileana. (1995–96). An "Italian" Observatory in India: The History of the Calcutta Observatory. *Studies in History of Medicine & Science*, XIV(1–2), New Series, 91–115.

Chowdhury, I. (2014). Fundamental Research, Self-reliance, and Internationalism: The Evolution of Tata Institute of Fundamental Research, 1945-47. In U. Das Gupta (Ed.), *Science and Modern India: An Institutional History*. Delhi: Pearson.

Cinchona Parliamentary Papers. (1863). *Return to an Address of the Honourable the House of Commons, dated 9 March 1863; -- for, "Copy of Correspondence Relating to the Introduction of the Chinchona Plant into India, and to Proceedings Connected with Its Cultivation, from March 1852 to March 1863*. India Office, 18 March; Published by House of Commons.

Cleghorn, H., Royle, F., & Baird Smith, R. (1852). *Report of the Committee appointed by the British Association to consider the probable Effects, in an Œconomical and Physical Point of View, of the Destruction of Tropical Forests, London*: Report of the Twenty-First Meeting of the British Association for the Advancement of Science held at Ipswich in July 1851, pp. 78–99].

Cleghorn, H. (1873). *Obituary Notice of Dr Robert Wight*. Edinburgh: Neill.

Conrad, L. I., Neve, M., Nutton, V., Porter, R., & Wear, A. (1998). *The Western Medical Tradition 800 BC to AD 1800*. Cambridge University Press.

Crawford, D. G. (1914). *A History of the Indian Medical Service 1600-1913*, 2 Vols. London: W. Thacker.

CSBS. (1819). *Second Report of the Calcutta School-Book Society's Proceedings*. Calcutta: School and Mission Press.

Cursetjee, A. (1840). *Diary of an Overland Journey from Bombay to England and of a Year's Residence in Great Britain*. London: Henington and Galabin (Reprint by Neville Wadia, Mumbai, 1994).

D' Cruz, I. A. (1991). Garcia da Orta in Goa: Pioneering Tropical Medicine. *British Medical Journal*, 303, 1593–1594.

Da Cunha, J. G. (1900). *The Origin of Bombay*. (Reprint, Asian Education Services, New Delhi, 2004).

Dam, H. J. W. (1897). Telegraphing Without Wires. *McClure's Magazine*, VIII, March, 383–392.

Dance, S. P. (1967). Report on the Linnaean Shell Collection. *Proceedings of Linnaean Society London*, 176(1), 1–34.

Das, S. N. (1991). Who Measured Mount Everest? *Himalayan Newsletter*, No. 44, 43.

Dasgupta, Subrata. (1999) *Jagadis Chandra Bose and the Indian Response to Western Science*. New Delhi: Oxford University Press.

De Asua, M., & French, R. (2005). *A New World of Animals: Early Modern Europeans on the Creatures of Iberian America*. Aldershot: Ashgate.

De Morgan, A. (1859). Editor's Preface, in *A Treatise of Problems on Maxima And Minima, Solved by Algebra*. W H Allen & Co. https://mathshistory.st-andrews.ac.uk/Extras/De_Morgan_1859_Preface/

De Vorkin, David H. (1994). Quantum Physics and the Stars (IV): Meghnad Saha's Fate. *Journal for the History of Astronomy*, 25, 155–188.

Deb, Raja Binaya Krishna. (1905). *The Early History and Growth of Calcutta*, p. 88.

Desmond, R. (1992). *European Discovery of the Indian Flora*. New York: Oxford University Press.

Dikshit, B. S. (1981). *Bharatiya Jyotish Sastra*, Part I & II. Civil Lines, Delhi: The Controller of Publications.

Dionne, R., & Macleod, R. (1978). Science and Policy in British India, 1858-1914: Perspectives in Persisting Belief. In M. Gaborieau, & A. Thorner (Eds.), *Asie du Sud: traditions et changements*. CNRS.

Dodd, E. F. (1956). *The story of Sir Ronald Ross and his fight against malaria*. Madras: Macmillan and Co.

Dongerkery, S. R. (1957). *A History of the University of Bombay 1857–1957*. Bombay: University of Bombay.

Dutta, M. (1977). *Jamshedpur*. Calcutta: Asiatic Society.

Earles, J. (1788). *A Treatise on Horses, Entitled Saloter, Or, a Complete System of Indian Farriery, In Two Parts: The First, Containing a Particular Description of the Different Colours and Marks of Horses, &c. The Second, a Description of All the Disorders They are Subject To, &c. Compiled Originally by a Society of Learned Pundits, in the Shanscrit Language: Translated Thence Into Persian, in the Reign of The Emperor Shah Jehan, by Abdallah Khan Firoze Jung, an Emeer of His Court which is Now Translated Into English*, by Joseph Earles, Calcutta: George Gordon.

Elgood, C. (1951). *A Medical History of Persia and the Eastern Caliphate*. Cambridge University Press.

Esch, G. W. (2007). *Parasites and Infectious Diseases*. Cambridge University Press.

Fenger, J. F. (1863). *History of the Tranquebar Mission on the Coromandel Coast*. Tranquebar: Evangelical Lutheran Mission Press.

Fisher's Memoir. (1833). *Memoir, dated February 7, 1827, compiled from the records of the India government at the East India House ...* printed in the Minutes of Evidence taken before the Select Committee of the House of Commons on the Affairs of the East India Company, February 14 to July 27, 1832, (I Public) Appendix I; Memoir and Supplement printed by order of the Honourable Court of Directors in January 1833, pp. 194–324.

Flückiger, F. A., & Hanbury, D. (1879). *Pharmacographia: A History of the Principal Drugs of Vegetable Origin Met with in Great Britain and British India.* London: Macmillan.

Foulker, T. (1861). Biographical Memoir of Dr. Rottler. *Madras Journal of Literature and Science,* 6(May), 1–17.

Fox, C. S. (1947). The Geological Survey of India, 1846 to 1947. *Nature,* 160, 889–891.

Frisch, O. R. (1979). *What Little I Remember.* Cambridge University Press.

Furedy, C. (1979). New Men Political Clubs in Calcutta in the 1870's and1880's: A Colonial Mix of Self-interest and Ideology. *Indian Journal of Politics,* 13, 63–73.

Gait, E. (1906). *A History of Assam.* Calcutta: Government Printing.

Gajjar, T. K. (1907). "Welcome Address," The Industrial Conference Held at Surat, December 1907: *Full Text of Papers Read at and Submitted to It, ed. by the Industrial Conference,* Madras: G.A. Natesan, 1–21, here: 9–10.

Garratt, Gerald R. M. (1994). *The Early History of Radio: From Faraday to Marconi.* London: Institution of Electrical Engineers.

Gawali, P., Doiphode, M., & Nimje, R. (2015). Colaba-Alibag Magnetic Observatory and Nanabhoy Moos: The Influence of One over the Other. *History of Geo- and Space Sciences,* 6, 107–131.

Geddes, Patrick. (1920) *Life and Work of Sir Jagadis C. Bose.* London: Longman, Green, and Co. (Written in Bose's life time, this is an authorized biography).

Ghose, Sarat Chandra. (1935). *Life of Dr. Mahendra Lal Sircar, M.D., D.L., C.M.D..* Calcutta: P.O. Bhar. Hahnemann Pub. Co.

Ghosh, A. (1997). Guru Jones – A Private Engineer in the Colonial Trap. *Indian Journal of History of Science,* 20(2), 139–159.

Ghosh, Siddhartha. (2002). *Rajendralal Mitra.* New Delhi: Sahitya Akademi.

Gill, P. S. (1992). *Up against Odds: Autobiography of an Indian Scientist.* New Delhi: Allied.

Glazier, A. (2020). https://euppublishingblog.com/2020/08/12/george-strachan-of-the-mearns-a-historians-biography/, introducing the book.

Goodman, D. (1991). Iberian Science: Navigation, Empire and Counter-Reformation, In D. Goodman, & C. A. Russel (Eds.), *Rise of Scientific Europe.* London: Hodder.

Gupta, Monoranjon. (1970). *Jagadishchandra Bose.* Bombay: Bharatiya Vidya Bhavan.

Harris, J. N. (1958). *Jamsetji Nusserwanji Tata.* Bombay: Blackie.

Hasan, F. (1991). Conflict and Cooperation in Anglo-Mughal Trade Relations during the Reign of Aurangzeb. *Journal of the Economic and Social History of the Orient,* 34(4), 351–360.

Hawgood, B. J. (1994). The Life and Viper of Dr Patrick Russell MD FRS (1727-1805): Physician and Naturalist. *Toxicon,* 32(11), 1295–1304.

Headrick, D. R. (1981). *The Tools of Empire Technology and European Imperialism in the Nineteenth Century.* Oxford University Press.

Headrick, D. R. (1988). *The Tentacles of Progress: Technology Transfer in the Age of Imperialism, 1850-1940.* Oxford University Press.

Heatly, S. G. T. (1842). Contributions towards a History of the Development of the Mineral Resources of India. *Journal of Asiatic Society of Bengal,* 1842, 11, Part 2, 811–835.

Heniger, J. (1986). *Hendrik Adriaan Van Reed Tot Drakestein 1636-1691 and Hortus Malabaricus.* Routledge.

Hodson, V. C. P. (1910). *Historical Records of the Governor-General's Body Guard.* London: W. Thacker & Co.

Holmes, J. D. E. (1913). *A Description of the Imperial Bacteriological Laboratory, Muktesar, Its Work and Products.* Calcutta: Superintendent Government Print., India.

Holland, J. H. (1932). Ledger Bark and Red Bark. *Bulletin of Miscellaneous Information, Royal Botanic Gardens,* Kew, No. 1.

Homfray, J. (1842). Description of the Coal Field of the Damoodah Valley and the and Poorooleah, as Applicable to the Present Date 1842. *Journal of Asiatic Society of Bengal,* 1842, 11, Part 2, 723–742.

Hooker, J. D. (1854). *Himalayan Journals,* Vol. 1. London: John Murray.

Hooker, J. D., & Thomson, T. (1855). *Introductory Essay to the Flora Indica.* London: Pamplin.

How, H. (1878). The East Indian Herbarium of King's College, Windsor. *Proceedings and Transactions of the Nova Scotian Institute of Natural Science,* 4(4), 369–379.

Howard, J. E. (1869). *The Quinology of the East Indian Plantations.* London: Lovell Reeve and Co.

Huguet-Termes, T. (2001). New World Materia Medica in Spanish Renaissance Medicine: From Scholarly Reception to Practical Impact. *Medical History,* 45, 359–376.

Hunter, W. W. (1876). *A Life of the Earl of Mayo.* Vol. 2, 2nd ed. London: Smith, Elder.

Hyde, H. M. (1962). Dr George Govan and the Saharanpur Botanical Gardens. *Journal of the Royal Central Asian Society,* 49, 47–57.

IACS. (1976). *IACS - A Centenary.* Calcutta: Indian Association for the Cultivation of Science.

Ingledew, C. J. D. (1858). *History and Antiquities of North Allerton, in the County of York.* London: Bell & Daldy.

IVRI. (1940). *Annual Report of Imperial Veterinary Research Institute,* 1940, Delhi.

Jacob, W. S. (1884). *Magnetical Observations Made at the Honorable East India Company's Observatory at Madras under the Superintendence of W.S. Jacob, in the years 1851-1855.* Madras: Lawrence Asylum Press.

Jacquemont, V. (1834). *Letters from India,* Vol. 1. London: Churton (Reprint, New Delhi: Asian Education Service, 1993).

James, Patricia. (1979). *Population Malthus: his Life and Times* (Reprint 2006: Routledge).

Jensen, N. T. (2014). Making it in Tranquebar: The Circulation of Scientific Knowledge in the Early Danish-Halle Mission. In E. Fihl, & A. R. Venkatachalapathy (Eds.), *Beyond Tranquebar: Grappling Across Cultural Borders in South India.* Hyderabad: Orient Blackswan.

Johnson, G. W. (1843). *The Stranger in India: Or, Three Years in Calcutta.* London: Henry Colburn.

Jürgens, H. (2004). German Indology avant la letter: The Experiences of the Halle missionaries in Southern India, 1750-1810. In D. T. McGetchin et al. (Eds.), *Sanskrit and Orientalism.* Delhi: Manohar.

Kennedy, J. (1910). English Education and Indian Ethics. *Asian Quarterly Review,* 30, 290–313.

Keynes, G. (1967). John Woodall, Surgeon, His Place in Medical History. *Journal of the Royal College of Physicians of London,* 2(1), 15–33.

Khaleeli, Z. (2001). Harmony or Hegemony? The Rise and Fall of the Native Medical Institution, Calcutta; 1822–35. *South Asia Research*, 21(1), 77–104.

Kling, B. B. (1976). *Partner in Empire*. Berkeley: University of California Press.

King, G. (1870). *Manual of Cinchona Cultivation in India*. Calcutta: Office of the Superintendent of Government Printing.

Kochhar, R. K. (1985). Madras Observatory: Buildings and Instruments. *Bulletin Astronomical Society of India*, 13, 287–302.

Kochhar, R. (1987). Shelton Clock at Kodaikanal. *Antiquarian Horology*, 17, 181–184.

Kochhar, R. (1991). Growth of Modern Astronomy in India 1651-1960. *Vistas in Astronomy*, 34, 69–105.

Kochhar, R. (1992). Science in British India. I. Colonial Tool. *Current Science*, 63, 689–694.

Kochhar, R. (1993a). Science in British India. II. Indian Response. *Current Science*, 64(1), 55–62.

Kochhar, R. (1993b). Ardaseer Cursetjee (1808-77), the First Indian Fellow of the Royal Society of London. *Notes & Records of the Royal Society of London*, 47, 33–47. https://prints.iiap.res.in/handle/2248/4772

Kochhar, R. (2004a). S.S. Bhatnagar: Life and Times (Review essay). In Life & Work of Sir S.S. Bhatnagar (by Norah Richards). (New edition, Delhi: NISTADS) (First published 1948). http://rajeshkochhar.com/data/publications/ssb_by_rkk.pdf

Kochhar, R. (2004b). Shanti Swarup Bhatnagar. *Resonance*, 7, 82–89.

Kochhar, R. K. (2008a). Seductive Orientalism: English Education and Modern Science in Colonial India. *Social Scientist*, 26, 45–63. (S. C. Mishra Memorial Lecture at the 68th Indian History Congress, Delhi, December 2007.)

Kochhar, R.K. (2008b). Cultivation of Science in the 19th Century Bengal. *Indian Journal of Physics*, 82(8), 1003–1082. http://www.ias.ac.in/article/fulltext/reso/007/04/0082-0089

Kochhar, R.K. (2008c). Science as a symbol of new neighbourhood: India and the International Geophysical Year 1957-58, *Current Science*, 94(6), 813–816.

Kochhar, R. (2014). Book Review Essay on M. K. Vainu Bappu. *Current Science*, 106, 1752–1755.

Kochhar, R. K. (2021). *English Education in India, 1715–1835 Half-Caste, Missionary, and Secular Stages*. Routledge.

Kochhar, R. (2022). *Sanskrit and British Empire*. Routledge.

Krishnan, S. (2013). *Empire's Metropolis Money: Time & Space in Colonial Bombay, 1870-1930*. PhD Thesis, Massachusetts Institute of Technology.

Kunz, G. F. (1915). *The Magic of Jewels and Charms* (Reprint, Kessinger Publishing, 2003).

Kumar, D. (1995). *Science and the Raj, 1857–1905*. Delhi: Oxford University Press.

Kumar, D. (1997). Medical Encounters in British India, 1820–1920. *Economic and Political Weekly*, 32(4, Jan. 25–31), 166–170.

Lach, D. F. (1970). *Asia in the Making of Europe*, Vol. 2, Book 1. University of Chicago Press.

Lach, D. F. (1994). *Asia in the Making of Europe*, Vol. 2, Book 3 University of Chicago Press.

Ledger, C. (1881). The Story of Cinchona Ledgeriana. *American Journal of Pharmacy*, 53(3), 9–12.

Lee, M. R. (2002). Plants against Malaria. Part 1: Cinchona or the Peruvian Bark. *Journal of College of Physicians Edinburgh*, 32, 189–196.

Leffer, C. T., Klebanov, A, Samara, W. A., & Grzybowski, A. (2020). The History of Cataract Surgery: From Couching to Phacoemulsification. *Annals of Translational Medicine*, 8(22), 1–46.

Lenox-Conyngham, G. (1944). Sidney Gerald Burrard. 1860-1943. *Obituary Notices of Fellows of the Royal Society*, 4(13), 507–522.

Lipner, J. J. (2005). *Anandamath, or The Sacred Brotherhood*. New York: Oxford University Press.

Lockman, J. (1762). *Travels of the Jesuits into Various Parts of the World: Particularly China and the East-Indies*, 2nd ed. London: Piety.

Lodge, P., & Oliver, J.. (1894). *Signalling across Space without Wires. Being a Description of the Work of Hertz & His Successors; His Successors*. London: "The Electrician" Printing and Publishing Company, Limited.

Love, H. D. (1913). *Vestiges of Old Madras*, 4 Vols. London: John Murray.

Macdonald, A. A., Warwick, C. M., & Johnston, W. T. (2005). *Locating Veterinary Education in Edinburgh in the Nineteenth Century, Book of the Old Edinburgh Club*. New Series Vol. 6, pp. 41–71.

Mackenna, James. (1915). *Agriculture in India*. Calcutta: Government Press.

Maclagen, E. (1932). *The Jesuit and the Great Mogul*. London: Burns, Oates.

Maitra, Somnath. (1959). One Friend to Another: A Few of the Letters Exchanged between Rabindranath Tagore and Jagadishchandra Bose. *Visvabharati Quarterly*, 24(4), 260–272.

Mann, H. H. (1918). *The Early History of the Tea Industry in North-East India*. Calcutta: Calcutta General Printers (Reprinted from *Bengal Economic Journal*, 2, 44–59).

Markham, C. R. (1871). *A Memoir on the Indian Surveys*. London: W. H. Allen.

Markham, C. R. (1913). *Colloquies on the Simples and Drugs of India by Garcia da Orta*. London: Henry Sotheran.

Martin, R. M. (1838). *History, Antiquities, Topography, and Statistics of Eastern India*. London: W.H. Allen.

Mason, K. (1956). Great Figures of Nineteenth Century Himalayan Exploration. *Journal of the Royal Central Asian Society*, 43(3-4), 167–175.

McInally, Tom. (2020). *George Strachan of the Mearns: Sixteenth Century Orientalist*. Edinburgh University Press.

McKie, D. (1960). The Origins and Foundation of the Royal Society of London. *Notes and Records of the Royal Society of London*, 15, 1–38.

Mehra, Jagdish. (1975). Satyendra Nath Bose, 1 January 1894–4 February 1974. *Biographical Memoirs of the Royal Society, London*, 21, 116–154.

Mehra, Jagdish. (2001). *The Golden Age of Theoretical Physics*, Vol. 1. World Scientific.

Mehta, M. (1985). In *Proceedings of Indian History Congress*, Aligarh, Vol. 45, pp. 669–677.

Mishra, S. (2012). The Economics of Reproduction: Horse-breeding in Early Colonial India, 1790–1840. *Modern Asian Studies*, 46(5), 1116–1144.

Mitra, A. P. (1985). *Indian IGY Programme: Achievements*. New Delhi: Indian National Science Academy.

Mittra, P. C. (1878). *A Biographical Sketch of David Hare*. (ed. G. G. Sengupta). (Reprint, Jijnasa, Calcutta, 1979).

Montgomerie, T. G. (1866). On the Geographical Position of Yarkund and Other Places in Central Asia. *Proceedings of the Royal Geographical Society*, 10, 162–164.

Montgomerie, T. (1868). Report on the Trans-Himalayan Explorations, in Connexion with the Great Trigonometrical Survey of India, during 1865-7: Route-Survey Made by Pundit ----, from Nepal to Lhasa, and thence through the Upper Valley of the Brahmaputra to Its Source. *Proceedings of the Royal Geographical Society of London*, 12(23 Mar.), 146–175.

Moorcroft, W. (1862). *Observations on the Breeding of horses within the provinces under the Bengal Establishment, submitted to the consideration of the President and Members of the Board of Superintendence*, Calcutta: Re-printed at the Military Orphan Press.

Moos, A. F. (1871). *Journal of Travels in India*. Vol. 1. Bombay: Education Society's Press.

Morrell, J., & Thackray, A. (1981). *Gentlemen of Science: Early Years of the British Association for the Advancement of Science*. Oxford: Clarendon Press.

Mouat, F. J. (1854). Notes on Native Remedies. No. 1. The Chaulmoogra. *Indian Annals of Medical Sciences*, 1, 646–652, p. 646.

Mudiraj, K. K. (1934). *Pictorial Hyderabad*. Hyderabad: Chandrakanth Press.

Mukherjee, N. (1975). *A Bengal Zamindar: Joykrishna Mukherjee and His Times, (1808-1888)*. Calcutta; Firma: K. L. Mukhopadhyay.

Mukherji, Visvapriya. (1983). *Jagadis Chandra Bose*. New Delhi: Publications Division, Ministry of Information and Broadcasting, Govt. of India.

Murchison, C. (1868). *Paleontological Memoirs and Notes of the Late Hugh Falconer. With a Biographical Sketch of the Author*. London: Hardwicke.

Murray, H. (1834). *An Encylopaedia of Geography*. London: Longman, Rees.

Natesan, G. A. (1921), *Sir Jagadish Chander Bose*. Madras: G A Natesan And Company.

Natesan, G. A. (1929). *Indian Scientists, Biographical Sketches With An Account Of Their Researches, Discoveries And Inventions. Dr. Mahendralal Sircar, Sir. J. C. Bose, Dr. P. C. Ray, Sir C. V. Raman, Prof. Ramachandra, Srinivasa Ramanujan*. Madras: G. A. Natesan & Co.

Natwar-Singh, K. (1981). *Maharaja Suraj Mal, 1707-1763: His Life and Times*. New Delhi: B.I. Publications.

Naz, N. (2004). University of Engineering and Technology, Lahore: 80 Years Passage through History. *UET Research Journal*, 15(1–2, Jan.–Dec.), 49–74.

Nehru, Jawaharlal. (1946). *Important Speeches of Jawaharlal Nehru Being a Collection of Most Significant Speeches Delivered by Jawaharlal Nehru from 1922 to 1946*, J.S. Bright (Ed.)., Lahore: Indian Print Works.

Noltie, H. J. (2006). *Robert Wight and the Illustration of Indian Botany*. Oxford: Blackwell.

Noltie, H. J. (2007). *Robert Wight and the Botanical Drawings of Rungiah & Govindoo*. Edinburgh: Royal Botanic Garden.

Noti, S. (1906). *Joseph Tiffenthaler, S.J.: A Forgotten Geographer of India*. Bombay: Javanji Dadaji.

Parker, L. A. (1915). A Brief History of Materia Medica (Continued). *The American Journal of Nursing*, 15(9), 729–734.

Parry, J. H. (1982). *The Age of Reconnaissance: Discovery, Exploration, and Settlement, 1450-1650*. California University Press.

Pascoe, C. F. (1901). *Two Hundred Years of the S.P.G.* London: Society's Office.

Pethiyagoda, R., & Sudasinghe, H. (2017). The Development of Sri Lankan Biogeography in the Colonial Period. *Ceylon Journal of Science*, 46(5), 5–18.

Phillimore, R. H. (1945–1958). *Historical Records of Survey of India*, 1–4 Vols. Dehra Dun: Survey of India.

Pigott, J. P. (1794). *A Treatise on the Horses of India.* Calcutta: Printed by James White.

Pinchot, G. (1947). *Breaking New Ground.* New York: Harcourt. (Reprint, Washington, DC: Island Press, 1998).

Playne, S. (1915). *Southern India: Its History, People, Commerce, and Industrial Resources.* New Delhi: Facsimile, Asian Education Services, p. 711.

Pocock, R. J. (1918). *Astrographic Catalogue 1900.0: Hyderabad Section. From Photographs Taken and Measured at the Nizamiah Observatory, Hyderabad.* Edinburgh: Printed for the Osmania University by Neill.

Pogson, N. R. (1887). *Results of Observations of the Fixed Stars Made with the Meridian Circle at the Government Observatory, Madras, in the Years 1862, 1863 and 1864.* Madras: Lawrence Asylum Press.

Prakash, O. (1998). *European Commercial Enterprise in Pre-colonial India.* Cambridge: Cambridge University Press.

Pres. Coll. 100. (1956). *Presidency College, Calcutta, Centenary Volume 1955.* Alipore: West Bengal Government Press.

Pritchett, F. W. (1986). The Chess-Players: From Premchand to Satyajit Ray. *Journal of South Asian Literature*, 22(2), 65–78.

Proudfoot, W. J. (1868). *Biographical Memoir of James Dinwiddie, L.L.D., Astronomer in the British Embassy to China.* Liverpool: Howell.

Raina, D., & Habib, S. I. (2004). *Domesticating Modern Science.* New Delhi: Tulika Books, pp. 182–198.

Raman, R., Raman, A., & Manohar, P. (2014). The Arsenic and Mercury-Containing Tanjore Pills Used in Treating Snake Bites in the 18th Century Madras Presidency. *Current Science*, 106(12), 1759–1763.

Ramanna, M. (1992). Profiles of English Educated Indians: Early Nineteenth Century Bombay City. *Economic and Political Weekly*, 27(14), 716–724.

Ranyard, A. C. (1879). Observations Made during Total Solar Eclipses. *Memoirs of Royal Astronomical Society*, 41, 1–792.

Rao, N. K., Vagiswari, A., & Birdie, C. (2011). Early Pioneers of Telescopic Astronomy in India: J V Jugga Rao and His Observatory. *Current Science*, 100(10), 1575–1581.

Ray, P. C. (1896). On Mercurous Nitrite. *Journal of the Asiatic Society of Bengal*, 65, 1–9.

Ray, P. C. (1918). *Essays and Discourses.* Madras: Natesan.

Ray, P. C. (1932). *Life and Experiences of a Bengali Chemist*, Vol. 1. Calcutta: Chuckervertty, Chatterjee. (Reprint, Asiatic Society, Calcutta, 1962).

Ray, N. R. (1986). *Calcutta: The Profile of a City.* Calcutta: K.P. Bagchi.

Ray100. (1962). *Acharya Prafulla Chandra Ray: Birth Centenary Souvenir Volume.* Calcutta: Calcutta University.

Ray, Pradyot Kumar. (1990). *Dewan Ramcomul Sen and His Times.* Calcutta: Modern Book Agency.

Reynolds, P. (2014). Afterword No 1 Professor John Gilchrist 1759–1841. *Leichhardt Historical Journal No 24*, 12–13.

Richey, J. A. (Ed.). (1922). *Selections from Educational Records: Part II*. Government Printing.

Robinson, W. (1841). *A Descriptive Account of Asam*. Calcutta: Ostell.

Robinson, T. F. (2003). *William Roxburgh (1751-1815): The Founding Father of Indian Botany*. PhD Thesis, University of Edinburgh.

Rockhill, W. W. (1891). *Land of the Lamas*. London: Longmans, Green.

Rosenthal, A. M. (1958). Indian Town Gets a Satellite Role. *New York Times*, Apr. 6.

Royal Awards. (1868). Presentation of the Royal Awards. *Proceedings of the Royal Geographical Society of London*, 12(25 May), 146–175.

Royle, J. F. (1840). *Essay on the Productive Resources of India*. London: Allen.

Saldanha, I. M. (1996). Colonialism and Professionalism: A German Forester in India. *Environment and History*, 2(2), 195–219.

Samad, M. A. (2014). Comparison of Veterinary Medical Education Programs between SAARC Countries and the United States. *Journal of Nature Science and Sustainable Technology*, 8(4), 495–521.

Sanwal, N. B. (1983). Seventy Five Years of Nizamiah Observatory. In: G. M. Ballabh (Ed.), *Nizamiah Observatory Platinum Jubilee Souvenir*. Hyderabad: Osmania University.

Sanyal, R. G. (1894). *Reminiscences and Anecdotes of Great Men of India*. (Reprint, Calcutta: Riddhi-India, 1980).

Schlagintweit, H., Schlagintweit, A., & Schlagintweit, R. (1861). *Results of a Scientific Mission to India and High Asia [1854-1857]*, Vol. 1. London: Trübner.

Sehgal, N., & Mahanti, S. (Eds.). (1994). *Memoirs of Ruchi Ram Sahni*. New Delhi: Vigyan Prasar, India.

Sen, K. C. (1901). *Keshub Chunder Sen's Lectures in India*. London: Cassell and Company, Limited.

Sharma, S. R. (n.d.). *Mughal Empire in India*, 10th ed. Agra: Lakshmi Narain Agarwal.

Sharpe, T., & McCartney, P. J. (1998). *The Papers of H. T. De la Beche (1796-1855) in the National Museum of Wales*. Cardiff: National Museum Wales.

Shridharani, K. (1953). *Story of the Indian Telegraphs: A Century of Progress*. New Delhi: Posts and Telegraph Department.

Shridharani, K. (1956). Sibu Nandy Lane, Calcutta. Amrit Bazar Patrika, Annual Puja Number, pp. 151–152 & 160.

Sinha, N. K. (1966). *Asutosh Mukherjee. Asutosh Mukherjee: A Biographical Study*. Calcutta: Asutosh Mukherjee Centenary Committee.

Smith, E. (1911). *Life of Sir Joseph Banks: With Some Notices of His Friends and Contemporaries*. John Lane.

Smith, Frederick. (1927). *A History of the Royal Army Veterinary Corps 1796–1919*. London: Bailliere, Tindall & Cox.

Sprat, T. (1722). *The History of the Royal Society of London*. London: Knapton.

Stansfield, H. (1957). The Missionary Botanists of Tranquebar. *Liverpool Libraries, Museums and Art Committee Bulletin*, 6(3), 19–43.

Sterll, M. (2008). Life and Adventures of Johann Gerhard König (1728-1785). *A Phantom of the Herbaria Rheedea*, 18(2), 111–129.

Subbarayappa, B. V. (1992). *In Pursuit of Excellence: A History of the Indian Institute of Science*. New Delhi: Tata McGraw.

Sur, A. (2002). Scientism and Social Justice: Meghnad Saha's Critique of the State of Science in India. *Historical Studies in the Physical and Biological Sciences*, 33(1), 87–105.

Tayler, W. (1871). Popular Education in India. *Journal of East India Association*, 5, Part 3, 1–36.

Taylor, T. G., & Caldecott, J. (1839). Observations on the Direction and Intensity of the Terrestrial Magnetic Force in Southern India. *Madras Journal of Literature and Science*, 9, 221–273.

Tea Parliamentary Papers. (1839). *Papers Received from India Relating to the Measures Adopted for Introducing the Cultivation of the Tea Plant within the British Possessions in India*. London: House of Commons.

Temple, Richard. (1896). *The Story of My Life*, Vol. 2. London: Cassell and Company, Limited.

Temple, Richard. (1900). *The Commercial Value of Wireless Telegraphic Communication with the Andaman & Nicobar Islands*. Calcutta: The City Press.

Ukers, W. H. (1935). *All About Tea*, Vol. 1. New York: Tea and Coffee Trade Journal.

Ullah, Mir Izzat. (1843). Travels beyond the Himalaya. *The Journal of the Royal Asiatic Society of Great Britain and Ireland*, 7(2), 283–342.

Unakar, M. V. (1936). Dr. N. A. F. Moos, Obituary. *Current Science*, 4, 862–864.

Van Gorkom, K. W. (1883). *A Handbook of Cinchona Culture* (trans. from Dutch by B. D. Jackson). London: Trübner, pp. 38–62.

Venkataraman, G. (1988). *Journey into Light: Life and Science of C.V. Raman*. India: Indian Academy of Sciences.

Visvanathan, S. (1985). *Organizing for Science: The Making of an Industrial Research laboratory*. Delhi: Oxford University Press.

Voelcker, J. A. (1893). *Report on the Improvement of Indian Agriculture*. London: Printed by Eyre and Spottiswoode.

Wadia, P. A. (1906). *Jamsedji Nussarwanji Tata. Indian Worthies*, Vol. 1. Bombay: Manoranjak Granth, pp. 67–116.

Walker, J. T. (1864). Extract of a Report by Majot J. T. Walker, Officiating Superintendent, Great Trigonometrical Survey. *Journal of Asiatic Society of Bengal*, 32(2), 110–123.

Walker, J. T. (1885). Four Years' Journeyings Through Great Tibet, by One of the Trans-Himalayan Explorers of the Survey of India. *Proceedings of the Royal Geographical Society and Monthly Record of Geography*, 7(2), 65–92.

Walker, G. K. (1927). The Punjab Veterinary College, Lahore. *The Veterinary Journal*, 83(7), 335–346.

Warner, B., & Hurly, R. (1976). J. E. de Villiers Observatory at Sea Point. *Monthly Notes of the Astronomical Society of Southern Africa*, 35, 57–62.

Warren, J. (1830). Biographical Sketch of the Late Col. Lambton, Superintendent of the Trigonometrical Survey of India. *Gleanings of Science*, 2(Mar.), 73–82. (The author is not explicitly named.)

Watson, E. R. (1907a). *A monograph on iron and steel work in the province of Bengal*. Calcutta, Bengal Secretarist Book Depot.

Watson, E. R. (1907b). The Exact Determination of the Fastness of the more Common Indigenous Dyes of Bengal, and composition with typical synthetic Dyestuffs, Part I, - Dyeing on Cotton. *Memoirs of Asiatic Society of Bengal*, II(3), 25–41.

Waugh, A. S. (1857). Papers Relating to the Himalayas and Mount Everest. *Proceedings of Royal Geographical Society*, 1, 345–347.

White, L. (2008). *The Collected Lyrical Poems of Luis de Camoes*. Princeton University Press.

Wight, R., & Walker-Arnott, G. A. (1834). *Prodromus Florae Peninsulae Indiae Orientalis*, Vol. 1. London: Parbury, Allen.

Wilkinson, T. T. (1853). Mathematics and Mathematicians: The Journals of the Late Reuben Burrow. *Philosophical Magazine*, 5, 185–193; 5, 514–522; 6, 196–204.

Williams, W. O. (1904). Veterinary Lieutenant-Colonel James H. B. Hallen, C.I.E., F.R.C.S.E., F.R.C.V.S. *Proceedings of Royal Society of Edinburgh*, 24, 642–645.

Williams, D. (1962). Clements Robert Markham and the Introduction of the Cinchona Tree into British India, 1861. *Geographical Journal*, 128(4), 431–442.

Winstone, H. (1984). George Strachan, 17th Century Orientalist: Plea for a Biographical Study. *Proceedings of the Seminar for Arabian Studies*, 14, 103–109.

Wood, H. T. (1913). *A History of the Royal Society of Arts*. London: John Murray.

Younghusband, F. (1922). Introduction. In C. K. Howard-Bury (Ed.), *Mount Everest: The Reconnaisance, 1921*. New York: Longmans, Green.

Yule, H. (1888). Concerning Some Little Known Travellers in the East. *Asiatic Quarterly Review*, 5, 312–335.

INDEX

Pages in **bold** refer to tables.

For Product Safety Concerns and Information please contact our EU
representative GPSR@taylorandfrancis.com
Taylor & Francis Verlag GmbH, Kaufingerstraße 24, 80331 München, Germany

* 9 7 8 1 0 3 2 7 3 8 7 1 0 *